ONLY ONE HEART

ONLY ONE HEART

THE STORY OF A PIONEER NUN IN AMERICA

Sister Patricia Jean, S.L.

Doubleday & Company, Inc.
Garden City, New York
1963

NIHIL OBSTAT: Rt. Rev. Msgr. F. N. Pitt
Censor Deputatus

IMPRIMATUR: ✠ Most Rev. John A. Floersh, D.D.
Archbishop of Louisville
November 25, 1961

The Nihil Obstat and Imprimatur are official declarations that a book or pamphlet is free of doctrinal or moral error. No implication is contained therein that those who have granted the Nihil Obstat and Imprimatur agree with the contents, opinions or statements expressed.

Library of Congress Catalog Card Number 63-10262

Printed in the United States of America

In gratitude to
my father and mother
who
also had only one heart

THE MORNING MANNA

O Dear Sisters and Scholars! Love
your Jesus, dying with love for you on
the Cross! Love Mary, your loving Mother
sorrowing at the foot of the Cross! Love
one another, have only one heart, one soul,
one mind! Love the Institute, love the
Rules, love Jesus' darling humility!

Father Charles Nerinckx

CONTENTS

"I WILL LOVE BAWNBOY, TOO"

With a slow, sigh-filled movement Moira lifted her head to the sun. The light of it caught her face, sharpening the wrinkles and changing the wisps of hair that stuck out at the edge of her shawl from the dull gray of old thatch to bright silver. It made her look triumphant, the little girl at her side thought. It seemed that the old woman could almost see the sun. Perhaps inside, down inside Moira's heart, beneath the shawl that hugged the bend of her skinny body and beneath the green of her faded blouse, perhaps inside the old woman *could* see the sun.

Susan began to make up the words that would ask old Moira if she could see the sun inside; but she did not speak. She knew that was the way it would be. They would walk along, not speaking, her pink-white hand on the brownly withered one, not held by it in the way children's hands are usually held, but holding it and telling Moira by the soft pressure of her thin fingers the way to take along the road.

Only the scraping of the old woman's worn bristies upon the rocky road and the scuffling of the little girl's gaiters as she matched her steps to Moira's made sounds against the silence. Small sound there was, and few things enough to make a sound in the listless morning; but many things there were to feel and smell, many things to see if one had just turned eleven. The road made a thin streak that ribboned together the white and yellow houses—not quite farmhouses and not quite village houses, close enough for friendliness yet scattered enough to breathe the country air. Between the houses, fields of freshly turned earth patched with green stretches where sheep moved lazily about spread their checkered pattern up to the darker green of the hills. Susan breathed in the savor of damp earth and new clover. She felt the warm pressure of the sun on her head and the rough gravel of the road beneath her feet. This, all of this was Bawnboy, her home. "Bawnboy in the parish of Templeporte, County Cavan," as her father would say.

As the two moved slowly along the road that day in May of 1865, the little girl wondered if Moira knew that white clover was hugging the edges of the road. Did Moira remember seeing it before she was blind? Old Moira hadn't always been a blind beggar, Susan had heard her mother say.

Suddenly the little girl knew by the stiffening of the old woman's fingers that she was going to speak. The two stopped. Old Moira turned her head toward the child. She put one hand on the little girl's light brown hair, feeling its soft warmth under her calloused palm.

"A donkey cart is near to the top of the hill, alannah. Do you see it yet? If it is Padriac, you will not have to be going all the way with me this day."

The little girl looked at the old woman and then turned to look back to where the road went up to the beginning of the sky. How did Moira know that a cart was coming? Then with the first glimpse of Padriac's red caubeen, the little girl clapped her hands.

"It *is*, Moira! It *is* Padriac coming. Hear him?"

"Yes, Susan, I hear. Every day I bless the good God for the hearing He puts in my ears. And it's not everything He keeps from my eyes either."

Old Moira squinted as she turned toward the road. It seemed to Susan that she was watching Padriac as he came closer in his clumsy cart.

Maybe Moira could see him. And maybe she knew about the clover. Maybe she even knew about the hawthorn bush where the fairies hid. Susan's eyes followed the road to where it curved out of sight. Just beyond the curve where the road dipped into a little valley, the dreaded hawthorn bush grew. Susan would not have to catch her breath and run past it with her eyes closed today.

Just last night her brother John had told about the hawthorn bushes in Kilkenny. They were found all bloody one morning after two fairy clans had waged a battle. Maybe Moira knew about this hawthorn bush. Maybe Moira likes to ride with Padriac so the fairies won't get her. She would ask old Moira some day, some day soon. It will have to be soon. She had meant to tell the old woman that she was going to America, but she forgot when they started to walk. Maybe Moira even knew that. Moira seemed to know everything.

"God bless you, old Moira, and the blessing of Himself be on the little one," Padriac called. Stopping his donkey, he got out of the cart as quickly as his stiff joints would permit.

"God give you long years, Padriac. And would you be giving old Moira a ride to the next house?" the old woman replied.

"In the name of Himself, I will be doing that," Padriac said as he almost lifted her into the cart.

Susan watched Padriac clamber back into his place. He heaved a deep sigh as he shook the reins again.

"The blessing of the blind go with you, Susan Carty," Moira called over her shoulder.

The little girl stood by the side of the road as they moved away. Had Padriac forgotten? Susan was picking up a pebble when the old man looked back and with a wink tossed a tiny piece of peat into the eddy of dust rising behind the cart. That was sure to chase the fairies who made the dusty cloud.

Susan turned around and started back the way she and old Moira had come. She could see her home looking scarcely white with the rose vines beginning to turn green. Whenever she saw the house, a warm feeling began to grow inside of her because then she could see other things too. She could see the big room with its long shelves of books where the family gathered to say their rosary and to talk. Talk which always seemed to turn to the penal days, of how Elizabeth had reached across the channel to Dublin and put there a House of Commons meant to snuff out the light of faith in the heart of the Irish, of how Anne had tried to smother the flame and had instead fanned it into an unquenchable blaze. Susan's father told of the penal laws that "hunted God

Himself" as priests offered Mass under the only roof the Irish could give Him, when the forests were His churches and the rocks of Ireland the altars for His sacrifice.

Susan's gait took on the air of a strut as she heard again her father's voice, "This is your heritage, my ones." Then suddenly her face grew serious, an invisible burden weighted her pace and she looked at the road as she walked. There had been other talk as the family gathered together these last few weeks. She must ask old Moira about America. Moira would know if a little girl would like it there. Was America like Bawnboy?

The hint of a distant voice interrupted her wondering and she stopped to listen. It was her mother singing. Susan said softly to herself the words that she had often heard her father say. "God bless her singing voice and her laughing heart." The little girl began to run, her wide blue skirt rippling in the breeze. She would run and throw her arms around her mother and tell her that she loved her. "God bless her singing voice and her laughing heart," she called to the quiet countryside as she ran.

At the low stone wall that curved to the bend of the road, Susan stopped running as she turned to start up the lane to the house.

"God bless her laughing heart and her singing voice," a high little voice echoed and Susan stopped abruptly as seven-year-old Jenny, holding a kitten by the tail, stepped out from behind a bush.

"Jenny," Susan gasped, as much frightened by her little sister's sudden appearance as alarmed by the plight of the kitten. "Jenny, what are you doing to that poor kitty?"

"I'm showing him how it looks with the sky on the bottom," she answered, a little annoyed that Susan should not have realized that for herself.

"But, Jenny, you might hurt him. Why don't you just tell him what it is like? He's too little to see for himself."

Without a word, Jenny hugged the kitten to her and proceeded to sit down right where she was. Yes, she would tell him how it looks. Susan knows a lot about kittens, Jenny told the ball of fluff in her arms.

Susan waited a moment, listening not so much to Jenny as listening for her mother's voice. She could not hear her singing now. As Susan started toward the house, her thoughts went back to Moira. The old lady must be at the neighbor's door by now.

It was funny to think that Moira had never seen her, that if suddenly the old lady could see like other people she would not know her. She would look at Susan and wonder, "Who is that little girl?" "How pretty the little one is today," old Moira would say as Susan took her hand. That's because she can't see me, Susan told herself. If she knew what Papa said she wouldn't call me pretty. Susan blushed recalling the time she had been hiding and overheard her father say, "Susie has not the looks of the others, Ellen; but Himself put gold in her heart."

Perhaps it was better to have gold in your heart than to be pretty like your sisters, but what fun it was to hope that old Moira might think she had beautiful dark eyes like Maria or that her hair was tinted with sunset like Eliza's. Had Moira ever heard Anne singing and did she think it was Susan? Susan thought that perhaps she was not even as pretty as Kitty or little Jenny; but, old Moira loves me and she needs me to show her the way, Susan thought. Two tears grew large in her blue eyes and she wanted to cry because she loved the old lady so much, and now when Susan went to America Moira would get lost on the road or maybe the fairies would steal her or maybe—or maybe. She stopped as a new idea pranced into her mind. Maybe I could stay in Bawnboy and wait for Moira to come and people would say, "That's Susan Carty. She didn't go to America because old Moira needed her." Even if no one ever noticed, she would be serving God. We serve God when we serve others. That was what the priest always said.

Ellen Carty, sitting by the kitchen window, looked up from her sewing in time to see the top of a little girl's head passing beneath. Her eyes went automatically to the door to confirm what the glimpse had told her. Yes, it was Susan, her two long braids fuzzy from the wind, her blue cotton dress looking slightly wrinkled, and her face flushed from running.

Mrs. Carty smiled. "Susan," she said to herself. With this thought came the whole litany of names, her children, Maria, Patrick, John, Kitty, Tom, Jim, Eliza, Anne, Susan, Jenny, and Delia. "God be praised for them," she said.

"Mavourneen, you're back so soon. Did Padriac give old Moira a ride? I saw him pass." Ellen Carty, slender and slightly smaller than medium height, was, in her late forties, still attractive. Her face, with its rounded Irish features, was dominated by eyes so brown as to appear black at times. Always neat in some dark house dress with a touch of her own crocheted lace at the neck and wrists, she relished well her roles as wife to the village's only miller and mother of eleven children. It had been only in the last few years that she had found time to enjoy being "good Mark Carty's wife." Older sons and daughters could at last take on some of the care of the younger ones. It was a good way of life.

Susan had meant to run and throw her arms around her mother, but instead she stood in the doorway hoping that the two tears would not spill down her cheeks. Before she realized it, the question in her mind had taken words. "Mama, what will happen to Moira?"

"What do you mean, what will happen to her? Someday the good God will be taking her off to heaven where Himself will be putting the light back into her eyes."

Susan sat on the stool next to the hearth, where a kettle was beginning to boil for tea. She does not understand, Susan was thinking.

"But what will happen to her when we go to America and I won't be here to take her to the next house?"

Ellen Carty smiled in her heart, but she did not look up from her sewing. "Alannah," she began softly, almost afraid of the sternness she must put into her voice. "Alannah, the good God Himself put darkness into Moira's eyes. He knows how to take her along the road, too. He only lets you help Him; but, mavourneen, He does not need your help."

Before she could finish the little prayer deep inside, which asked that the words be not too harsh for a little girl, Susan's arms were around her.

"Oh, Mama," she was sobbing, and Ellen felt Susan's tears on her own cheek. Ellen herself began to cry. America is too far from Bawnboy, she was thinking. Why must Mark be so bent on tearing us all from our home?

As the fire in the hearth fingered the tea kettle, steam nudging its lid, Ellen started suddenly.

"Why, Susie, here we sit being sentimental and the kettle almost popping its lid and your father wanting a bite to eat this day."

Wiping the tear traces from her flushed cheeks, Susan ran to the cupboard for the pandee, which would hold just enough tea for her father's and Patrick's and John's noon bite.

"Papa will be wondering what's kept his little girl so long." Mrs. Carty smiled as she poured the steaming brew into the pitcherlike container and placed it along with some freshly baked biscuits in a small basket for Susan to carry along the boreen, across Paddy Flynn's turf field to her father's mill.

"And I mustn't run or there will be no tea when I do get there," Susan laughed in anticipation.

Ellen Carty tucked a fresh white napkin over the top of the basket and handed it to Susan. "Now be off with you," she said, and leaning over she wiped away a last bit of tear on Susan's cheek. "And mind that you have no more bad dreams about old Moira. What's God to be doing if you take care of all His worries?"

Susan, with the basket held firmly in both hands, started for the mill. Knowing just where to look, slightly left of the rocky mound in Paddy's field, she could see the thatch roof of the mill outlined against the blue sky. For as long as she could remember, her father had spent his days there milling flour for the surrounding countryside and sending wagons piled high with neat sacks of flour and grain as far as Dublin at markettime. Patrick and John, her eldest brothers, worked with their father there, and, as Mr.

Carty himself said, "There aren't two better millers in all County Cavan than Mark Carty's sons."

Edging through a break in the stone wall that separated the lane from the turf field, she was soon past the mound. Now she could see the mill in full view ahead. It was not a large mill, at least that was what her father said; but it was the only one in Bawnboy and that's why it gives us all "position," or anyway that was what her mother said.

The mill held a fascination for Susan. She felt at home there; but since it was a place of business and her visits were seldom, there was always a sense of adventure in her heart as she approached the mill. This day was one of those rare Saturdays when she enjoyed the privilege of taking a lunch to the mill so her father and brothers would not need to return home until late afternoon.

As she walked quickly along the path to the side door, Patrick, tall, curly-headed, his work clothes powdered white with flour, stepped into view, a broad grin on his face.

"Why, 'tis Susie, the fairest colleen in all Cavan, come with tea for three starving men." And he bowed low and, smiling, tried to take the basket from her.

Susan dodged his hand and slipped past him through the doorway.

"It's to Mr. Mark Carty, the miller of Bawnboy, that I'm giving the tea," she said with a lift of her head.

"What's this?" Mr. Carty asked, looking up from the ledger where he had just entered a purchase.

"May all the holy saints in heaven smile on our Susie for her kindness in coming all this way with a bit of a meal for her father and brothers!" His voice seemed to smile as his face smiled.

Mark Carty was a tall, heftily built man with ruddy cheeks and blue eyes that laughed merrily beneath bushy graying brows. Although he had always tried to brush down any sign of a wave in his hair, it curled mischievously at his temples.

"Papa dear, the biscuits are newly baked. See," she said, lifting the napkin to show him. "Where is John?" she asked, looking at Pat.

"Oh, probably sleeping in the loft," he answered.

Susan put her hands into the pockets of her apron and cocked her head to one side as she frowned.

"Now look at the fair colleen," Patrick teased. "Can't say a word against John Carty without the Brady side in her hopping to his defense."

Just then John, balancing a sack of flour on one shoulder, came down the narrow ladder from the floor above. "Papa, this is the last one for . . . why, Susie mavourneen, it's good to see you." Putting down the sack, he grabbed one of her pigtails and drew her around in a complete circle.

"Susie was just about to start a war to save your good name, John me lad," Mr. Carty said as he poured the tea.

"I think the wee one is fond of you, John," Mr. Carty said, patting him on the shoulder. "But come, let's have our tea."

Mr. Carty bowed his head to ask a blessing of the good God who had provided the tea and biscuits, asking Him in turn to bless dear Ellen and fair Susan for their kindness. In a minute the chatter had begun anew. Susan, sitting on a low bench near her father, was a silent listener as the three men turned their talk to America and their coming departure from Ireland.

"Roden's letter here," Mr. Carty said, pulling a wrinkled envelope from his pocket, "says that now that the war is over and the farmers are back in the fields again, the mills of St. Louis will have more work than they know what to do with. Roden says there'll be no trouble finding work."

"How long have the Rodens been in St. Louis, Papa?" John asked as he reached for another biscuit, handing the basket on to Susan.

"Well, let me see now. It must be twenty years since they left Ireland, but they went first to New York and stayed there for a while. Yes, it was twenty years because Patrick here was no higher than my knee and John, my lad, you were but a scrap of a man tumbling about the floor when they left."

John blushed and Patrick winked at Susan.

Balancing his cup of tea on his knee, Mr. Carty looked beyond

John and out through the open door to the turf field, and, as if talking to himself, he said, "We were great chums, David Roden and myself. As boys we roamed these hills and the bogland together dreaming of the day when Ireland would be free and we would be great men in a great land. But as we grew older, we came to understand better that the freeing of our country was not so easily done as boys would think. And when the famine came years ago and O'Connell stood up before Parliament and pleaded that they stop exporting potatoes when Ireland was starving for want of them, Roden and I dreamed of sailing for the land of America where such things don't happen. I was cautious, maybe too much so; but he being more adventuresome took his family and left. Ah, no one knows how much I missed that lad. We had been friends a long time, like brothers we were, though only cousins. All this time he's been faithful to me, writing and asking me to come along and see how good America is. Ah, she's been good to him and his wife and children all thrivin' and happy. He's even got a daughter Mary who's a nun, a nun mind you in America!" He paused and only the sound of a cart rolling along the road on the other side of the mill made a muffled sound in the distance. At last he turned to Susan, "Mavourneen, you are being too quiet. What's going on in that wee head of yours?"

"Papa, is St. Louis like Bawnboy?"

"Ah, Susie, my child, I have to say to you that it is not." Then he smiled lovingly at her and patted her hand. "It is a city, not a village like this. Oh, you might say it is a giant village, a place many times bigger and grander than wee Bawnboy."

"But Papa, I like Bawnboy even if it is only a village and even if there are places many times grander." There was a hint of sadness in her voice.

"Ah, mavourneen, I know that you do. And I do too. This is your home, the place where you were born. The part of the earth where God Himself chose to put you as a wee babe. But, Susie, the place on the earth matters only because God has chosen it; and so you see, my dear little one, now that He has chosen for you and for me and for all of us to go to St. Louis in far-off

America, that must be the dearest place on the earth for us, the dearest place because God has chosen it to be our new home."

Susan smiled at her father. And turning to John, she said, "Then I shall love St. Louis more than Bawnboy; but," she looked back at her father, "I shall love Bawnboy too."

When Susan had gone and the boys had returned to their work, Mark Carty sat staring at the ledger. Next month a new page and a new owner. He hated to think of the mill not being his. It had given him a fair enough life, but it couldn't give four sons and someday four families a good life. And what was there for a boy to go on to in a place like this? Well, the mill would give them all a start in a new land. If he could only count on Ellen being as determined to love their new home as Susan was. "Then I shall love St. Louis more than Bawnboy," he could hear Susan say. "But we won't be selling this house, Mark dearest," he could hear Ellen plead. Ah, it had been foolish! He had told her so. They'd never come back. Why, she couldn't ever want to come back. He brushed his calloused hand over the smudge of flour on his trouser knee. But his concern he could not brush away.

Outside, halfway down the hill, Susan turned around and waved; but no one waved in return. Papa always waves, she told herself. Shrugging her shoulders, she took the path that led to the road. "When I go to the mill, I hurry," she had once told Moira; "but when I come back, I take the long way. Can you guess why I do?" But old Moira had said that she couldn't guess so Susan had explained that it made the visit last longer.

Susan turned around again. Now she could not see the path to the mill. This was where John had shown her how to make the mill sink into the earth. Slowly she walked backward. One step, two steps, three steps. Now it was gone. Then she made it come back. One step, two steps, three steps forward. "I can make it go up and down," she said aloud to herself.

One step, two steps backward. One step, two steps forward.

"Here, here, what do you think you are doing?" a big voice behind her asked.

Startled, Susan looked over her shoulder. In the middle of the road stood Mr. Shawn. Mr. Shawn was a man who wandered about the village. The big boys said his wife wouldn't let him into the house.

"You scared me," Susan said.

He threw back his head and laughed. "And you scared me, going back and forth like that. I was thinking that the fairies had stole your wits away. What are you doing?"

"Just seeing if I can make the mill go up and down. Do you want to try it, Mr. Shawn? I'll show you how." She put the basket down on the road and took his big rough hand. "Now watch the mill. You take one . . . you have to walk with me, Mr. Shawn," she insisted as she tugged at his hand. "One step, two steps, three steps up. See? Now one step, two steps, three steps back."

"Anybody seeing us would think we'd had too much, Miss Susan."

"Too much what?"

"Oh, just too much," he chuckled.

"Mr. Shawn, would you like a biscuit? I have two in the basket." Susan had once heard Maria say that Mr. Shawn would be found starved to death someday because he didn't eat right.

Mr. Shawn leaned over Susan as she showed him the biscuits.

"Mr. Shawn, what makes you smell different from other people?" she asked.

Laughing, he pulled out a big blue handkerchief and wiped his mouth. " 'Tis the nectar of the gods, Susan. Ah, but it's also the curse of men," he added.

Susan did not understand Mr. Shawn. He was always so nice, but he said such peculiar things. Maybe that was why his wife locked him out of the house. Poor Mr. Shawn.

"Do you want a biscuit?"

"Oh no, Miss Susan, not this time of the morning. I'm on me way to speak with your father."

"You like Papa, don't you, Mr. Shawn?"

"Aye, and who in Bawnboy doesn't? It will be a sad day when he leaves. Well, I'll be on me way. And mind you walk forwards. No one ever got very far walking backwards."

Susan smiled. She liked Mr. Shawn. Sometimes she prayed that God would tell his wife not to lock him out.

Back at the mill Mark Carty was weighing the sacks of wheat flour that had just been ground. He had to be finished in time to walk into the village to see Mrs. Colin before midday. For two months he had been promising her that he would build the little cabinets in her big room; and if he was to do it before he left, he would have to see what she wanted so he could get the lumber in Dublin next week. He had not done as much cabinetmaking in recent years as he did when he was younger, but many times when the milling business was slack he had been glad that he knew another trade.

He glanced up as he heard footsteps on the path. It was Shawn! Poor Shawn.

"Greetings, Shawn, old man. How are things with you?"

It was hard to tell that Mark and Shawn were the same age. Shawn's ill-treated body was bent whereas Mark stood erect and tall. Shawn's face was puffy and lined, although it might once have been handsome.

"What is on your mind, Shawn boy?"

"I want to be returning the money I am owing you, Mark. I guess you thought you'd not be seeing it again. Well, maybe you wouldn't have but that little piece of work you told me they needed done at the church gave me more than I had first thought. I figured that I ought to be repaying you before I got to drinking it up."

"Now, Shawn boy, if you need this, don't be giving it to me. What about your Eileen? Maybe she could be using something."

"I gave her some. She's happy as a lark with me now. But it won't last. I can't be staying away from the drink and she won't be having me with it. It's a rotten fellow I am, Mark."

"Ah, it's too bad you two didn't ever have any young ones. I guess a woman just doesn't know how to act if she hasn't a child to look to," Mark said.

"That's it, Mark. But it don't seem right to me that I should be blamed for that. She don't say nothing about it now any more, but that's where the trouble first started. She was so fixed on the idea of having children; and then when we didn't, she got all mixed up inside, making out that it was everybody else's fault. I guess I should have listened to her and been more ready to sympathize. It's turned out pretty bad, Mark. Thank God that you have good Ellen Carty to see eye to eye with you. There ain't nothing in my way of thinking worse than a woman who can't be seeing what's a man's fault and what ain't." Shawn shook Mark's hand and blinked quickly. "I'll be seeing you. God bless you, Mark."

By this time Susan had arrived home, where she was excitedly telling Jim, just two years older than she, about playing the game with Mr. Shawn.

"And, Jim, I was going back and forth and back and forth when Mr. Shawn came along. I showed him how to do it too."

"Mr. Shawn? You mean that you were showin' that old drunk how to make the mill go up and down?"

"He is not an old drunk! He is a friend of mine. I like Mr. Shawn very much."

"You ought to tell his wife that."

A dark-haired, dark-eyed girl of twenty emerged from the shadows of the kitchen doorway.

"Maria, Jim called Mr. Shawn an old drunk. And he isn't, is he?"

"Jim, Papa would be very unhappy if he heard you say that. Susan, don't you think that you ought to bring that basket inside? Mama has been wondering why you were gone so long."

"I had a long talk with Papa and John. And then I showed Mr. Shawn how to play the game. All that takes time, Maria," she said.

"Yes, I know, Susie."

Susan looked up at Maria out of the corner of her eye. Maria smiled. Maria is beautiful, Susan was thinking. Maria is more beautiful than anyone else in the world.

"What have you in your hand, Susie?" Maria questioned in her best big-sisterly tone.

"I picked up a stick, Maria. If you look at it just right, it looks like a man. See. Arms, legs, the head!"

Maria's dark eyes laughed, but her expression did not betray Susan's seriousness.

"Look, Mama, I found a funny old stick that looks like a man," Susan said to her mother as she followed Maria into the kitchen.

"Why, so it does, Susie! Now be putting it down and washing your hands. Then you can be calling the boys."

Susan put the end of the stick into her apron pocket, holding it against her with one elbow as she went to wash her hands. "If God wanted to, He could breathe on this kippeen and make it into a real man, couldn't He, Mama?"

"Yes, He could, Susie." She smiled, glancing to see if Maria had heard.

Three weeks later, on an afternoon in mid-June, Ellen slammed the lid of a small trunk in the low-ceilinged attic and turned to back down the ladder for the last time when she noticed Susan's kippeen on the floor. Ellen herself had carried it up with her that day in May. Strange that she had not noticed it there before on one of the many trips she had made to the attic these weeks. Sitting down on the old trunk, she fingered the stick. "And God could breathe on this kippeen and make it into a man."

"Yes, Susie, He could," Ellen repeated now out loud. Her fingers caressed the stick as she thought of her Susan. What would become of her in America? If they were to stay in Bawnboy, it would not be difficult to picture her ten years from now married to some village lad, a boy with laughing eyes and a broad Irish grin, a boy not unlike one of Susan's own brothers. But in America? What would happen to all of them in America? Could she control them all? What would happen to Mark? He thought now that he would like working in one of those big mills with no responsibility for the place, but he wouldn't. He'd been the town's only miller for too long to come down to working for someone else. Why she probably wouldn't be seeing him from sunup to sundown. That was no way to live. And how would they keep their children at home with neighbors so close and all the allurements of the city? Why, she'd never even see them half the time. They'd certainly grow away from her. Well, Mark would see and then he'd thank her for insisting that they hold on to the old house in Bawnboy. She gave the trunk an affectionate pat.

"Mama," a voice from downstairs came up to her. Reluctantly Ellen left the darkness of her own thoughts and looked down through the bright opening of the trap door to see Susan's face looking up to her.

"Yes, and what is it?"

"Mama, I told Moira and she thinks America is a very fine idea."

ST. LOUIS, MISSOURI—1865

Susan ran the dust cloth back and forth across the narrow window sill. Back and forth. Her movement took on the rhythm of the Terry clock on the mantle as she absent-mindedly pushed the cloth from side to side. Still lost in thought, she tried once to sit sideways on the sill, but it was too high. Twisting the cloth into a long cord to wind into a bracelet from wrist to elbow, she stared blankly out the front parlor window, past the white slats of the porch bannister, across the brief front yard to the red brick street. But she did not see the porch railing, nor the narrow strip of lawn, nor O'Fallon Street; her mind was on a road in Ireland.

"When are you going to stop daydreaming and be finishing the dusting?" her mother asked.

Without turning, Susan answered, "I'm all finished, Mama. I was just thinking about Mr. Shawn."

Ellen came up behind her daughter and rested her chin on Susan's soft hair. Putting her arms over Susan's, she too looked out the open window; but she saw only an ugly city street.

"It's lonesome you are for home, isn't it, mavourneen?"

"Some, Mama, but I like it here, don't you?"

Ellen did not answer.

"If when you look out, Mama, you look above the houses, the sky looks like Ireland's. And besides, we never had red brick streets with gas lamps!" Susan wiggled free of her mother's embrace and turned toward her. "I love the street lamps best." A clip of horses' hoofs drew her attention back to the window. "And such carriages, Mama! I do hope we can get a carriage someday."

"Now never you mind wishing for things we can't be affording. Shake out that cloth and put it away, then up to the sewing room with you."

"I didn't know Anne and Eliza came home."

"They didn't."

"But I thought you . . ."

"Never you mind what I said. We'll be waiting no longer for those two. Call Jenny. She's in the back yard with the boys."

Ellen straightened the red plush cushion at the end of the settee. She sighed. Things were so simple for children. Five months and they'd forgotten their real home. Five months and already some of her worst worries had come true. Just take those girls, Anne and Eliza, fourteen and fifteen, running hither and yon, over at the Bryants', over at Rodens', walking clear up to Washington Avenue to watch the trolleys. She had told Mark that this had to stop. When was he going to realize that this was no place for rearing children?

She sighed again as she started up the straight, stiff stairway. This wasn't her idea of a house either. She even had the feeling that all of them looked less like a family in this place. Perhaps that it did not really belong to them—though heaven forbid that she'd want to own it—bothered her the most. Well, at least she had a sewing room. Though the good Lord knew it was all she could do to get the girls together to use it. Pausing in the doorway, she tried to regain her composure.

"Look, Mama." Kitty walked toward Ellen holding out a long piece of crocheted lace. "I think it will be ready for Maria's table runner."

"Who ever heard of giving gifts for a month's wedding anniversary?" Mrs. Carty teased.

Kitty gave her a satisfied grin as her mother inspected the work. Knowing her mother's nod was high praise, she returned to her wicker chair near the window.

"I can't quite believe that Maria is away from us only a month. It seems she's been gone forever," Ellen said as she picked up the sampler Anne had been fiddling with for days. She frowned. Those blue stitches would have to come out. All going the opposite direction!

"I think David is very nice," commented Kitty, who at seventeen thought the combination of David Roden's elegant manners and Maria's dark beauty something right out of *Lippincott's Magazine*.

"Yes, he's a fine enough lad, Kitty, with his easy way." Ellen's voice carried a note of reservation; "but mighty sure of himself. You are old enough to be knowing what I mean. Why when I think that he had the very boldness to ask Maria to marry him after only being acquainted four months . . ." She paused. "But maybe his father being your father's distant cousin made him think it wasn't as if they were exactly strangers. But I said to your father . . ."

"Here we are, Mama," Susan announced as she and Jenny bounded into the room.

"Well, good! Now, Susan, your shuttle's over there on that table between the windows. Have Kitty show you once again how you are to hold the thread. Jenny, you—Jenny, did you wash your hands after playing with those cats?"

"Yessum. See." She held her hands, palms toward her mother.

"All right, then you can be undoing this embroidery thread for me. The baby got into it again."

"Ah, why do I always got to undone it?" Jenny complained as she took the box of tangled thread and sat down in the middle of the floor.

"Because you don't keep it out of Delia's way," Kitty laughed.

Ellen glanced around the room. She looked at Kitty crocheting, at Susan struggling with the tatting, and at Jenny "undone-ing" the thread. She picked up one of Mark's work shirts to mend the collar. Well, he was pleased enough with America. My, how he talked about the mill! You'd think he owned the place. Men and children found everything so simple—bring them half around the world and they thrived, but with a woman it was different.

"This always looked so easy," Susan was saying to Kitty.

Ellen stopped a moment to watch Susan. The tiny soiled knots of thread were increasing in number around the hassock. How like Susan; she never gives up. She will keep trying until she learns.

"Why don't you try knitting for a while, Susie?" Kitty asked.

"No, I think I've almost got it." She walked over to her mother. "Look, Mama, is this the way?" And she drew the thread around her slender fingers and slid the shuttle through with the greatest ease.

"Why, mavourneen, that's fine!" her mother laughed.

"Mama, will I ever learn to tat?" Susan asked.

"Of course, you will. What are a few soiled knots to the likes of Susan Carty?"

The engine made small, harsh groans inside the boat. Lapping the muddy water with slaps of sound, the big wheel churned one more circle of spattered brown drops, and stopped.

As Susan turned to look up at David, a streak of sunlight mirrored across her face. Squinting, she watched him for a moment. He was scanning the small crowd on the landing, totally oblivious of Susan's questioning expression. Since he paid no attention to her, she turned to Maria instead.

Tilting her head to one side like a little bird, she asked, "Is this Cape Girardeau?"

Maria nodded; and Susan, satisfied, turned her attention again to the activity on the landing. Far below them, she had seen two fat ropes come flying out of the boat like wild serpents leaping at the big black men on shore; but the men, polished and shining in the sun, caught the serpents and were now winding them around and around two posts on the dock. These were junglemen who turned serpents into dead rope. My, but she'd like to tell Moira, and Mr. Shawn, too, about this.

Maria, watching Susan's obvious delight with all that was happening, could not help but think how grown-up she acted. Susan, in a blue taffeta dress with flounces of ecru lace and a wide sash that puffed out into a stout bow at the back, hardly seemed the same Susan who had once provoked her mother into saying, "You wouldn't be knowing how to take care of fine clothes," when Susan had come home with her cotton apron stained purple with raspberries. Yet here she was a prim little miss of twelve.

"There they are!" David almost shouted, jolting Maria out of her reverie. "See, Maria. Look, Susie, there they are. I think they see us." And he began waving his hat frantically.

Beyond that rainbow of color, which was really a cluster of ladies in hoop skirts and feather-decked hats, stood two women in identical black. The older of the two smiled to herself as she watched the young nun at her side. If I gave her half a nod, she was thinking, she would gather in her skirts and run to meet them.

But Sister did not have long to wait. Maria and David came down the plank with Susan following them. As they reached the landing, Maria smiled at David, who, leaving his wife and Susan, made the last few feet in a sudden flash of boyishness.

"We are so glad to see you, Mr. Roden," the older nun said as he came up to them.

Sister Cecilia, watching her brother and Mother Bridget exchange greetings, hugged her hands together like a little girl at her first surprise party. Then holding out both hands to him, she said, "Oh, David, I am so glad you could come."

"You're taking good care of our Mary, Mother Bridget." He smiled, delighting in the flush of pink his remark brought to his sister's cheeks.

"Where's the baby, David? I thought surely you'd bring him."

"We didn't want to take him traveling too young. He might turn out to be a vagabond like you," David teased.

"Mother Bridget, how are you?" Maria asked warmly as she and Susan joined them. "And Sister Cecilia," she said, giving the young nun a hug.

Tapping Susan's bonnet lightly with his hand, David said to Mother Bridget, "Here is your prospective student, Mother, one of the most charming colleens," he glanced at Maria, "to come from the Land of Saints and Scholars." Then with all the charm of his Irish ancestry, he made a slight bow for Susan's benefit. "And, Susie, this is Sister Cecilia."

Susan looked over from the older nun to young Sister Cecilia and then back again at Mother Bridget. Her eyes rested for a moment on the two red hearts embroidered on the front of Mother Bridget's habit. The nun's veil was like a hooded bonnet caught under the chin and falling cape-like to the waist. Except for the two red hearts on their capes and a white collar, both sisters were dressed completely in black. Susan wanted to stare at the lovely hearts, but instead she looked to the edge of her own skirt, where the tips of her cloth-top slippers shone in the morning sun.

"You're going to love our school, Susan," Sister Cecilia was saying.

Mother Bridget suggested that it was time for them to start for the academy. As they walked, they soon saw St. Vincent's Academy high on the hill ahead. Facing the river, it looked, with its three rows of white porches against the rusty red of the brick, more like a spacious, gracious home than a convent boarding school.

The morning sun sifting through the great oaks made splashes of light along the way like the occasional bits of laughter that punctuated the conversation of the happily chattering group. As they neared the grounds, edged by a stone wall, Maria was asking, "How many years have the Sisters of Loretto been here, Mother?"

"Since 1838," she answered.

"Could the building be that old?" David asked.

"Oh my, no," Mother laughed. "That building wasn't built until 1851 after a tornado destroyed the other one."

"Oh, tell them about the mill!" Sister Cecilia encouraged.

"What about the mill?" David asked.

"When our sisters bought this property in 1838, they also got plans for the mill that was to have been built here. With their pioneer ingenuity, they took the plans and with a few changes used them for the school."

Susan had been listening to Mother Bridget's story. The word "mill" had struck a nostalgic note in her young heart and with a child's simplicity of logic, the very association in her mind between a mill and her father cast a spell of enchantment over the academy on the hill. She smiled at Mother Bridget as they all became aware of other voices, high and clear, the voices of little girls at play, coming softly like a murmur on the still July air. The few children who had stayed on during the vacation were out near the orchard behind the school, Mother Bridget explained. As they went through the gate, she took Susan's hand.

"We'll go join the fun," she said to Sister Cecilia, "while you take David and Maria up to the house."

"Why are the children at school on Sunday?" Susan asked Mother, as the two walked along the path between the academy and the frame house that served as the sisters' convent.

"The children live here," Mother Bridget said simply, adding, "This is a boarding school and a boarding school is home and school all in one. When school is in session, there are many children here."

"Oh," Susan gasped. "When I was little," she drew herself up tall to emphasize the fact that she was no longer little, "and we lived in Ireland, our school was along a road that went past the boogie bush. Fairies live there and steal children if they aren't careful; but my brothers and Jenny and I always ran past with our eyes closed and they never got us. I wish we'd had a school like this one," she said as she got to the point of her narrative about the fairy bush, "because I was always scared to go that way to school. The boys used to laugh but they were afraid too; I could tell."

"How many brothers do you have, Susan?"

"Just four. We did better on girls. There are seven girls and one dead which really makes eight."

"My, that is quite a large family!"

Susan looked at Mother Bridget. "How many in your family?"

"Oh, there are hundreds, Susan."

The child looked puzzled. Then Mother Bridget gave a knowing laugh. "Oh, you mean *my* family. Well, since you ask, there were eight of us and two of my sisters are also *sisters*."

"You mean sisters like you and Sister Cecilia?"

"Yes, that's right."

Just then a voice behind them said, "I thought you were going to find the children, and here you are." It was Sister Cecilia.

"So we were, but we got very much taken up with family matters," Mother Bridget said, smiling down at Susan.

"Mother, as we came across the lawn, Mr. Tom was looking for you. He's waiting at your office."

"Thank you, Sister. I must go now, Susan. Will you excuse me?"

Turning toward Susan, Sister Cecilia smiled. "David and Maria have gone to visit our chapel, Susan. Would you like to go too?"

Susan looked up at the young sister with eyes that saw more than a black-garbed nun, with eyes that somehow were claiming what she felt was hers. With that claim came a question. "I would like to see the chapel, but there is something I would like to know. Would it be all right to ask?"

"Oh, I'm sure it would. What is it, Susan?"

"Those." She pointed to the red hearts on Sister Cecilia's veil. "What do they mean?"

Touching the hearts with her hand, Sister Cecilia looked beyond the curve of Susan's bonnet to the blueness of the sky and smiled.

"They mean a great deal, Susan. They represent the hearts of Jesus and Mary." Then looking directly into Susan's serious blue eyes, she added, "They say that I am a friend of Our Lord and His dear Mother."

When Susan returned home from her visit to Cape Girardeau, she talked continuously about the school "where the little girls stay even at night." The art room with its border of brightly colored birds and flowers, its easels and paint pots, sounded often in her story; but she never seemed to tire of saying, "Why, they have a real little church in their own house and, do you know, the sisters have the hearts of Jesus and Mary on their black dresses!"

"Is it there that you're wantin' to go, mavourneen?" her father asked.

"Oh yes, Papa!"

"Well now, I think that a grand idea. We shall plan on it."

In the heat of a late July evening, thirteen months after their arrival in St. Louis, Mark and Ellen sat alone at the kitchen table. Putting down the newspaper that he had been pretending to read, Mark watched his wife's motionless figure. She looked so tired, her hands holding loosely the undarned socks in her lap. For months he had been aware that Ellen no longer sang at her work. He had thought that Maria's marriage would help, but it hadn't. Then he had offered to buy the house, but that had only brought out how much she disliked it. Now as the family gathered for the evening rosary, her voice would die away in the chorus of children's prayers and Mark knew that tears were the reason. This had to be settled. He had done everything a man could do, or he thought he had. Maybe he didn't understand how deeply a woman's heart can be rooted in a homesite, clinging to hills and fields, imbedded in its mother soil. But sometimes he felt that she hadn't tried to like America, but maybe she had. Who was to judge? Finally he said, "Elly, would you like to be going home to Ireland for a bit?"

Slowly she raised her head. Her lips parted in a whispered, "Mark!" Before she could say more, a tear ran down one cheek. Yes, of course, she wanted to go home, back to Ireland.

"Oh, Mark, you mean you've decided that this isn't the place for us after all?" She got up and walked around the table and put her arms around his shoulders. Resting her head against his, she almost laughed. "Oh, Mark dearest, I've been knowing for a long time that this was no place for us. I hoped and prayed that you'd see it too."

He reached up and took her left hand with his right and gently swung her around in front of him. "Now just a minute, Ellen Carty," he said. And before she knew what was happening, he had set her on the kitchen table in front of him. "Now, Elly, don't be building any false hopes. I'm sorry, but I was not meaning to give you the idea that I've changed me mind one bit about this fine country. I know that you've been homesick. No man could mistake that. And I'm clear sorry for it; and I want to see you singing and gay again; but, Elly, this is the place for our children.

There's no chance for a young lad in Bawnboy. Farming's the same as starving and even the milling business is a poor one now. You know yourself that for years I did the work of three men to give us enough to eat. When the milling was bad, I could carpenter a bit or tend the eel lines at the river. I'm not complaining, but I'm not for having me sons do the same. And I'm not bringing me daughters up to be wives for some other man's poor lads that may take to drink for their lot in life."

"But Ireland's a God-fearing country where you can keep your children decent and good. You don't seem to give that any thought at all."

"Now, Elly, don't make me angry. If it were thinking straight you are, you'd be knowing that there are as many sinners in Ireland as any place else. That's not what we're arguing. I expect me children to love and fear God no matter where they are. And it's to my way of thinking that they can do it better here where they can get a decent education and find more ways of serving God than just by being patient in adversity."

Ellen put her head down. He was shouting at her! It wasn't enough that she had tried to do everything he wanted. Now he was shouting at her and saying she wasn't thinking straight.

"No, Elly," Mark went on, his voice calmer now, "I'll take you back if you want to go, but I'm not taking the children."

She looked at him with amazement meant to shame. "Why, Mark Carty, would you be asking me to make so hard a choice?" These words fortified her self-pity enough to add, "How can you be so cruel?" And then she cried.

Mark did not answer. Was he cruel? Was he trying to force her to choose to stay? Finally he patted her shoulder. Then he lifted her down from the table. He drew her close to him and his right hand pressed her head against his chest. "Now, Ellen, stop crying. We'll go back to Bawnboy for a while. Then maybe you'll feel better."

He let her cry. At last she said, "But how would they get on without us?"

"Now, I've wondered that, and I think that John and Kitty

could manage things for a while. Maria's not far away. She'll look in. Who knows, maybe David would not be minding moving here for a time. But we'll see. We'd take the baby with us, and the rest are no trouble at all."

While Mark made plans to sail for Ireland in August, Susan continued to dream of Sister Cecilia and Mother Bridget and the academy on the hill. Her small trunk was already partially packed with dresses and things she would need for school, and there was no thought that her mother and father's trip to Ireland would change her plans for the fall. She was perhaps the one least affected by the thought of parting since she had already accustomed herself to the thought in terms of her own departure.

The first hint that her dream was to fade before it was fully conceived came when she heard Maria telling her mother that St. Philomena's School was not far from her home and that if the children came to live with David and her on Pine Street, they could walk those blocks to school. Susan thought it over and decided that Jim and Tom must be the children Maria meant. Even when it was decided that they would move in with David and Maria, Susan did not worry. Then one rainy morning after she had said something at breakfast about learning French when she went to Sister Cecilia's school, her father called her into the parlor.

Susan sat very straight on the edge of the wicker chair, her toes just touching the bare floor. Her father, standing with his back to a pile of boxes, the carpet in a long roll at his feet, looked unusually tall. The house was strange now, most of the furniture gone, the windows, free of curtains and draperies, seemed bigger than before. Susan smiled at her father. Searching for the words that would take the sting out of her disappointment, he seemed almost oblivious of Susan herself.

"Susie," his voice sounded husky. "I'm sorry about the school. What I mean, mavourneen, is . . . forgive me for not having told you sooner, but you can't be going like you planned."

Susan stared at her father. She swallowed back a gasp of surprise as she realized what he was saying. "You'll love our school,

Susan," Sister Cecilia was saying again. "You'll love our school."

"Susie, I know it's disappointed that you are." His voice seemed faraway. "It was my fault for not telling you before."

"But, Papa, you promised! You said yourself that I could go!" She jumped from the chair. "Papa, I have to go to Sister Cecilia's school!" Her eyes were wild. "Isn't there some way?" she sobbed.

"Now, Susie darling, if there were, you know I'd not be disappointing you. But I just can't afford it now with taking your mother back to Ireland. There just isn't the money I'd hoped there'd be." Mark wanted to say that maybe she could go next year, but there had been enough of false hopes for all of them.

"Susie, I'm that sorry," he said, putting out his right hand to touch her quivering shoulder, but she pulled away and ran toward the window.

"Susie!" Mark heard himself shout. "I will not have this nonsense! I said you can't go and that's that!"

Susan turned around and stared at her father. Had he really shouted at her? "Papa?" came a half-sob, half-question.

Mark rammed his right fist into his other hand. "Come here, mavourneen," he said marshaling a deep tenderness to the words.

Susan looked at him. Tears filled her blue eyes. "Oh, Papa, I don't want you to go away!"

Mark, crouching on his heels, held out his arms to enfold her. "Oh, Susie, I'm that sorry." And his heart echoed, I'm sorry.

The days passed and with their passing the time for Mark and Ellen's departure came. Strained silences that were foreign to the house on O'Fallon Street filled these last days. There was pretense at nonchalance on the part of the boys. Mr. Carty's repeated assurance that they would all be together again grew unconvincing; all wore a front of laughter for the others, only to shed tears when no one was looking.

Early one morning Mark and Ellen left St. Louis as quietly as they had come; more quietly, for children's voices, once anxious with questions about a new home, were hushed now and the few words they spoke had not the excited ring of a year before.

There were those last few minutes, minutes cruelly short, before the ferry pulled away from the levee. Throats tight, hearts pounding, tears, a child's nervous giggle, and then the last warmth of embrace. The boat whistle, shrill and unfeeling, cut like a knife the mother and father from their children. Suddenly there was space between and each watched the others grow smaller until finally they waved at what they could no longer see.

Had anyone noticed Mr. and Mrs. Carty as they boarded the train on the other side of the Mississippi that day in 1866, they might have wondered at their silence and thought the one small child with them a granddaughter, so old did they look. They were going home to Ireland, poor with a poverty that only those who have known the wealth of children can experience when they find themselves alone.

With the opening of school, the days of September moved a bit faster for the family on Pine Street; but for Susan these were days of bitter comparison. St. Philomena's School was not on a grassy hill covered with great shade trees, but on a plain city street; St. Philomena's School did not have a little "church" inside or an art room; but worst of all St. Philomena's School had no Sister Cecilia who wore the hearts of Jesus and Mary. True there were sisters. And Susan had to admit, they were very kind sisters in blue. And one sister was almost as nice as Sister Cecilia; but, of course, she had no hearts on her veil. She really did not even have a veil. "John, they wear great white hats!" she had said the first day.

"You're going to like it then," he said.

"I'll try; but, John, you should see Sister Cecilia's school."

The rise and fall of children's voices, like a sea of foreign tongues, eddied back and forth across the playground at St. Philomena's School on the corner of Summit and Clark avenues. In the far corner of the yard a line of little girls was lost in contemplation of counting to the swish of a jumping-rope. Nearby, in the shade of the school, six heads hovered in silence over a circle of marbles. Smaller children ran frantically in and out between the clusters of older children in an effort to keep from being tagged. Two boys, still wearing summer's mark of freckles, peeked through the fence at the girls. Above this running, whirling sea of sound and activity, the coronets of three Sisters of Charity glided slowly like white sea gulls.

As Sister Elizabeth stopped for a moment to watch the game of jump rope, a small girl with two straw-colored pigtails came skipping toward her. Emily bore the air of one who is not the only daughter in a family of sons for nothing.

"'Ster, please," she put her hands into the pockets of her calico pinafore and looked up at the tall sister. "'Ster, that new girl won't tell me what she's got in her pocket and I think she should."

Sister Elizabeth smiled and looked beyond Emily to where three other little girls had paused as if awaiting a decision.

"Susan is only teasing you, Emily. She probably doesn't have anything in her pocket."

"Oh yes, she does." Emily, emphasizing her reply with a vigorous bob of pigtails, turned toward the three. "It sticks out and it's soft!"

The little group moved a bit closer to Sister and Emily.

"I told her it's a bird, Sister," Susan called. "But she won't believe me."

"It can't be a bird or it would fly away, wouldn't it, 'Ster?" Emily retorted.

Sister Elizabeth looked at Susan's clear blue eyes and the mouth unspoiled by pouting.

"Emily, you should believe Susan when she tells you that she has a bird. Perhaps it is a play-bird," Sister suggested.

Susan had reached into her pocket and there in the cup of her white hand the soft down of what had been a bluebird lay very still.

"No, Sister," she answered, the trace of a brogue adding tenderness to her tone, "it isn't playing. The poor thing is really dead. I found him under a birch tree on the way to school." She closed her slender fingers gently around it and looked up at the sister. "At home in Ireland we used to find lots of birdeens after the rain. They haven't the strength for staying in their nests, I guess."

Emily looked at Sister Elizabeth with an expression that suggested Sister tell Susan to throw the ugly thing away.

"What are you going to do with it, Susan?" the sister asked kindly.

Susan's eyes widened with surprise. Do with it? "Why, take him home for a Christian burial," she answered.

Late the same afternoon as Susan finished her mortuary duties in the back yard, a man's voice asked over her shoulder, "What do you think you're doing?"

Susan swung around. "Oh, John! John, you'll never guess who you sounded like."

"Man or beast?"

"Man," she laughed.

"Hmm, Papa?"

She shook her head. She wished he were Papa.

"Patrick, that scamp?" he asked.

"No, wrong again."

"John, meself," he assumed a thick brogue, "that's who."

"All right then, I won't tell you at all."

"Ah now, mavourneen, please?" He pretended he was going to get down on his knees.

"If you want to know, you sounded like Mr. Shawn."

"Well, now there's a compliment."

"You know, John," her eyes grew very serious and very big, "I've thought a lot about Mr. Shawn and I think I know why Mr. Shawn's wife always locked him out. Sometimes he drank," she whispered, as if revealing a great secret.

"No!" John feigned amazement.

"John, do people ever lock other people out without any reason at all? Even if they don't drink? Can they just shut them out even if they love them?"

"Now, Susie darling, you're getting into the fast channel there. You had better stop asking more questions than you can handle."

"John, I just wondered."

"Well, you know, you still haven't answered my question."

"Yours?"

"Yes, I asked you what you were doing when I came out."

"I was burying a dead bird. Poor thing!"

"Well, now that's fine." He started toward the back steps before she could go back to her other question. "Are you coming in?"

"John," she called. "Did Mama shut us all out?"

"What?"

"Oh, nothing. I was just getting into the fast channel again."

ST. LOUIS, MISSOURI—1868

Susan stood in the dim upstairs hall with one hand on the door knob. She was taller now, with thick curls instead of flying pigtails, but still, fourteen was not so very old; yet today it *had* to be old enough for the care of three little boys. Straightening her shoulders to draw on whatever of maturity she had, Susan prayed, "Don't let them see me cry," as she opened the door to the room where Maria's three little boys slept. "Where are my boys?" she called softly, forcing a false calm into her voice.

At first she saw only Frank sitting in the middle of the high-backed bed. But as her eyes grew accustomed to the pale light of the single kerosene lamp near the head of the bed, she saw that Charles was a small mound asleep beside him. Maria's "wee one" was cooing to himself in the crib near the window.

"Here we is," Frank called, sliding from his place on the bed. "The boys," he said, using the expression the family of aunts and uncles had given them, "the boys was prayin' to go to heaven with Mum."

Susan walked over to the crib and scooped the baby into her arms. Charles was already asleep. When she had seated herself in the cane rocker, Frank crouched at her feet. Susan ran her left hand gently over Frank's tousled head, then patted his cheek affectionately.

"You know, I'm surprised at you, wanting to go with your mother."

Frank looked up at her, puzzled.

"Have you forgotten about your father? Who would love him if you went traipsing off to heaven?"

Susan wondered if this was the way to talk to a little boy about to begin a motherless childhood with innumerable aunts trying to care for him.

"But I want to go with her," Frank sobbed.

"I know, dear." Susan pressed the baby's head against her own—Oh why must Maria die when they all needed her?

Maria's illness had started with chills and a sore throat, then a high fever ending in delirium. At first the doctor had said she had a mild case of typhoid fever. "Must have gotten polluted water someplace." Then he decided that she had pneumonia. Whether it was typhoid or pneumonia or both, they did not know; but Maria was dead. And with her death, they were all without a mother again.

Susan sat in the dimness, not speaking, only waiting, as though someone might tell her why Maria died. After a few minutes she realized that Baby David had grown heavy in her arms. Looking at Frank, she put one finger to her mouth, then whispered, "He's asleep."

Susan carried her sister's youngest to his crib. When he was tucked in, she stooped down and lifted Frank into her arms. She carried him to the big bed. Giving him a tight squeeze, she put him down. "Now, you my darling," she said, holding the covers high to make a wide opening for him beside Charles.

When he was in, Susan tucked the covers around both boys. She kissed them. Then she tilted the chimney of the lamp to blow out the low flame.

Frank smiled up at her. "Aunt Susan, *you* won't go away, will you?"

"No, Frank." She smiled. Then blowing out the flame, she said, "I won't ever leave you."

The skip and pause and last throb of Maria's heart sounded a hurt echo many days later in a little house in far-off Ireland when Mark and Ellen received word of their eldest daughter's death. They said little to each other. What could be said? Both saw all the days of loneliness they had known spread before them as a futile reality.

One evening after nearly a week of silent grief, Mark looked across the table at Ellen. The sputter of peat punctuated the silence.

"Ellen, dearest, I've been thinking."

"Yes, Mark?"

"I've been thinking as I sat here that life has not been too kind to us since we came back to Bawnboy." He hesitated, then added, "And Ireland herself is not the place she was when we had our family with us."

"Mark, what is it you are trying to say?"

"Only this. The dream you had of being as we once were here in Ireland with our family gathered around us will never be. Maria, God rest her soul, is gone now and the rest do not want to be coming back here to Ireland. If we want our children with us, it is we that must go back to them."

"Oh, Mark, my thoughts have come by another road to the same idea. May God forgive my selfishness in wanting to stay here." She wept for a few minutes, but Mark did not try to restrain her. At last she went on. "It's the little boys that Maria has left that have tugged at my heart this evening. Perhaps if we were to go back to St. Louis, it would be to our grandchildren I could be giving the care and love I've kept from our own these years."

They passed into silence once more. The years had been lonely since their return. Each night as they knelt with little Delia to pray the beads, they were reminded that their family was not as God had meant it to be; one child where there had been eleven was loneliness that gnawed at their hearts.

"Ellen, dear one, would you be willing to leave your home for good?"

"Ah, Mark, you know as well as I that this has been no home. The hills and valleys of Ireland, though dear, make not a home. It is no home a man and a woman have that lacks children."

Mark, getting up from his place, crossed the room and laid one strong hand on her silvered hair.

"How can you ever forgive me, Mark?" she sobbed.

"It isn't forgivin' I must do."

"But I was selfish, Mark! I thought only of my own feelings."

"And which of us doesn't? 'Tis hard to know what is selfish and what is not. We must trust the good God to know the difference."

She leaned against his strong body and sobbed. How had God made one man so good?

"Susie, when you've finished stretching the parlor curtains, you could help Jenny wash the china in the dining-room cabinet," Kitty buzzed as she sat at the long kitchen table rechecking the marketing list. "This afternoon Jim can take the big carpet out in the back and give it a good beating. Mama was always so particular about keeping the carpets nice."

Susan wrinkled her nose and turned her face away from the steaming starch she was stirring. "When's Eliza going down to Union Market?" she asked.

"When I get this list made out. Tom's going along to help carry things."

"Kit, I think I heard the vegetable man."

"Frank's watching. I told him not to budge off the front steps until he sees the wagon."

"If the scissors' grinder comes first, he'll never remember." Susan laughed.

"No, I think David made it clear last night that he's not to follow him any more."

"Aunt Kitty, the vegetable man from Gravois Road's here!" Frank shouted from the front hallway.

Even David was not left out of the preparations. That evening Kitty had him up on a ladder cleaning the hall chandelier. He was in this position, with a big checkered apron tied around his middle, when Patrick and his wife came by to see if there was anything they could do.

"Pardon me, madam," Pat chuckled. "But is Mr. Roden anywhere about?"

David wiped a dusty hand across his face. "No, my good fellow, he isn't. This is a house of women, didn't you know?"

If the rest of the family was excited, Frank and Charles, who had heard so much about Grandpa and Grandma Carty since they could understand anything at all, were no less so. Frank wanted to know if they talked "Irish" and if his father thought that Grandpa would teach them to talk that way.

"Aunt Susan, is Delia our sister or who is she?" Frank asked.

"No, dear, Delia is my little sister. She is your aunt."

"Oh," he said. Then after a moment of apparently deep thought, he remarked, "We sure have lots of aunts."

It was spring 1869 when Mark and Ellen Carty returned to St. Louis. David Roden, who now had three motherless sons to rear, could see no reason for them finding another place to live if they were willing to share his home. So at least for the time the entire Carty clan decided to remain on Pine Street. And for this time there were the old storytelling hours in the evening, the kneeling down to say the rosary together, the Carty laughter, and the Carty singing. Ellen Carty again found a use for her sewing needles that had been too long idle.

Ellen, sitting by the dining-room window mending Frank's overalls, looked up to see Susan standing in the doorway. It was hard to believe that her Susie had grown so tall. Almost-fifteen was a strange age for a girl—one day a woman, the next a child again.

"Alannah, come sit by me," Ellen said.

Susan pulled up a little hassock, the same one that had been in the sewing room when they lived on O'Fallon Street.

"Mama, you look tired." Susan smiled at her mother. "After just having Delia around for so long, I guess you aren't used to so many children."

"Oh, but it is good to have all of you again! You must know that."

Susan looked at her mother. Why if she loved them so much had she stayed away so long? She wanted to ask but she did not. Instead she would ask another question that bothered her more now. Half consciously, Susan ran her fingers across the worn blue overalls that lay in her mother's lap.

"Mama, I've been wondering about something."

"Yes, I could tell that you were."

"It's about Maria, Mama. I know that God does things because they are the best to do; but, Mama, I cannot help wondering why it was He took Maria away when she had three little boys to love and care for. And when the rest of us—" She stopped before she added, had come to think of her as our mother.

"It's not for us to be asking the good God His reasons for things, alannah. Yet it is natural to wonder, and I'm thinking that He who made us that way would not be blaming us if we get to wondering about Himself and His reasons. Maybe He saw how ready Maria's heart was or maybe—" She paused and looked away. "Or maybe He wanted to bring your Papa and me back. There might be many reasons all at once, Susie. Heaven's for finding out all that. But just because we don't know the reasons now, doesn't mean that He's without them."

"But, Mama, does God want people to suffer, to be lonely, to miss other people?"

"Now, alannah, there are many things I'd not be knowing about the good God. I know that He chose suffering for Himself and for His Mother. Suffering's a strange thing. Some of it we make ourselves and then we can't be saying that God wants us to have that, but suffering that we don't make for ourselves, like Maria dying, should make us turn to God, and then if we turn to Him and use our suffering like He wants, He can take whatever of value there might be in it and maybe save a soul from sin. Or maybe—maybe make saints of us. Susie, do you remember the kippeen you once found back home in Ireland, the one that you said God could breathe on and make a man?"

Susan nodded. She did remember.

"Well now, just as God could be working a miracle and making a man of a stick by breathing on it as He did once with a man of clay, it's by breathing suffering on a man that He can be making of him a saint. But it's the man who must breathe *in* the suffering. It's the man who must use it." She seemed to talk to herself. Finally, she said, with a catch in her voice, "Some of us learn that too late."

Susan looked at her mother. It didn't really matter now why her mother had stayed away so long. She was back and it was so good to have her again.

"I understand a little better, Mama."

"Well now, 'tis easy enough to speak of being a saint; it is going beyond the talking that's the trick." She smiled. "But now it seems to me that I recall hearing Kitty ask you to get the things from the market for her. Going to the market's good for making saints, too." She patted Susan's cheek.

Susan hopped up from her place. "I'll never be a saint, Mama," she said, giving her mother a quick kiss on the forehead.

"Ah, who knows, Susan Carty?"

"Do you like this dress, Mama?" she asked, twirling around to make the pink gingham skirt billow out.

"'Tis lovely. But 'tis a little vain I think you are."

"Oh, Mama, it isn't vain to want to look nice."

"No, but when a girl spends a long time putting ribbons in her curls and looking at herself in a glass, well then—"

"When did I ever do that?" Susan swung around again.

"Oh, go on with you. You better go to the market."

"Mama, would you have a quarter I might use?"

"A quarter now? And for what?"

"Well, there's something I'd like to buy."

"Another ribbon?"

"No, Mama, this is not for me." She whispered, "It's for Kitty! A surprise. A surprise to make her vain, too," she teased.

"Well, then take a quarter out of my tin box in the top drawer of the chiffonier. But let me warn you, Kitty'll not be for wearing any ribbons, so you might as well be saving my money."

With the market basket on one arm, Susan almost skipped down the front steps. It was such a beautiful day! Once on the brick sidewalk, she slowed her pace. It was only eleven o'clock. "There's plenty of time," she said aloud. She took a deep breath. Last night's rain had left the air clean, the whole world was clean, and even Pine Street looked better for its bath.

"Susie. Oh, Susie."

Susan looked back over her shoulder. She waved at Delia, playing with the O'Brien children in the empty lot across the street.

Today she was going to do something about Kitty. Kitty had a pretty face, but her hair! Unconsciously Susan brushed her own hair back from her face. She liked her own curls. They were soft and thick. They felt good bouncing lightly against the back of her neck.

Was Mama right? Was she vain? Mama had just been teasing. But if only Kitty had curls, she said to herself. Well, she could at least help her brighten up her hair. Now what was the name of that restorer? Adams, Abbott? Oh yes, Allen's! Mrs. Allen's Hair Restorer, guaranteed "to restore youthful color to faded hair." And Kit's was faded all right.

Just around the corner was the barbershop. For a long time now, another idea had come to mind each time she passed this place. Today she stopped. There was Mr. Ben, the barber, working on someone covered with shaving suds. There weren't any other customers waiting. She touched her hair again.

Mr. Ben looked up and waved the hand holding the razor. Susan waved back. Mr. Ben was more than what Susan's father would term a waving acquaintance because she had spoken with the barber several times when she had seen him standing outside waiting for customers.

She walked on slowly. She should get the hair restorer first anyway.

The market was on the next street. Susan was in and out in a few minutes; only getting the bottle of Mrs. S. A. Allen's Hair Restorer took any time. At first the man acted as if he hadn't even heard of it.

Susan crossed the street to walk home on the other side, but when she reached a spot opposite the barbershop, she stopped.

Maybe the hair restorer would be enough, but then if the curl would help Kitty . . .

Mr. Ben was standing outside leaning against the red and white pole and reading. No one else was around. Susan took a big breath and darted across the street. A boy on a new English bicycle almost lost his balance as he swerved to keep from hitting her.

"Hey, miss, watch out," he yelled.

"Sorry," Susan called after him, as she continued on across Twenty-third Street.

"Well, Susie, good morning," Mr. Ben said. "You nearly got yourself run down there."

"I was thinking about talking to you," she said. "Mr. Ben," she glanced around, "could I see you inside the barbershop?"

"Sure thing!" He opened the screen door and followed her inside.

"Mr. Ben, do you have a scissors handy?"

"You know me, Susie. Lots of scissors." At this he drew a narrow, pointed pair from his vest pocket. "Want something clipped?" he asked.

"Yes, I do. Here," she said, taking hold of one of her curls, "will you clip this off for me, Mr. Ben?"

The barber was so taken aback that his mouth dropped open in surprise.

"I'm not fooling, Mr. Ben. I want it cut off."

"Now, Susie. You can't be serious."

"Oh yes, I am. I'm going to give it to someone. It's quite stylish now for ladies to wear a false curl. I want to give it to someone," she repeated.

Mr. Ben was reluctant. "Well, I guess you know what you're doing. Does it matter which one?"

"No, just so you cut one off."

"Well, I'll take this one. It won't be so noticeable as that one there." And with that the scissors freed the curl from her head.

"I'm sorry I don't have anything but some newspaper to put it in."

"Oh, that's all right. Oh, Mr. Ben." She suddenly remembered she had no money left. "Does that cost the same as a haircut?"

"Oh no, there's no charge for that. But remember, you can't put it back on."

"I know," Susan said, as she glanced at herself in the mirror to make sure that her beauty was not completely gone.

As Susan walked out of the shop, a feeling of loss took possession of her. On her left arm she carried the market basket and in her right hand the newspaper-wrapped curl for Kitty. She wondered if she looked like Jenny had when Maria had to cut the tar out of her hair.

"Susie, is that you?" Kitty called from the dining room when she heard the kitchen screen door close.

"Yes."

"Come in here a minute, will you?"

"Yes, in a minute." Susan was still standing near the door. How was she going to tell Kitty about the hair restorer?

"I want you to see the flowers Grandma Roden brought," Kitty was saying as Susan came into the dining room.

"Kitty," Susan began.

"What's wrong, Susie? Is something wrong?"

Susan held out the newspaper package. "It's a present for you, but it's a different kind of a present. Promise that you'll wear it, Kitty. Please promise."

"Well now, what is it all wrapped up in newspaper? If it's something fancy, I don't know if I will or not. Did you make it yourself?"

"Well, in a way I did."

Susan handed her sister the gift.

"Well now, it feels soft enough." She turned it over in her hands as she unwound the paper. Then Susan saw that same expression she had noticed on Mr. Ben's face when she asked him to cut off the curl. "Why, Susan Carty, where ever did you get this?" At the sound of her own question, Kitty realized the answer. "Susan Carty, you've cut off one of your precious curls!"

"I want you to have it." She paused. "I want you to wear it. It's very stylish to wear a false curl, Kitty. And besides—"

"Wouldn't I be a fine picture going about with one of your curls dangling from my dull hair?"

"But, Kitty, I got you something else. Just wait till you see." She put the basket on the table and pulled out the tall narrow bottle of dark liquid. "It's hair restorer!"

"Well, I never in all my life knew that what I needed was hair restorer. Good Lord, child, I'm not bald!"

"Oh, Kitty, it's only to bring back the natural beauty of your hair. See what it says."

"Well, you can just take your hair tonic. I'll have none of it."

"Don't you want the curl either," Susan asked rather pitiably.

Kitty marched toward the kitchen without a word. When she got to the doorway, she turned around. "Of course, I want the curl. You gave it to me, didn't you? Just don't expect me to wear it, that's all."

Life on Pine Street between Twenty-third and Jefferson Avenue took on a pattern where month followed month and season season with not much change until a new decade began. Then it was 1870, but even in 1870 some things had not changed. The marketing still had to be done. One sunshiny day Jenny rested the brown basket against the hitching rail in front of the new meat market while Susan once more consulted the list.

"Please hurry, Susie, I'm tired of carrying this."

"I am hurrying, but I can't figure out what Kit means by this. Here, look. What's that?"

"Ah—ah—it looks like s-o-c-l-a. I don't know. Socla? Never heard of it."

Susan laughed. "You should be in the circus. Such faces!"

"Let's see it again," Jenny said. "Maybe that's not a *cl*. Maybe it's a *d*—soda!"

"Oh, sure, soda for baking. Jenny, you are a genius! I've changed my mind, you do not belong in a circus, you belong—well, some place where it takes a great deal of intelligence. Why don't you go back to the market and get the soda? And then to the confectionery. I'll meet you there."

"Where are you going?"

"I saw something in Hilliker's window. I want to see if it's still there. Here, take the purse. I'll meet you in the confectionery in about five minutes."

Susan turned around and went back the way they had come. The sign had been in the dry-goods store window for three days now; by tomorrow it could be gone.

Susan walked slower as she got in front of the store. That same young man with the black hair and the thin mustache was there again. Susan shifted the bundle in her right arm to her left and reached for the handle of the door. The store was almost deserted except for a few women in the back trying on shoes. The young man looked a little better close up. In fact, he looked almost nice, she thought.

"Good afternoon, miss," he said. "Could I help you?"

"Yes, you could." Susan smiled. "I noticed that you have a sign in the window."

"Oh yes, we want a saleslady for Saturdays. Do you know anyone who might be interested?"

What did he mean, did she know anyone who might be interested? What was wrong with her? "Well, frankly, I do," she said with such a slight edge of indignance that he apparently did not notice.

"Good! Tell her to drop around some morning. Mr. Hilliker, the man who owns the store, my uncle in fact," he cleared his throat to allow the comment time to register, "is only here in the morning."

"Well, thank you," Susan said as she turned to go.

"Tell your friend that I think the position pays eighty-five cents." His voice had a smile in it.

Was he laughing at her? Susan turned around; his face was still serious. "What all would she have to do?" she asked.

"Oh, you know. Ask people if they want anything, help them decide, take the money, make change, wrap the purchase. Nothing too hard; *I* do all the book work and Mr. Wilkes checks stock."

Susan hurried out of the store. She wondered why Mr. Hilliker wanted a sales*lady* when his own nephew wasn't even a gentleman.

Jenny was coming out of the confectionery when Susan got there. Jenny was going to ask what she had done at Hillikers, but Susan didn't look too happy.

"What's wrong, Susan? Couldn't you find the sign?"

"Oh, I found out what I wanted all right. Jenny, how old do you think I look?"

"I don't know. You just look like you, that's all."

"No, seriously, if you were guessing my age, what would you say?"

"First tell me how old you are."

"Sixteen, you know that."

"Well, that's it. You look sixteen."

When everyone was seated at the long dining-room table that evening, Tom announced that he had gotten a raise.

"Congratulations, son," Mr. Carty said, reaching across the corner of the table to shake his hand.

"Mark, you nearly upset the gravy," Ellen scolded.

"Sorry, Elly, but I'm that proud of the lad. I'm proud of you all," he added.

There were fourteen of them around the table. At Mark's right sat Ellen, and then came Delia, who was seven, next Jim, Eliza, and Kitty, all grown persons now. Next to Kitty was little Charles, David's second boy. At the end of the table sat David Roden with Frank at his right, and then Susie, little David, John and Tom, and finally Jenny at their father's left. That was the whole Carty clan except for Patrick and Anne, who were both married now. "They are a fine-looking, healthy lot," as Mark was fond of saying.

As the conversation subsided for a moment, Susan heard Jenny tell their father that Susie was going to go to work in a store. Suddenly everyone grew silent. Little David piped, "I didn't get my milk, Daddy." And everyone laughed. Susan could have hugged him for filling in the quiet.

"What's this Jenny's telling us?" Mr. Carty asked in Susie's direction.

In a way Susan was glad that it was out. She was dying to tell, although she had no idea how everyone would take it.

"It's a job at Hilliker's Dry-Goods Store being a saleslady on Saturdays."

Kitty looked across the table with an expression of horror. Susan thought that Eliza was going to faint. Her mother looked at her father to see what he would say next.

"That sounds mighty ambitious for a slip of a girl," he said.

"Say, our Susie will be joining up with those woman suffrage people if we don't watch her."

"That's enough, Tom lad. I'll be discussing this with Susan privately."

Susan could not tell from her father's tone just what he thought about the idea, but he had called her *Susan* and that usually meant he was serious. She was glad, though, that he had said that they would discuss it privately because she knew that he would understand when she explained how she felt about it.

There was no time to talk until after the dishes were done and the rosary said. Susan waited for a chance to get her father's attention. When he was looking at her and she was sure that he was listening, she said, "I think I'll go out to the kitchen."

In a few minutes he followed, saying that he would have a few words with her.

"Papa, I'm sorry that you had to hear about it the way you did. The only reason why Jenny knew first was because I told her on our way home."

"Oh, that part is all right, Susie. You are a big girl and you don't have to be saying every thought that comes into your head. But it's wondering that I am if this is the sort of a thing for you to be doing."

"Papa, it is a fine store. I am sure I could be a help to people there. I've watched clerks. Some are so gracious it's a pleasure to talk with them, but others! Well, Papa, some are really un-Christian."

He chuckled at her seriousness. "Susie, mavourneen, I am quite sure you'd be a help any place, but if it's wanting to help you can be a great help here at home."

"But, Papa, I'm not really needed here!"

"Now, Susie, you shouldn't be thinking that way. Why the little lads and Delia look to you as much as to the rest. And you are a great joy to your mother."

"But she and Kitty are always making up things for me to do, Papa." Susan smiled and her blue eyes sparkled. "Just think, I will be able to bring you my earnings just like Tom and Jim do and maybe you can be buying things you would not buy otherwise."

"You are a good girl, mavourneen."

"With gold in my heart, Papa?"

"Aye, with gold in your heart; but mind you that a bit of gold in your pocket does not rob your heart."

"Oh, Papa," she hugged him, thinking that he did not know that there were tears in her eyes.

Susan had one problem to solve before seeing Mr. Hilliker the next day: she had to look older. If Eliza would just lend her a dress to wear. When Susan got upstairs to the big, front bedroom that she shared with Eliza and Kitty, Kitty was not there yet. Susan was in luck because she was sure Eliza would help if Kitty wasn't there.

After the dress was picked out, Eliza had one more suggestion. "If you put your hair in a bun instead of in curls, you'll look older. But, Susie, you can't look grotesque and expect that man to hire you to wait on his customers."

"Why aren't you two in bed?" Kit asked as she came into the room.

"Oh, Kitty, Liza has just said that I might wear her blue alpaca. And she's going to fix my hair so I'll look older."

"I didn't say that I was going to fix your hair," Eliza protested.

"But you will, won't you Liza? I can't look grotesque, you know."

Kitty glared at Eliza. "And you the very one who said you

wouldn't lift a finger to help her." Kitty dug her hands into her hips to emphasize her disgust.

"Well, Kit, if she's going and if Papa approves of her going, we can't do a thing about it."

"I guess she'll be wanting all of us to wish her success," Kit said.

"You will, won't you, Kit?" Susan tried to look pitiful but her eyes were laughing.

"Yes, Susie. I hope you will look fifty-five in your bun and alpaca." Then she smiled in spite of herself.

Mr. Hilliker was just pulling up the green shades the next morning when Susan tried the front door. He smiled and nodded, signaling that he would be there in a moment.

"My, you are early today, miss. We don't open until eight."

"I wanted to get here before you got too busy. You are Mr. Hilliker, aren't you?"

"Yes, I am." He tugged at his dark green vest. "And what might I do for you, miss?"

"I've come about that sign in the window. I would like to be your saleslady."

"Well now, you would, would you? Hmm. Had any experience?"

"I've had the experience of a lot of salesclerks and I think I know the difference between the good ones and those that aren't so good. And I know I could be a good one."

"Hmm, you seem to know your own mind, which is a good trait in any business. And you don't seem to mind getting out early either."

"I would like a chance, sir. It would take me a while to learn all your merchandise and where things are kept, but I'd be willing to come in on my own time and learn about your store."

"That seems fair enough. Maybe you'd like to look around right now?"

"Yes, thank you, if you have the time."

"We sell just about everything in the way of dry goods. Over to the right, in that front section there, we have all the small items like ribbon and button hooks. Then next, back along that side is the yardage. As you can see, the shoes are at the rear of the store. Up on this other side, we have the ready-to-wear section for gentlemen, everything from spatterdashes to suspenders. And then up here towards the front are the ladies' things. Since ladies do most of the buying, we have what they like up front. Years back we used to carry food staples but now the straight grocery and meat markets are coming in. You know, miss, I didn't ask your name."

"My name is Susan Carty."

"Irish, I kinda thought so. Well, I don't have nothin' against the Irish myself. It's just as well you don't have much of a brogue though. There are lots of people come in and out who have some pretty strong national feelings. You know how it is. Just don't make any remarks."

Susan was not sure what Mr. Hilliker was trying to say, but she decided not to ask just now. Apparently this was a subject in some way connected with good business.

"Before I start on Saturday, I'd like to come in and really get acquainted. You know, with prices and all."

"Sure thing. My nephew can help you learn the place. He comes in the afternoon on a day like today; but if you want to come back after dinner, he could get you lined up on matters."

"Mr. Hilliker, may I ask what you expect to pay me?"

"A real business woman, aren't you? Well, Miss Carty, I think maybe . . . of course, you haven't had any experience and I could probably get someone who knows the business." He paused. Even the last remark sounded hollow to him. She had such a clear, straightforward expression in her eyes that it wouldn't do to try to fool her. "But you have been honest with me and I want to be honest with you. If you come in at eight and stay until six—with half an hour for dinner—I think that I could pay you a dollar a Saturday. A nice new silver dollar."

"Oh, thank you," she gurgled, almost forgetting that she was trying to look eighteen. "I'll be back this afternoon at one o'clock if that is . . . um . . . satisfactory."

"Sure thing. Very fine." As she left the store, he could not help but wonder just why a girl like that would want to work on Saturdays in a dry-goods store.

Susan had a hard time to keep from running home. Several times she looked back over her shoulder to see if Mr. Hilliker was trying to call her back to say he had changed his mind. At the corner of Jefferson and Pine, she waved to the dairy man, who had stopped to fix his horse's harness. Safely across the street, she ran the last fifty feet to the house, and rushed smack into her mother, who was just coming out onto the porch.

"You must have persuaded the man that you were old enough," her mother said.

"Oh, Mama." She swung her mother around, almost lifting her off her feet. "He gave me the job and he didn't even ask how old I am!"

Mrs. Carty's face was flushed and she was laughing. "My, Susan, I never expected a daughter of mine to lift me off my feet."

"Oh, Mama, I'm going back after dinner to find out all about it."

Following her mother through the hallway to the kitchen, Susan called to Eliza, who was peeling potatoes at the table. "Liza, the hair did the trick. I am hired!"

"I take for granted that you are now a woman of the business world," Kitty said stiffly as she came in from the dining room.

"Oh yes, Kit, Mr. Hilliker is wonderful. He said that I might come in any time and learn all that I like about the store."

"Well now, that's generous of him," Kitty said with a flavor of vinegar.

"What time will you be starting on Saturdays?" her mother asked.

"Eight, Mama. And I get half an hour for dinner and then I work until six. And, this is the surprising part, I'm to get a dollar every Saturday!"

"That's a mighty long day, Susie."

"You know, Mama, Mr. Hilliker said one thing that puzzled me. When I told him my name, he recognized it as Irish right away. Then he made some kind of a remark about a brogue and strong national feelings and 'just don't make any remarks.' I didn't understand what he meant."

"You have a lot to learn, Susie," Kitty added.

After dinner Susan walked back to the store. As she passed the front window with its display of yard goods, shirts, and shoes, she was sorry—and yet a little glad—to see that Mr. Hilliker's nephew was there moving a pair of ladies' pearl-buttoned shoes to make room for a pair of gray gabardine ones. Three dollars! Three Saturdays' pay!

"May I help you, miss?"

"I'm not a customer. I'm the new saleslady," Susan said, with a light emphasis on the *lady*.

"Oh yes, Unc—, Mr. Hilliker told me. Miss Carty, I believe." He could have sworn that she was the girl who had been in yesterday.

"I don't believe I know your name," Susan said.

"Burgess, Burgess Hilliker." He expected her to make some comment. People usually did, but instead she just grinned.

"Where shall we start?" she asked, looking around.

"Any place you like, Miss Carty. It's a big store."

The door opened and a stout woman sauntered in.

"Why don't you practice on her," Burgess urged.

"Oh, I couldn't yet," Susan giggled.

"Sure you can. Just ask her if you may help her."

Susan glanced at him skeptically. Was he making fun of her? Well, she'd show him. She would!

"May I help you, madam?" She smiled as she walked over to the woman.

"Yes, dearie, I would like a box of Lucifers." The woman smiled complacently.

"Lucifers?" Susan repeated. She had a mental picture of little red devils with pitchforks. "What kind would you like?" she asked, hoping to get some clue.

"Oh, it doesn't matter, any kind."

"Did you have any particular size in mind?" Susan tried again.

"No, but if you have sizes, I guess it's the biggest I'd want. My husband uses them for his pipe. Ten a day, at least."

"Oh, that's—if you'll excuse me, I'll see what I can do." She looked around for Burgess. Surely he had heard. Why did he just stand there fiddling with those shoe laces. Walking in his direction, she demanded through her clenched teeth, "What are they?"

"Matches. Lucifer matches." He gave a smug nod toward a shelf behind her.

When the woman had departed with her box of Lucifers, Burgess leaned against the counter and laughed aloud. "Say, you were great! 'What kind, please? What size, please?'" He smiled as he mocked her.

"Are you always this cruel?" Susan asked, in her best, grand ladies-romance tone.

"No, not if I'm treated kindly. You did grin at my name, you know."

"And you were rather obnoxious, you know."

"When?" he demanded.

Susan's face flushed.

"I thought so! I thought so! You are the girl who came in yesterday. That's funny!" And then he really did laugh.

On a Saturday evening late in October, when darkness came early, Susan was returning home from the store about six-fifteen. As she crossed the street, she noticed a man coming down the front steps. She quickened her pace. Maybe it was John going out early. In a moment she realized that she did not know the man.

"Good evening," Susan said as she passed him.

"Good evening, miss." He raised his hat. Then Susan noticed the medical bag in his left hand.

Susan hurried up the steps. Opening the front door, she found the hall deserted. Then she saw Kitty coming down the stairs.

"Kit, is someone sick?"

"Yes, Susie. It's Papa. He was brought home about three o'clock. The doctor says it's Papa's heart." Kit wiped her eyes.

"Where's Mama?"

"She's upstairs in our room lying down. She's awfully upset."

"Did you call a priest?"

"I should say not! Do you want to frighten Papa into his grave?"

"Well, Kit, if it's his heart, he might die!"

"Don't talk that way! He's going to be all right."

Susan swished past Kitty and started up the stairs.

"Where do you think you're going?"

"I'm going to see how Papa is."

"The doctor gave strict instructions that no one is to bother him. He has to get lots of rest. John is with him if he needs anything."

Susan continued up the stairs. She would see about Mama then.

She could see her mother lying on her bed with a white cloth across her forehead. Eliza was sitting on a chair next to her with her back to the door. Susan looked at the closed door to her father's room. What if he were dying and he did not have a priest? How could they all let him die without the sacraments? You have to let Papa live, she prayed. We need him. And there she was standing in the middle of the hall praying the same prayer she had prayed for Maria.

The door opened and John looked out. "Oh Susie, would you tell Kit that Papa is breathing easier now?"

"John, let me see Papa."

"Ah Susie, it's best right now if you don't come in showing emotion. That would be bad for him."

"John, I won't cry. I just want to see him."

"All right, but don't tell the rest that I let you in. He just can't have a lot of talking and fussing around."

Susan tiptoed into the darkened room. Her father looked strange lying on his back with his eyes closed. He was breathing in long throaty sighs. She stood at the foot of the bed wondering how he had been breathing if this was breathing easier.

"Well now, is that my Susie?" he asked slowly. He had opened his eyes slightly and was trying to smile at her.

"You mustn't talk, Papa," John said soothingly.

"Now, Susie, darling," her father said, "don't look so solemn like. Only the good die young, and I'm a very bad young fella."

Susan felt tears in her eyes. O God, please don't let him die. She tried to smile at him, and he moved one hand as if to wave at her.

Susan went back downstairs to find Kit, but instead she met David coming in the front door.

"David, did you hear about Papa?"

"Yes, Susan, I've just been over at St. Patrick's. Father McCaffery will be over in a few minutes."

Susan laid her head against David's shoulder as she burst into tears. "Oh, David, he can't die. He just can't!"

David patted her shoulder. He wanted to say that her father wouldn't die, but he knew.

"Well now, Father, I'm fixed! That's the medicine," Mark whispered when Father had anointed his mouth and his eyes and his feet and had given him all the blessings of the Church.

"I'll bring Communion in the morning, Mark. The doctor thinks it's best not now."

Mark nodded.

For two days Mark slipped back and forth from consciousness to unconsciousness.

At last Mark's lips were so parched with fever and his tongue so dry that his family took turns dampening them with a cloth. Even the few drops of water that reached his throat gurgled so threateningly, they thought he would choke.

On November 1 the doctor said he could not live another day. But he was still breathing in the evening and his chances for living through the night seemed as good as they had been the night before. Desperately Ellen Carty and her children clung to the thin thread of hope. God knew how they needed him.

After going through the motions of eating a supper which she could not swallow, Susan went back to her father's room. Her mother, worn and shrunken, sat in a chair near the bed. Susan went over and placed a hand on Ellen's shoulder, unconscious that she did what she had so often seen him do. Then she went to the other side of the bed and knelt on the floor. She took her father's big, calloused hand and held it between her own. It was not feverish as it had been. Tenderly she stroked it. This was his big strong hand, the hand that could easily swing a child or a sack of flour. If only he would grasp her hand now. She wanted to call to him. She wanted to cry out to him to hold her hand. It seemed that she was the one who was slipping away. He would go on. It was she who would change. He would somehow go on and on and always be just what he was—a gentle man with strong hands.

His hand was colder now, but it was still his hand. His face was drawn, but it was his face. The whole of her was a throbbing loneliness with a pain that tore her. This was the birth pang of a life she did not want. She was coming forth into a world where he would not be. Suddenly her sorrow erupted in tears. She knew. She knew that he was dead, but for one long moment she held onto his hand to keep from being lost. But she was lost. Maria was gone; her father was gone; and she was all alone. She breathed in all the suffering of loss.

ST. LOUIS, MISSOURI—1873

"Look at that one, Aunt Susan! See it? That one!" Charles was jumping up and down, pointing to another steamboat, but this one had a giant gilded eagle perched between its puffing smokestacks.

"I see, Charles. Don't get so excited." Susan patted his shoulder.

Frank's face was serious. He had been watching the slow advance of a coal barge since it had first emerged from the span of shadow riding the river beneath the unfinished bridge.

"It's going past," he said, disappointed. "I thought everything stopped at St. Louis."

"Not everything, Frank. Probably that barge is going down to Memphis or Vicksburg."

"Boats from everywhere, Charles!" Frank exclaimed to the six-year-old beside him.

Just then a boat marked U S MAIL LINE blasted a deafening signal that seemed to shake the river front. The boys clamped their hands over their ears; Susan frowned. As the blast died, she heard Frank spelling out the letters on the side of another boat.

"That's Cape Girardeau, Frank. You know who lives there."

"I do?"

"Sure, you do."

"Do I know?" Charles asked.

"Yes, you both do. That's where your Aunt Mary, Sister Cecilia, is."

"Oh, ya, I forgot. Is it far?"

"Not too far, Frank. Sometime we'll have to take a boat ride down. When I was just a little older than you two, your father and mother took me to Cape Girardeau."

For a few minutes Susan was a little girl again, looking up at

Sister Cecilia. The nun was saying, "The hearts say that I am a friend of Our Lord and His dear Mother."

"Pardon me, miss, may I help you?" a familiar voice asked.

"Oh, Burgess!" She smiled. "What are you doing here?"

"Looking for you, of course. I went to your house and your sister said you had taken the boys down to see the boats."

"How nice! Frank and Charles, you know Mr. Hilliker."

"Yes," Frank nodded his head.

"Do you have your horse with you?" Charles wanted to know.

"Yes, I do, young man. Would you like to take a ride?"

"Gee, could we, Aunt Susan? Could we?"

"It looks as if my steamboats have been surpassed by your mare."

"I thought you might *all* like to take a ride."

"We would *all* love a ride!"

Burgess' two-seated buggy was his latest mark of success. From clerk in a small uptown store to manager of a larger downtown business in less than four years wasn't bad, thought Susan.

When the boys were safely deposited in the back seat, Burgess helped Susan in. She looked like spring itself in her light-yellow muslin delaine suit with a gold-colored silk ruche down the front of the well-fitted jacket. At least a dozen times in the past three years, Burgess had told her how glad he was that she had discarded the bun for the curls. Now that all seemed so long ago.

"Do you have time to go out Washington Avenue and past Missouri Park?" he asked as he got in beside her.

"Of course we do."

Burgess swung the buggy around and threaded his way across the levee toward Locust Street.

"Watch for St. Louis University when we get out a little ways on Washington Avenue, Frank," Susan called back over her shoulder. After a few minutes, Susan turned to Burgess. "What's on your mind?"

Burgess pretended to be absorbed in the traffic on either side as he urged the mare to turn at the corner of Third Street. "What makes you think that I have anything particular on my mind?"

"You didn't come all the way down to the water front to give the boys a ride," Susan smiled.

"No, I came to see if you will change your mind about—"

"About the store? We've talked about that, Burgess. You know I couldn't do that to your uncle."

"Well, that's what I mean. I talked to him last night. I pointed out that his business downtown would benefit. I reversed his argument for keeping you uptown. Of course, he said that you would have to decide."

Susan did not answer. Burgess was dear. He really thought this would please her, but there was more to not wanting to work for him than she could explain.

"Burgess, I appreciate all this. Please know that I do, but I'm just not ready to make a change. I think that I am helping people as much where I am as I could downtown."

"Maybe it's time you helped yourself," he retorted. "It isn't only the job that I'm thinking about."

"I know that, too; but let's just leave things as they are. You are very sweet, and I think a great deal of you—"

"Yes, I know." His tone carried a tinge of sarcasm.

"I really do, Burgess!"

"Yes. And Mary, the dressmaker, and Ben, the barber, and my mare. You love everybody!"

"Is that so very bad?" She laughed.

Frank called over the seat that he saw the university, and Burgess made some comment about a new store as they turned onto Thirteenth to pass the park, but Susan felt the strain of Burgess' disappointment.

"Won't you come in?" Susan asked as they walked up to the door.

"No, not today," he answered.

"We're home!" Susan called, taking off her ribbed-silk hat and placing it with her gloves and bag on the seat next to the hall tree.

"So soon?" Kitty asked from the kitchen. "Did Mr. Hilliker find you?"

"Yes, thank you." Susan turned to Charles and Frank. "You two run upstairs and take off those good knickers."

"Aunt Susan, why didn't we stop in the park?" Charles wanted to know.

"There were reasons, Charles, but now let's change clothes."

"All right, but I thought—"

"Thanks for taking us to see the boats, Aunt Susan," Frank interrupted as he started up the stairs.

"Ya," Charles echoed.

Susan watched them both clump up the stairs. Wouldn't Maria be proud of them?

"Why didn't you ask Mr. Hilliker to come in?" Kitty asked as she came through the narrow hall that led from the kitchen to the front hall.

"I did, but he seemed to be in a hurry."

"We don't see so much of him since he moved downtown. How's he getting along?"

"Just fine. He really is a very good businessman, Kit."

"Did I tell you that the Lenahans are coming over this evening? Mrs. Lenahan doesn't know that I know today is her birthday. I'm baking her a cake and I thought it might be nice to have a little surprise party."

"Is George coming, too?"

"Yes, of course, and I've asked the O'Briens."

"It's going to be a big party!"

"Everyone except the Lenahans will be here at eight. I told her eight-fifteen. Then I told George not to let her get here early."

"That should be fun. What can I do to help?"

"Nothing dressed in your good suit, but maybe after we have dinner and you put on something else, you could ice the cake for me. Oh, my heavens, the cake! It should be coming out of the oven!"

Susan picked up her hat and gloves and started up the stairs. She couldn't forget Burgess' comment about it being time for her to help herself. Maybe that was really what she had been doing all along. Maybe she was actually being selfish by not going downtown to work; maybe she was being selfish in staying, too. She had to admit that it was rather satisfying being the only woman in the store. It was comfortable knowing she knew how to help people there.

Susan put her hat and gloves on the dresser. Then with a gesture that had become ritual, she picked up her mother's picture in its prim, black frame. Poor Mama, Susan thought, remembering those months after her father's death. Ellen Carty had faded—so desolate, so alone.

As Susan held the picture, she remembered, not without sorrow, the evening some six months after her father's death when she and David had been alone with her mother in the downstairs parlor. David had said that it was time for Mother Carty to think of herself. Susan had turned to see her mother's face strained with pain—a pain of despair. "No, David," she had said in that soft whisper that had always belonged to times of strong emotion. "I did that once and it will be the one regret I take to my grave."

A few months later, when Ellen Carty had become ill and knew, almost happily, that she would not live long, she had told Susan always to weigh well her responsibility to those who loved her. Since her mother's death, Susan had done just that—or so she had thought until today. More and more she had assumed a central role in the lives of David's children. She had thought that to be the way. Now she wondered. In some ways this was a selfish role. Had all the gold of being hero to these children somehow robbed her heart the way Papa had warned? Susan looked long at the picture. *Mama, I will weigh well my responsibility; I will.*

"Now let me show you this material." Susan loosened whole yards of a filmlike silk. "You'll love it! It is so delicate. Just feel it!"

A slender, well-dressed woman in her mid-thirties was examining the material with Susan.

"It is beautiful," she agreed, as she ran the silk between her fingers. "Now, how did you say it might be made up?"

Susan reached under the counter and pulled out a small magazine. "Like this," she said as she paged through the ladies' magazine. "For days I've been thinking how lovely this material would be made up this way." She turned the magazine around and pointed to a picture for ready-made dresses which could be purchased downtown. "Only I wouldn't use piping around the neck and bodice, I'd use a ruche down the front to the waist."

"That is pretty, but I don't like such a full sleeve."

"That could probably be altered. Perhaps the softness of the material would take care of it." Susan made a puff of the material to illustrate.

The woman felt the silk again and held it up against her to get the effect of the melon color. "I like your idea, but I doubt that the seamstress I have could make a dress with only a picture to follow."

"Have you ever had Mary Peters over on Market Street? She's excellent. Mary can do anything and she is such a sweet person. You'd love her."

"Well," the woman hesitated. "Now I'll have to think. My mind's in a whirl. About how many yards do you think I'd need?"

"I would guess ten, but I think that you should not buy it until you see a seamstress. Take a sample of the material and the picture. Then you can see how much you'd need and if she can copy it."

"Well, my, that's very good of you to suggest that; but after all your time I feel I ought to buy the material now."

"Oh no." Susan smiled. "You wouldn't be satisfied that way. If you are going to have a dress made, you would rather know that the woman can do it and when she could have it for you and just how much material you would need. We have a whole bolt of this. It just came in last week and it is much too expensive to be bought up in a hurry. Here, let me give you Mary Peters' address and the picture."

Susan was going to tear out the page. "Oh, why don't you take the magazine. I'll write her name and address on the edge of it. Then you'll have both together."

"You've been very kind," the woman said. "Thank you. I'll be back."

Susan glanced at her lapel watch. She had told Delia to meet her at Market and Jefferson at ten minutes past twelve. She wanted to get something for Kitty at the jeweler's.

"Mr. Wilkes," she called to the baldheaded man arranging boxes in the rear of the store. "I'm going home for lunch now. Could I bring you anything on my way back?"

"No, thank you, Susan. Take your time though. I have my lunch bucket with me today."

"Why don't you stop now and eat?"

"Oh no, I'm not hungry just yet. You go along."

Susan felt sorry for Mr. Wilkes. He must be lonely without a family. She would ask Kitty if they might have him over to Sunday dinner again soon.

Walking along the brick sidewalks, Susan thought about her life at the dry-goods store. She smiled. Now she was doing all the book work that Burgess was once so proud of doing. But this wasn't the answer. And she knew that working for Burgess wasn't the answer either. Burgess wasn't only offering her a job in the store. This was his way of making sure that she didn't forget his other proposal. When she thought about it, she wasn't really sure why it didn't seem like the obvious answer. He was everything she had ever thought a man ought to be. Oh, he wasn't as understanding as Papa, but Papa had been an exception in that. Was she being selfish? Was she thinking only about herself? She didn't think so. Burgess didn't really need her, at least not the way she thought someone ought to need someone. No, the new job wasn't the answer. Marrying Burgess wasn't the answer. There was only one thing she was certain of: she wanted to serve God and the only way to serve God was to serve others. Who were the others?

Looking up, she saw Delia waving frantically from her perch on the green bench at the streetcar stop. Susan smiled.

"You should have been here a minute ago, Susie," Delia almost shouted as her sister got within hearing distance. "A trolley conductor almost punched a man who shouted at him. Was he ever mad!"

Susan laughed. "Who was mad?"

"All three of them. A man trying to get on was mad too. He said it was all Brown's fault that the trolley drivers didn't keep their minds on their work. Who's Brown, Susan?"

"He's the mayor. Some people blame everything on the mayor."

"Oh." Delia seemed satisfied.

"If you can pull yourself away from that bench, we'll get Kitty's birthday present."

"I almost forgot. Do you have any idea what to get? Maybe some earrings? How about some of those sparkly combs for her hair?"

"Do you really think she would wear sparkly combs, Deal?"

As Susan opened the door, the quaint little brass bell over it jerked a happy jingle.

"Could I do it again?" Delia whispered.

Susan nodded. "But just once."

"Good afternoon, Miss Carty. How are you today?"

"Fine, Herbert. Delia and I came to pick out a birthday present for our eldest sister."

"Did you have anything in mind?"

"Not definitely. She doesn't usually care for jewelry, but I thought if I could find a rather plain locket maybe I could persuade her to wear it."

"I see." The man opened a glass case behind him and drew out a plush tray covered with lockets of various shapes and sizes. "We have some lovely plain ones."

As he turned the tray toward her, Delia stood on tiptoe to see too. "My!" Delia exclaimed wide-eyed.

"Maybe Kitty would like a heart-shaped locket," Susan said. "Do you like this one, Delia?"

"Why a heart, Susan?" Delia was obviously enthralled with one that flashed a blue-glass setting.

"Kitty is a friend of Jesus and Mary, too, Delia."

Delia looked at Susan. "She is?"

Susan held the locket in one hand, but her eyes went to a plain oblong one with a simple cross engraved on it. Kit probably wouldn't wear the heart.

"I think I'll take this one," Susan said, pointing to the oblong locket.

"Let me see." Delia stretched her neck. "I thought you were going to get the heart. Why not the heart, Susan?"

"Hearts and crosses really mean the same thing, you know."

The man loosened the locket and put the tray back into the glass case. "They do? You know, Miss Carty, if you don't mind my mentioning it—I think you are rather partial to crosses. Your watch case has a cross of sapphires on it, and not too long ago, I believe, you bought earrings that were tiny crosses."

Yes, Susan thought. He was right. But she liked hearts too.

"You won't be satisfied until you walk through the streets of St. Louis with a cross on your shoulders." He laughed.

That was a strange thing to say, she was thinking as they left the shop.

"Where are we going now?" Delia asked.

"Home. Do you want to carry the package?"

"Umhum. When do we tell Kitty?"

"Not until tomorrow, but she'll probably guess that this had something to do with her birthday. We just won't tell her what."

Waiting at the corner for a chance to cross Pine Street, Susan noticed that the bricklayers were sitting on the steps of the half-finished school eating their lunches. She wondered why she hadn't ever seen any of the sisters around? Didn't they ever come to see how the work was progressing? She must ask Kit if she had seen any of them there.

"I wish they would finish that school," Delia said. "If it takes much longer, I'll be too old."

"What makes you think you're going there anyway?"

"David said I could maybe. I think Aunt Mary's going to be there."

"No, Delia, honey. Sister Cecilia's not going to be there. David meant that sisters from the same order are going to be there."

They crossed the street and turned left. Funny, wasn't it, Susan was thinking, the way 2310 Pine had turned out to be home. It was to have been for only a short while, just until Papa and Mama came back from Ireland, and then when they did come back they all stayed. Now both Mama and Papa had gone.

While she was eating lunch, Susan remembered to ask Kitty if she had ever seen any of the sisters over looking at the school.

"Oh yes. Didn't I ever tell you? Oh, Susie, I'm sure I did. During February one day I saw two over there so I went over and introduced myself. They were from the Cathedral school. Somebody had brought them up to see how it was coming."

"You didn't tell me."

"Oh, I guess it was David I told. Yes, it was. I remember now. One of the sisters knew Sister Cecilia very well."

"Kit, what do you think about nuns?"

"Why, Susan, whatever do you mean, what do I think? I think they are marvelous, giving up all they do to help people. I could never do it myself, but I admire anyone who can."

"Kitty, you won't laugh if I tell you something?"

"When did I ever laugh at you?"

"Kitty, I wish I could be a nun."

"Lord save us, Susan. You a nun?"

"Well, what's so ridiculous about that?"

"Oh, it isn't exactly ridiculous, but you with all your love of fine clothes and parties and running around spending money. I just never thought about it."

"I don't think I'll ever forget the way Sister Cecilia's face radiates happiness. You can just see how happy she is."

"Well, look who's talking about radiating happiness. Since when have you taken to being an old gloom?"

Susan laughed. "Well, I can't join the convent tonight. I promised George I'd go to the first band concert of the season. And he always wants to sit near the bandstand so he can watch the drummer he thinks is so funny."

Susan knew that Kitty was right. She did love a good time and pretty clothes, but these weren't everything in life. Maybe this idea of the convent was foolish; maybe it was impossible; and yet, she couldn't get it out of her mind. All summer and into the fall she thought about it.

The Sunday night after Thanksgiving, Susan found an opportunity to talk to John about it. She knew that John, now twenty-eight and still unmarried, would—because he was so like her father—know that she was sincere.

"Aren't you going down to play pool tonight?" she began.

"No, I think I'll reform." He put down the *Daily Times* and took his pipe out of his mouth. "Say, this is unusual. Where is everyone?"

"Kitty and David took the boys over to see Grandma Roden. Delia said she has to study—imagine!—and Liz went to a friend's house for the night."

"And Jenny?"

"Probably upstairs weeping over *Uncle Tom's Cabin.* It's nice to have things quiet for a change, isn't it?"

"Since when are you interested in quiet?" John picked up the paper again. "How's everything at Hillikers, Incorporated?"

"Perfect!" she answered. When he didn't respond, she said, "John, I have something I'd like to ask you."

"Umhum," he grunted from behind the paper.

"John, what would you say if I said I were going to the convent?"

"Umhum," he grunted again.

"Did you hear me?"

"Umhum." Then he put down the paper, and, taking the pipe out of his mouth, he asked, "Where did you get the idea?"

"Oh, I've been thinking about it for a long time. What do you think?"

"I think I'm a poor one to ask. It sounds great, but I'm not much of a judge. Look at me. I'm still sitting around not sure where I'm going."

"Then you don't think it would be impossible?"

"Susie, my sweet, when did you ever find anything impossible?"

"But Kit thinks I'm too fond of clothes and having a good time."

"Ah, what does she know about nuns?"

"For that matter, what do I know about them?"

"That's why you should talk to someone who does. Why not Father McCaffery? He's levelheaded. He'd give you the straight facts."

Susan took John's advice. Father McCaffery had been a good friend of the family. He had been with them when Maria died and later he had come when their father was sick. She decided to ask to see him after Mass the next Sunday.

"And what can I do to help you, Susan?" he asked as they sat down in the stiff rectory parlor.

"Father, I've been thinking . . ."

"Oh?"

Susan had thought that this would be easy, but she couldn't find the exact words to express what she wanted to say. "Yes, I've been thinking about life." She hesitated. "Father, mine doesn't seem to have much purpose."

"Oh? Has something gone wrong?"

"Oh no, Father, everything is fine. That's part of the trouble. Everything is perfect, but I'm not really doing anything worth while."

"Well, how old are you, Susan?"

"Nineteen. I'll be twenty in March!"

"Well now." He laughed. "You must be patient. Some nice young man will come along and then you'll find purpose in life."

"No, Father, what I want to say is that I think maybe I ought to be a sister."

"A sister? You mean a religious? Well now, Susan. Convent life isn't all soft music and candle light. Have you seen some of those sisters herding a crowd of little urchins to church?"

"Yes."

The priest paused to think. "And your life, you must admit, has been pretty far removed from penance and abnegation."

"Abnegation?" she repeated, not sure what he meant by it.

"Yes. I've known you for a long time now. You are the sweet darling of that household, Susan. Just talk to David or Kitty or your brother John. Susan can do no wrong in their eyes. And that's natural, I suppose, but convents aren't like that. Could you take a back seat? How would you like being just one of the sisters? And obeying rules you might disagree with?"

"Then you think I couldn't do it?"

"I'm not saying that. I think you should think about what is involved. If you were to marry George Lenahan, for instance," he watched to see if George's name would bring any reaction, "you could have a nice little family and a home where your desire for human love would be satisfied. You'd have someone to share your troubles and someone to look out for you. Have you thought about that?"

"Are you trying to talk me out of the idea, Father?" Susan asked with a touch of pique.

"Certainly not, but there's no room for illusions in the convent. This idea of sweetness and light just doesn't fit the reality."

"But, Father, doesn't God give us the grace to face the reality?"

"He does, but He doesn't work miracles."

Susan did not know what else to say. He had really said the same thing Kitty had said, only in different terms. They were both probably right; and yet, she kept telling herself, it was only by serving others that she would ever serve God.

After a long pause, Father asked, "What kind of a sister do you want to be?"

"A long time ago I had thought that maybe I'd like to be a Daughter of Charity like the sisters who taught me at St. Phil's. But being so tall, I'd scare little children in one of those coronets."

"And now?"

"You know, Father, David's sister is a Sister of Loretto. Once I thought maybe I could be a sister like she is."

"But now you aren't too sure about the sister idea at all?"

"Oh, I think I'm sure," she answered so vehemently that she surprised herself, "but all the things you said about me are true. And yet, I really feel that it's only by serving others that I'll ever be able to serve God. At home in Ireland, I used to lead the blind beggars to the next house. It may sound funny to you, Father; but I knew even then that I could be happy only if I could help others."

"Fine," he snapped, as he stood up and looked down at her. "I don't doubt at all that you will make a very good sister, Susan; but I wanted to see how sincere you are. Why don't you write to David's sister and see what she has to say. Who knows, maybe the Sisters of Loretto won't even have you."

One thing, her responsibility to Maria's little boys, bothered Susan as much as her uncertainty about herself. Hadn't she promised to look out for them? As long as her own mother was alive, she knew that they had no want of mothering; but for the past year Susan had grown more accustomed again to thinking of them as her responsibility.

"Father, there's one other thing: the boys, David's boys. Since my mother died, they have been almost like mine. I think I understand them, and—"

"And you feel that you have some obligation to look after them."

"Yes."

"Well, Susan, that is very commendable, but not too realistic. Now I'm not minimizing your love for them nor theirs for you, but those three boys are David's responsibility and—with the help of you and Kitty—he has done very well so far. You know, Kitty did all right with you older children so I think she can manage the little boys too."

"But what if Kitty ever marries?"

"Now, Susan, you can't take care of every eventuality."

For one fleeting moment Susan was reminded of another time when she had been told not to take care of someone else's problem. "My mother once asked me what God was to do if I tried to take care of all His worries."

"She was a wise woman, Susan. I suppose she knew you would eventually get enough of your own to take care of."

When Susan told David and Kitty that she had definitely decided to become a Sister of Loretto, Kitty again wondered how she would ever be satisfied in those black clothes, but David said he should get a straight ticket to heaven with a sister and a "daughter" in the convent.

Telling the adults had not been difficult, but telling the three boys was different.

"I'm going to live with God," she said, and then caught her breath. "Oh, not like your mother or grandma in heaven. I'm going to live with Him on earth."

"You are!" Frank's eyes grew wide as he sat up in bed. "Where does He live?"

"Why, He lives in church," Charles said disgustedly. "Are you going to live in church, Aunt Susie?" He wrinkled his nose at the thought.

"Oh no." Susan laughed. "Would you know what I meant if I said I am going to be a sister and live in a convent?"

"Sure," Charles answered. "Like the sisters at school who wear funny clothes. And besides," he added, "Aunt Mary is a sister 'cause Daddy said so."

"That's right. And I'm going to be a sister like Aunt Mary."

"But, Aunt Susan, why don't you want to stay with us?" Charles asked.

"It's not that I don't want to stay with you; but it is something like your mother going to heaven. God wanted her, so she went. God wants me to be a sister and take care of little children like you and Frank and Davey so that is what I must do. Everyone should do what God wants. You must be good and obey your father because that is what He wants of you. Do you understand?" she asked.

"Sure," Frank said.

"I do too," Charles agreed. "But, Aunt Susie, when ya comin' back?"

Susan laughed. "Goodness me, I'm not gone yet and you asking me such a question. Come on, you two, and get to sleep. It's late and Aunt Kitty will be in here seeing what we're doing."

"Good night," Charles called.

"Aunt Susie?" Frank's voice was questioning.

"Yes?"

"Aunt Susie, when you see God will you tell Him somethin'?"

"Yes, Frank, what is it?"

"Will you tell God if He doesn't need Mum any more, we'd like to have her back."

Susan blew out the lamp and walked to the doorway.

"Will you tell Him?" he asked.

"I'll tell Him, Frank," she whispered. "I'll tell Him."

LORETTO, KENTUCKY—1874

The heat of the day still hung heavily on the air, reluctant to stir as the first breeze of evening rustled the tree tops outside the open window. Burdened with the monotonous drone of locusts beating their wings in slower and slower rhythm, the air was an almost suffocating pall hanging over the small room. In the shadows a young girl in somber black sat waiting.

"Tomorrow," she whispered softly, and straightened her shoulders in defiance of the heat.

No longer the Susan of lovely curls, her hair was now drawn back severely from her face. Convent plainness had replaced the ruffles and frills; yet in other ways she was the same. Six weeks had not wrought all the changes that religious life must bring, for these changes would be more a growth, a maturing, rather than a remolding.

As Susan sat there waiting, her mind went back to the first morning when she and Father McCaffery, and three other postulants, Nora, Catherine, and Mary, had arrived at Loretto. It seemed like yesterday; and yet, it might have been years for all that had happened since they rode slowly along the Bardstown Pike and first glimpsed the academy which told them that they were at the mother house of the Sisters of Loretto. There had not been much excitement that day, except the wild beating of Susan's own heart. The very slowness of the spring wagon that brought them from the train station was indicative of the quietness with which vocations are accepted by those whose duty it is to fashion a religious from the raw material God sends to them.

There was no great ceremony, no line of dignified nuns to gaze at her with questioning eyes, critical of her silk and lace, only a motherly sister who expressed her thankfulness that she had arrived safely, and a very quiet portress who scarcely looked at her after they had been introduced. The sisters had shown her and her companions to a neat little room in the guest house, where they were to stay until some minor arrangements could be made for their entrance into the novitiate. From the simple yet cordial reception they received, they might have been old friends whose familiarity made ceremony unnecessary.

The only novelty of that first day at Loretto was meeting the robust, jolly priest with whom the four girls and Father McCaffery dined. Father Wuyts was ecclesiastical superior and chaplain at Loretto; but since he himself seemed little impressed by his position, Susan had not felt out of place or thought it strange to be entertained by him. She smiled to herself now as she saw herself actually clapping her hands like a child and exclaiming, "Oh, will I ever look like that?" when she glimpsed a novice in blue habit and white veil crossing the stretch of tall grass beneath the window of Father's office. She had thought the novices would wear black too. What would Kitty say?

"Shust, you will," Father Wuyts had answered in his heavy Belgian accent. "If we can make from you an anchel. The dear novice chillen, they shust anchels."

Now, the six-week postulancy was over.

"Tomorrow," she whispered, "tomorrow I will be a novice. Tomorrow I will be God's for always."

The locusts had momentarily paused. The trees outside swayed in the breeze and at last the cool air found its way through the window. It seemed as though she had been waiting for hours. All the other postulants had been called. She was last.

"If Mother asks me if I have a choice, I'm going to tell her that I have," she said to herself. Her heart began to pound faster again as she thought of the awaited interview. "Oh, I hope she lets me have it," she thought, and then she whispered a "please" to God.

A low voice fashioned to silence came from the dimness of the hall. "Susan, you may come now."

She followed the dark figure without comment, moving as if

in a dream. In spite of the heat she shivered slightly. She didn't remember ever being this excited.

At Mother Dafrosa's door she was left alone, and after rapping gently, she entered. Mother Dafrosa, the mistress of novices, seated in a low chair behind the desk, looked up and indicated by a nod that she was expecting Susan.

Mother Dafrosa smiled. She smiled as one growing old smiles at seeing the promise of the future in one much younger than herself. Folding her worn hands on the desk before her, she looked at Susan. In six weeks she had come to know that here was character, tall and broad, character that reached out and influenced. *Steady,* best described her.

Now there was a question of a name for Susan. What was to be Susan Carty's religious name? What name could tell of her laughing Irish heart? Of her grave seriousness? Of her determination? What name would be hers when tomorrow, for the first time, she would wear Loretto's habit and begin her religious life?

Not one to waste time with nonessentials, Mother Dafrosa got immediately to the business at hand. "Susan, have you any choice as to a name?"

"Yes, Mother, I would like Wilfrid," Susan replied without the least hesitation. Then she held her breath a moment as Mother's face grew very thoughtful.

"Wilfrid," she repeated. "Wilfrid? Well, who gave you that name?"

Susan remembered Mother Placide's remark of several weeks before. "I hope you get the name Wilfrid, dear. It suits you." Ever since then she had rather thought of herself as Sister Wilfrid. It was like divine inspiration that Mother Placide should have said that, or at least Susan had thought so.

"Mother Placide suggested it," Susan said simply, wanting to add, oh, please let me have it.

"No, I don't like it," Mother said with finality in her voice. "It's too wolfish."

"Henrietta?" Susan asked.

"Henrietta!" Mother repeated as if she even disliked saying the name. "And who gave you that name?"

"Reverend Mother Elizabeth." Susan smiled.

"Well, I don't like it, Susan. It's too Dutchy for an Irish girl like you." She smiled at this and Susan got the courage to ask for another name she liked almost as well as Wilfrid.

"Mother, do you think that Sister Mary Henry is a nice name?" Then, remembering that Mother Dafrosa didn't like any masculine name for a sister, she suggested, "Decarose?"

Mother Dafrosa just sat there almost as if she hadn't heard this last suggestion. Susan knew what Mother was waiting for, and she also knew that if she said what Mother wanted her to say, the name that she had most dreaded would be hers. Why had the old Sister Praxedes died leaving that name of all names free for some unsuspecting postulant? Praxedes! what a horrible name!

At last Susan said, "Well, Mother, you will have to give me the name you think God wants me to have." She swallowed nervously and her face grew pink with embarrassment. Her heart was pounding wildly, and she could not look at the sister behind the desk.

"Susan, I think Praxedes is just the name you should have. It's a strong name, the name of a Roman martyr, someone who faced challenges, who died for her belief."

"Sister Praxedes," Susan said slowly. A saint was fine, but a martyr? And with a name like that? It really was rather funny—her named for a martyr. There was a long moment, and then Susan smiled in spite of herself. With sincerity, she finally said, "Thank you, Mother."

"Susan," Mother's voice grew matter-of-fact, which indicated that the discussion of her name was settled, and that henceforth and forever, like it or not, she was to be Sister Mary Praxedes. "Susan, since you are the youngest in the class, you will naturally come last in the order of reception tomorrow." She glanced at Susan to see the reaction. Ever since arriving, partly because she was the tallest, but more because she fell into leadership naturally, Susan had been first in precedence. Her companions had taken to calling her the "Old Miss," the title usually given to the oldest in a class.

"God plays games with us, doesn't He, Mother? He knows how anxious I am so He's teasing me. When reception was postponed from the second to the sixteenth, I thought I couldn't wait and now that tomorrow is almost here, I am to be last." She smiled and looked away wistfully. "I can wait." Then she added, "I could wait forever, I suppose, just so it would be sometime."

"That's a good child," Mother Dafrosa said. "Now run along and mind that you sleep tonight." She gave a little laugh. "That will be difficult, won't it, Sister Praxedes?"

The sky was pale gray, with pinkness rimming the fields to the east, when the first soft strains of organ music joined the silence. It was the long-awaited morning of July 16, 1874, and four young girls were walking in slow rhythm down the aisle of Loretto's chapel. Now that they wore the blue habit and white veil of novices, all except God would in a short time forget that they were hardly more than little girls. The world would look on them as religious and neither guess nor care that young hearts beat quickly and that the dreams of youth were still held sure inside of them. All the loveliness of being young they carried in their hearts to Him that day and He accepted it, a gift apart; and in silent beneficence, offered them eternal youth.

Here there was no sense of hard-felt sacrifice. An oblation was being made, but not one of the novices was counting the cost to self or questioning in her mind if this was the wisest thing to do with life. This was generosity and wholehearted giving. They were but a fragment like that fragment of each generation who reach high, dream of true greatness, and know the way of attainment. As they walked down that aisle, while morning spread the sky with greater radiance, earth looked up to heaven and heaven smiled on clay's unselfishness. An alliance was being entered into between four little girls and the King of heaven and earth.

The fingers on the organ keys stilled and the last notes hushed into quietness. Kneeling now in their places, they began the Mass with the priest and as his words rose audibly above their heads, "*Introibo ad altare Dei,* I will go unto the altar of God," their spirits soared up and up like larks mounting to the zenith of the sky. "I will go unto the altar of God." Freely with no regrets, giving my all, I go unto God.

"*Ad Deum qui laetificat juventutem meam,* Unto God who giveth joy to my youth." They brought their youth. And no one could guess and no one could know the joy He gave to them as they knelt at the place closest to heaven, His altar.

Now the song of the angels is their song as the words of the *Gloria* take possession of them. "Glory to God in the highest and on earth peace to men of good will." Peace, the angels sang and peace descended on those hearts that were right with God; now it settled in stillness on these wildly beating hearts, peace deep and sure, peace that God gives only to those who give their very wills to Him.

Laudamus te, sings the heart of freckle-faced Nora. *Benedicamus te,* rises Mary's chant. *Adoramus te,* comes the awed words of young Catherine. *Glorificamus te,* beats Susan's heart. We give Thee thanks for Thy great glory, they chorus. *Gloria in excelsis Deo* is their song as they kneel waiting for the moment when the celebrant will turn, and, pausing in the Mass, will receive them as companions of God's Mother at the foot of the cross.

The fingers lightly touch again the organ keys and music floats like a whisper on the air. There is a breathless moment, and then together they rise, together they go to the altar of God, to Him who gives joy to their youth. Together, as one, they kneel and the priest turns and the music stops and now the moment that was planned from all eternity has come. God has again seen fit to regard the humility of His handmaidens. Infinitely unworthy though they be of Him, He has desired these hearts and is about to take them to Himself.

"Sister, is it your desire to enter the novitiate of the Society of the Sisters of Loretto at the Foot of the Cross?" As the celebrant asks this question that has been put to all the young women wishing to serve God in Loretto's way, Nora and Mary, Catherine and Susan, each in turn, responds unhesitantly, "Yes, it is my sincere and earnest desire."

There is no more of questioning, words play poverty to meaning, and only the heart can know how much is held within the simple phrase, "sincere and earnest desire."

"Sister, express your desire in form," comes the celebrant's voice again.

"I, Nora Quinlan, now known as sister Mary Decarose . . ." Her clear blue eyes look down the years of religious life with no hint of what they hold.

"I, Mary Condon, now known as Sister Mary Oswin . . ." The merriment of a generous heart rings in her voice.

"I, Catherine Gorman, now known as Sister Mary Evangeline . . ." Her hands are folded prayerfully, awaiting their task.

And now for the fourth time the question is sounded and the youngest of them responds in tones tinged with the breath of Ireland.

"I, Susan Carty, now known as Sister Mary Praxedes, do freely and truly declare before you, Reverend Father, and before all present that it is my ardent desire to enter the Novitiate, and God assisting to become and to continue a member of the Society of the Sisters of Loretto at the Foot of the Cross. Amen. Jesus and Mary. Amen."

"Freely granting your petition, I, in the name of the most Holy Trinity, admit you into the Novitiate of the Society of the Sisters of Loretto at the Foot of the Cross and in blessing yourself and your habit, I shall pray that you may ever be found a worthy spouse of the Son of the Living God."

"'I, Susan Carty,' no longer Susan Carty, 'spouse of the Son of the Living God.'" The words are spoken and forever they will echo in her heart as a sacred trust. She knows that this is only the first of promises, a pledge that will someday be fulfilled in holocaust in the pronouncing of her vows of Poverty, Chastity, and Obedience, but to Sister Praxedes this is the day of oblation. There is to be no turning back, no retaking of her gift.

"I, Susan Carty, now known as Sister Praxedes," belong to God alone, body and soul, in life and in death. I am His eternally.

The novices return to their places. Blue habited, white veiled, they return newly named, consecrated now and forever to the service of God at the foot of His cross.

Sister Praxedes, with a yawn, put one finger into her half-filled wash bowl. "Oh, ice again!" She was so sleepy, and it was cold, so cold. Hurriedly she slipped into her clothes. They were cold too. Everything was cold. As she put her shawl about her shoulders, she shivered. Was anyone in the whole world as cold as she? Digging her hands into her wide sleeves, she reflected that the cold would at least keep her from growing drowsy during prayers. "Dear Lord," she breathed as she started for the chapel, thinking in spite of herself and all the holy maxims she had been hearing, "I wish I were warm in bed."

The chapel was chilly and looked even more so in the semi-darkness of early morning. She genuflected and went to her pew. The clock struck. It was a quarter after five. Kneeling down, she looked across the expanse of empty pews toward the Tabernacle. She smiled and said in a whisper, "It's cold in here. May I come warm myself at Your red lamp?"

Another novice came in and lighted an oil lamp on either side of the chapel. The soft tread of feet grew more frequent as Sister Praxedes became aware that the emptiness in front of her was gone. Almost everyone was in the chapel. The clock chimed and every head bowed low. "Holy, holy, holy . . ." the prayers began.

The voices rose and fell with unconscious rhythm. Sister Praxedes forgot the cold and the early hour. She forgot as she had forgotten every day. And as she prayed, she smiled and talked to God from her heart. It was good to know that He understood the feel of earth's coldness and the ache of a lonely heart. She looked at the sanctuary lamp. He was letting her warm herself by it.

Within a few weeks Sister Praxedes had found that there was more to novice life than the loveliness of blue and white. She had floors to sweep and pots to scour, clothes to patch and mend. She learned that laughter ripples freely at recreation time, but that there are days when homesickness aches in the heart until tears ease it away. Life does not change its pattern of joy and sorrow in a convent, only the point of view is different. It is the getting and keeping this point of view that creates novitiates. One day when she complained to Mother Dafrosa that she still disliked answering bells that called her from one task before she was finished with the one she was doing, Mother smiled. "You don't have to like them, Sister, you just have to respond to them."

"I know it when you say it, Mother. And I think I believe it, but when I'm just about finished sweeping the corridor, when I just about have time to get all the way to the end for once—the bell rings! And there I am. I revolt! I just revolt!"

"And what do you do when you revolt?"

"I get furious. I want to leave the broom right in the middle of the hall or, even worse, I want to dump the dust right there and just leave."

"And do you?"

Sister Praxedes laughed. "I haven't yet."

Mother Dafrosa did not say anything. She just waited.

"Mother, don't you think it is just a little inefficient never to allow enough time to finish things the way they should be?"

"Give yourself time, Sister. You'll come to realize that some things are only relative. To learn efficiency is not your reason for being here."

Coupled with this problem was a strange new longing. At times she felt her heart reaching out for her own identity. Everything that had made her Susan seemed to be gone. It wasn't so much that she no longer looked like Susan Carty—without mirrors she could forget that; but Father McCaffery had been right. She had been the center of the dearest family in the world. That was where she had been herself—Susan, Aunt Susan, Mavourneen. And now? Now she was Sister Praxedes. And who was Sister Praxedes? No one—just a novice who didn't much like answering bells.

Those bells again. Bells for this and bells for that. A bell for choir practice, a bell for prayers. Bells for sewing, bells for reading. Meal bells, bed bells. Bells and more bells.

The novices were seated at desks and their mistress was standing near the front of the room. They had been discussing why Father Nerinckx, the founder of their society, hadn't left Belgium long before he did, since he was in danger of being captured by the revolutionaries.

"It isn't easy to leave one's native country, Sister, even a country where one is not able to live in the way that one knows is the only way to live."

Sister Praxedes smiled. That was really right. Moira had thought America was a very fine idea, but Moira had stayed in Ireland. But Susan's mother had gone back. Leaving her native land had been too hard. Mother Dafrosa was right: it isn't easy to leave one's native land.

A hand was raised near the back of the room. Mother Dafrosa nodded.

Sister Evangeline stood up and cleared her throat. "Mother," she said almost dreamily, "what do you think Father Nerinckx thought about all the days he was alone hiding in the hospital at Dendermonde?"

"I don't know, Sister. What do you think?"

"I've been thinking that perhaps he liked being alone."

Some faces showed wonderment. Like hiding in a hospital for almost four years? Like being alone? Like not being able to go out and see people? Almost everyone in the room looked skeptical except Mother Dafrosa. She was visibly pleased, and asked, "Why, Sister?"

"Well, after he came over here—and, really, all his life he longed to join the Trappists—so he must have loved silence. He made silence so important in our lives."

Sister Praxedes visualized Father Nerinckx hiding in a tiny dark room. Even locked away from people, he could still serve them. "Physical isolation does not cut us off from the community of love. Only putting self before others will do that." She was wondering something else. Perhaps he loved Kentucky for its solitude. In his day it was empty of people. It was rugged and full of silence. As he rode his horse, Printer, over the hills trying to reach outlying districts in his far-flung parish (half of the state of Kentucky) he must have been glad for solitude; and yet she thought, he must still have been very lonely at times. A person could be serving God and yet be lonely—she wondered if the little boys missed her.

Coming out of her own maze of thought, she heard Mother say, "We were an institution of necessity. Father Nerinckx knew that the hope of Catholicism in pioneer America lay in the children. He was one man, and one man cannot minister to seven thousand parishioners and still find time to instruct them properly. So he thought of us."

"Mother, why do you think that God stopped him so many times before the order was finally established?"

"God didn't stop him, Sister—God tried him. There is a great difference. The fact that, as a young community, we had so many hardships only proves that we have divine approval. We are like the Church in that. Persecution makes for increase in the things of God. Father Nerinckx had to suffer everything from fire to apathy before the Society was successfully established.

"I think we should learn a great lesson from all that Father Nerinckx and the first sisters endured. Our title is Friends of Mary at the Foot of the Cross. Notice that Father Nerinckx put us in the position where he stood all his life, the culmination of which was actually a crucifixion. When he was forced by opinion to leave Loretto to another's charge, he suffered the complete death of self. The first sisters had to stand and see his crucifixion; and like Mary, they voiced no objection. There is a great lesson for us. Just meditate on our founder's life and you'll find much to learn."

Sister Praxedes had a thought. She raised her hand. "Mother," she said, "is that what you meant about it all depending on how you look at it?"

"That's right, Sister. And if you follow the thought through you'll find out as you go through life that the same thing can happen to two people. One looks at it God's way and the other in a purely human way. Humanly speaking, Father Nerinckx might have revolted and tried to justify himself when he was accused of severity with the community he had established; but he didn't. Humanly speaking he could have faced every situation in his life differently, but he used what came as a saint would. And, Sister Praxedes, I can assure you and every one of you that your life will bring as much in the way of opportunity for holiness. The element that makes for holiness is not what comes as much as how it is taken. See it from God's point of view and you're holy and joyous, see it from a human standpoint and you aren't even happy."

As Sister Praxedes left the classroom, the words "you aren't even happy" kept coming back to her. It was true. She knew it was true. Yet how did one go about always having God's point of view?

The next day was Monday. As Sister Praxedes cracked the ice on her basin again, she shivered. "Now what is God's point of view on this?" she asked herself. She smiled. She put one hand into the water; icy as it was, she could at least thank God she had some water. Mother Dafrosa's words about the bells came back to her. "You don't have to like them." Bells a bother or bells a blessing depended upon how you looked at it. "What a wonderful life!" she said to herself, trying to convince herself that it was true. "I love hot water for washing. Kit always had hot water for me in the wintertime. At home I never had to crack ice in the pitcher and then use it to wash. But God doesn't seem to think hot water is important in my life, so I shouldn't either. I hate cold water but as long as God doesn't provide anything else, who am I to complain?" As she dressed and hurried off to chapel she thought the idea was fixed. "It's all in the point of view," she told herself during meditation.

After breakfast the novices went over to the two-story brick building just across the garden from the novitiate to do their Monday duty. It was here that washing, rinsing, and ironing followed each other in quick succession. Quietly yet happily, with only the noise that swishing water and pausing irons can make, the novices worked.

Sister Praxedes had been helping at the tubs; but this morning Sister Thecla, the professed sister in charge of the work, said she would like to try her at ironing altar linens.

"Just do what sister does, dear child," Sister Thecla said in a high-pitched voice as she left her with an older novice.

Sister Praxedes remembered the time she had first tried to iron one of David's shirts to suit Maria's taste. This shouldn't be hard, she thought.

After watching the novice iron an amice, she was given a plain linen altar cloth to iron. As she tried to glide the iron lightly across one edge, something happened. The iron caught. Starch gathered on it. She waited a moment, letting it cool a bit, and then tried again only to have the same result.

"Try this piece of candle wax," the sister who was supposed to be teaching her whispered.

Sister Praxedes smiled gratefully and took the lump of wax. She rubbed it on the bottom of the iron and wiped the excess wax and starch on a cloth. She started ironing again. Soon more starch formed on the iron. It seemed forever until the cloth was finished. She was aware at the same time that the older novice had finished two cloths.

As she was putting her piece of work to one side and reaching regretfully for another, Sister Thecla was at her side.

"Sister, dear child, I think you would do better over there sorting clothes for the postulants to hang up."

"But I should like to try another one, Sister," she said softly.

"I know, dear child, but I think you'd do better separating clothes."

Sister Praxedes went over to the table where a mountain of clothes was waiting to be disentangled. It's all in how you look at it, she was thinking to herself. If I had stopped on the first shirt I ever tried to iron, I never would have learned to do them. She picked up a nightgown and folded it. If I had let the knots bother me when I was learning to tat, I wouldn't be able to do that either. It was that iron. She knew she could iron altar cloths as well as anyone else. "It's all in your point of view," came to her again. "Now Susan," she mentally scolded, "you are proud. You don't want anyone thinking you can't do things. What difference does it make? Where's your 'God-slant' on this?" She folded and argued with herself. The ice water had been a snap, but that old starch was too much. She was still trying to straighten out her thoughts when a bell sounded. A bell a blessing! All the novices burst into happy talk as they moved to one end of the room, where sorghum sandwiches and milk were spread out neatly on a large tin tray.

Sister Evangeline put her iron back on the stove and hurried to catch up with Sister Praxedes, who was already talking to little Sister Oswin.

"Oh, I'm tired," Sister Oswin said as she puffed to a stop on a bench.

"Why, Sister, dear child," Sister Praxedes said teasingly, imitating Sister Thecla's high voice, "the day has just begun. What's wrong with your point of view?"

"What's wrong?" Sister Evangeline said as she joined them. Sister Oswin had closed her eyes to give the proper impression of weariness.

"I've been washing habits, and I'm exhausted," she said with her eyes still closed.

"Your point of view is wrong, Sister," Sister Evangeline laughed.

"While you two are readjusting your vision, have a sorghum sandwich," Sister Praxedes said, handing Sister Evangeline one and placing one in Sister Oswin's limp hand.

Just then Sister Thecla came up. She was smiling as usual. Looking at Sister Oswin, who had recovered enough to taste the sandwich, she said, "Sister, dear child, will you run out and get an armful of wood for the stove while you are resting?"

Sister Praxedes turned her face so Sister Thecla could not see her. Sister Evangeline took another bite of her sandwich to keep from laughing. The bell sounded again as Sister Oswin picked up the wood basket and went through the doorway to the woodshed.

Being sure of her point of view was not Sister Praxedes' only problem. A new one was arising and she sensed it long before she was willing to admit it even to herself. For the first time in her life she was aware of how she felt physically. Sister Oswin had joked about being tired, but as the weeks went on Sister Praxedes became cognizant of a weariness she could not shake off. She was tired, but it was different from what she had known as tiredness before. It made her feel sick. She didn't even like the thought of food. Going to meals became an effort. One morning before the rising bell rang she lay awake. She had been awake for some time. She felt tired, but she couldn't go back to sleep. Suddenly she coughed and felt that her throat was full. She groped for her handkerchief and then she knew what it was that had awakened her. Blood came from her mouth—not a great deal but enough to frighten her. She lay back on the pillow and waited. Nothing else happened.

During the night it had snowed, so after breakfast Mother Dafrosa appointed a crew of six to clear the walk around the novitiate and down toward the academy building.

Sister Praxedes, not having mentioned the hemorrhage, put on her rubbers and shawl and a pair of woolen gloves. Somehow in the morning light her predawn experience seemed less real. Maybe it was nothing.

As she was going out the door, Sister Oswin came up to her. "Mother said we may talk while we clear away the snow. Isn't this fun?"

The two went out the door equipped with brooms. The snow was not very deep so brooms would do it nicely.

"Let's work together," Sister Praxedes said. "You're short and I'm slow so we should keep up with one another."

"Isn't it beautiful!" Sister Oswin exclaimed, leaning on her broom.

"Yes, lovely, but we'll never get finished if we're going to admire the view."

"Oh, you're too practical," Sister Oswin rejoined as she started sweeping.

"That's true," came the reply.

They worked silently for a while. Finally Sister Oswin paused to catch her breath and she smiled enviously at the long strokes Sister Praxedes was taking.

"Don't give up," Sister Praxedes called as she stopped herself for a moment's rest, and leaned lightly on her broom. Seeing Sister Evangeline coming toward her, she resumed her sweeping, though with less vigor.

"Look who's quitting." Sister Evangeline laughed as she joined them.

"I'm letting Sister Oswin catch up with me." Sister Praxedes smiled.

"You can't fool me. Why don't you quit? You look sick. Anyone can see that."

"I think I will stop," she answered seriously. Then with a twinkle of mischief in her eyes, she added, "I just remembered that Mother said she had something she wanted me to do." And before her companion realized it, Sister Praxedes had started up the steps.

Sister Evangeline stood there looking bewildered. "Something's wrong with her," she said audibly.

"And something's wrong with you, too," Sister Oswin, who had been standing behind her, replied. "It isn't a good sign when you find people talking to themselves."

"Something's wrong with Sister Praxedes. I know it," Sister Evangeline repeated, ignoring Sister Oswin's remark.

"Oh, she's all right. She just isn't used to working hard, that's all." Sister Oswin shrugged her shoulders and resumed her sweeping.

"I hope she tells Mother if she doesn't feel well." Sister Evangeline stood watching Sister Praxedes until she had gone inside.

With the temperature below zero and deep snows keeping dampness in the air, the winter months were naturally marked by sniffles and coughs that seemed to be waiting for spring to chase them away. Mother Dafrosa spooned out the needed remedies, warned against sitting in drafts, and saw that all novices bundled up in shawls and rubbers when they went out-of-doors. Sister Praxedes, like the rest, took her medicine and spent a few days in bed.

"Sister," Mother Dafrosa said one morning, with a look of concern, "you don't seem to be shaking off that cold as you should. Perhaps you ought to go to bed and stay there until it leaves completely. It worries me."

"This must be a special kind of Kentucky cold." Sister Praxedes smiled. "I never had one like this before. I feel so strange at times." As she described what she meant by "strange," Mother's brow furrowed. "Sister, are you telling me everything?" Sister Praxedes felt strangely like a little girl again. "No, Mother." As she told about the blood, she grew smaller inside.

"Sister, why didn't you tell me this sooner?" Her voice was more anxious than severe.

"I guess I was afraid to," she said simply.

"Child, remember this, your health is not your own. When you aren't well, you must tell me. God needs strong nuns who are able to do His work." There was great kindness in her words. Looking at Sister Praxedes, her eyes betraying her anxiety, she said calmly, "We'll see what the doctor says. Until then we must pray that it is nothing serious."

The doctor confirmed Mother Dafrosa's fear that Sister Praxedes was threatened with tuberculosis. Fortunately, Sister Praxedes was strong and the ailment had not progressed far; however, if possible, she should go west, he advised.

As Sister Praxedes listened to Mother repeat what the doctor had recommended, a new fear gripped her young heart. Could it be that she had no vocation to the religious life? Health was essential, and if she were really sick enough to be sent west . . . was Mother trying to tell her that she did not belong here at Loretto after all? Unable to say anything, she waited helplessly for the answer to her unspoken questions.

"We must pray," Mother said, adding, "I'm sure God will show us what to do." She smiled and looked at the young novice, whose face reflected the struggle going on within her. "You mustn't think the thoughts you have now, Sister. God is not going to give you up so easily."

"Oh, Mother." Sister Praxedes laughed, tears filling her eyes. "Oh, Mother, He just has to keep me."

In spite of Mother's reassurance, the prospects were not favorable. Sister Praxedes was still a novice, her health was in danger, there seemed adequate reasons for the superiors to decide in favor of her returning home. Her prayers were at once petitions that she be allowed to remain in the convent, and acts of resignation should the decision be that she had no true vocation. From day to day she awaited news one way or the other until a week had passed and it seemed that the matter had been forgotten. Then on Tuesday morning, while the novices were having class with Mother Dafrosa, Father Wuyts knocked at the door and asked if he might come in as he had some news which might interest them all.

"Do come in, Father," Mother said cordially, and offering him a chair, stepped to the back of the room.

Father Wuyts told the sisters about the honor which the Pope was giving the Church in the United States by conferring the pallium on Bishop Lamy of Santa Fe.

Sister Oswin asked just what receiving the pallium meant and Father explained that now Bishop Lamy would be an archbishop and the diocese of Santa Fe would be an archdiocese.

"Bishop Salpointe, who has been in the east, is going to take the pallium to Bishop Lamy," Father told them.

Looking at Sister Praxedes, Mother Dafrosa remarked, "Sister will be going west before long, too."

No further explanation was given. Sister Praxedes found herself wondering if she had heard correctly as no one else mentioned it or seemed to have noticed.

Knowing that the most discreet thing was to wait until Mother sent for her, Sister Praxedes decided not to wait. Ten minutes after the class had been dismissed she knocked at Mother Dafrosa's door with trembling hand.

As Sister Praxedes entered the room, one glance at Mother's serious expression caused a lump in her throat and she had the sudden impulse not to mention her real reason for coming. Before she could say anything, Mother spoke.

"Sister," she began, smiling now, "you know about Bishop Salpointe's journey to Santa Fe. Reverend Mother Elizabeth has told me that I may tell you that arrangements have been made for you and Sister Florence to meet His Excellency in Kansas City the latter part of May. You are probably destined for our novitiate in Las Cruces. I don't know, but at any rate God has answered our prayers. It will be a long and difficult trip, but I know that you are willing to endure it to get into a climate that suits you better."

"Mother, I'll go any place just so I don't have to go home. It seems that the harder I prayed for resignation, the more impossible it became." She smiled now, a sad smile as tears filled her deep blue eyes. "But my heart is heavy, Mother. Loretto is my home now and I love it here."

Fully aware of what leaving the home of one's first days of religious life can mean, Mother Dafrosa longed to sympathize with Sister Praxedes, but here was no need for sympathy.

After a moment Sister Praxedes took a deep breath, which crushed back the tears, and smiled. "He's good to keep me at all, isn't He, Mother?"

KIT CARSON, COLORADO—1875

"We're going to have a storm to christen the last lap of our journey," Sister Florence shouted above the persistent roar of wind. Although she had not intended the remark for the white-haired priest who was briskly approaching Sister Praxedes and herself, it was he who answered.

"A storm? Oh, you mean because of this wind." Bishop Salpointe chuckled. "My dear Sister, wind and prairie go together."

"And dust, too, Your Grace?" Sister Praxedes smiled wryly.

"The most annoying part, you'll find." Then, pointing at the pile of cinders that marked the abrupt end of the iron rails, he went on, "Take a good look at that railroad, Sisters. Before we even see the beginnings of Santa Fe, you'll be wishing that they went all the way."

"Will we be leaving soon?"

"Just as soon as you two Sisters get aboard our chariot."

The chariot was an unpretentious three-seated carriage, which promised, if not comfort, at least fair assurance that it could weather the miles between the end of the railroad at Kit Carson, Colorado, and Our Lady of Light Academy in Santa Fe, New Mexico.

Perched side by side on the back seat, with their small black valises on the floor and a yellow wicker basket between them, the two young sisters watched the last-minute preparations. Men browned by either natural pigment or wind and weather, Sister Praxedes could not tell which, checked harnesses, dislodged stones from under wagon wheels, and shouted incomprehensible words that were apparently related to the whir of activity.

Watching this strange ritual, Sister Praxedes felt a tingle of excitement in her fingertips. Was this the way the forty-niners had felt as they headed west? Seventy-fiver didn't sound as romantic; but the thrill was the same, or so she fancied. True, she wasn't seeking gold in some unmarked stream or mountainside, but what she did seek might prove as illusive. She did not let herself think what would happen if she failed to find health in the West. She only knew that she must find it.

She and Sister Florence, although still novices, wore the black habits of professed sisters; but the somberness of their clothes could not hide their common youthfulness any more than it could hide their differences of height and build. Tall, slender Sister Praxedes was a contrast to the medium-height, plump Sister Florence. But their greatest contrast, not even they realized. Each carried a secret of her own: Sister Praxedes' was fear; Sister Florence's was doubt.

"Look at the Bishop." Sister Praxedes nudged her dreaming companion. "He's like an old lady getting her house in order."

Bishop Salpointe, who as representative of the Holy Father was taking the pallium to Bishop Lamy in Santa Fe, felt keen responsibility for every detail of this journey. At the moment he and Father Bourgade were listening to something the small boy seated in the wagon ahead was saying. These three had been a long time journeying, the Bishop from Rome and Father Bourgade and his small charge, John Carbonier, from Paris. Their travels had made them a family.

Father Bourgade was telling the Bishop in French that John wanted to sit with the driver, but that he was afraid the boy would bounce out.

"Not if we tie him in. Domingo," he called to a dark, weather-worn man in dungarees, "give me that rope, please." Then to the priest, "We'll see that our boy doesn't tumble out."

Assured of his place with the driver, the little boy smiled broadly, displaying the space once filled by two front teeth.

"Why they're tying him in!" Sister Florence exclaimed.

"Do you think that we will get tied in too?" Sister Praxedes asked.

Sister Praxedes was lost in looking. This was all a new world of activity to her. Ahead, perhaps two hundred feet, she could see something she would not have thought possible. One man was maneuvering a whole team of horses to hitch them to the lead wagon. She was glad no one knew her ignorance, but she would have thought that the horses had to be attached one by one.

"Oh, look!" she exclaimed. "A little donkey!"

The man the Bishop had called Domingo, removing a block from in front of the carriage wheel, smiled up at her.

"Is he the Bishop's, Domingo?" she asked.

"Oh no, *hermana;* but she is not a donkey," he said with soft, genuine courtesy. "She is a burro!"

"A burro?" she repeated, trying to roll the rs the way he had done.

"Si! A burro! Burro good animal. She carry *mucho* but not so stubborn like a donkey. You see many burros in Santa Fe." His teeth glistened and his eyes smiled. He seemed to reflect in his very manner the musical quality of his lilting, questioning speech.

As Domingo went on to the wagon behind them, Sister Praxedes whispered to Sister Florence, "Don't you love the way they say Santa Fe? They say it with the same warmth of tone that my mother used to have when she said Ireland. What does Santa Fe mean? It must be holy something."

"Oh, look! The first wagon is moving!"

"And here comes the dust!"

Great clouds of dust rose into the air as first one wagon and then another jerked into motion. Both sisters were so busy fanning that they missed seeing Bishop Salpointe leap onto the seat in front of them, nor did they note that he made a triple Sign of the Cross. The sway of the carriage told them that he was there, however, and the rocking and the rumbling complaint of the wheels announced their departure.

"Here we go!" the Bishop called above the noise. "I hope that child will be all right." Then he glanced back at Sister Praxedes, remembering the letter in his pocket.

Slowly the caravan groped its way along the rut-ribbed road

that swung southwest as it left the solitary frame house. Here, too, they left the last railroad tie, poised like a period at the end of the Kansas Pacific Railroad. From the boundary between Kansas and Colorado, the rest of their ascent to Santa Fe would be over a trail which cut across the southeastern corner of Colorado through Las Animas and Trinidad, then climbed high over the Raton Pass into New Mexico, winding down to Otero, south to Cimarron, across the rolling desert to Las Vegas, and then rose steadily up and up through the hypnotic waves of *piñon*-dotted sand hills until it wound slowly to a stop at seven thousand feet, high against the sharp peaks of the Sangre de Cristo mountains in the adobe capital of the Southwest: Santa Fe.

But on that day, May 25, 1875, as Sister Praxedes looked back over her shoulder in time to see the frame house slip below the horizon, Santa Fe was thirteen days away and she, who was only vaguely aware of what the fever was doing to her body, still had no hint of how the same fever would sap her spirit before the caravan reached the heights of Santa Fe.

Nearly six hours after their bustling departure, stiff, dust-saturated, and already marked with sun and wind burn, Sister Praxedes looked out across the profusion of undulating grass and wild flowers, which stretched in what seemed like an endless flow of greens and yellows. Without realizing it, she sighed and put one hand to her eyes.

"Tired?" the Bishop asked as he closed his breviary and looked back at her.

"A little," she smiled.

"How would you Sisters like to walk for a while? It won't be long until sunset. Then it is not safe to walk." A signal to Domingo stopped the horses. Slowly, almost painfully, they managed to climb out of the carriage. After sitting for so many hours, the first few steps came grudgingly.

"I can't stop swaying," Sister Florence laughed.

"You'll feel it for days," said the Bishop.

"How do those poor little burros keep going with so much piled on them?" Sister Praxedes asked.

"Oh, burros are made for heavy burdens, Sister."

They walked for about half an hour, then the caravan entered a rambling canyon, where rusty scars left by the spring thaw showed on the gray walls. The trail grew too rough for walking so the three walkers once more took their places in the carriage. At first the hard seats felt almost comfortable, but as the trail grew steeper and rougher, the illusion of ease vanished.

No one even attempted to converse now. Every measure of strength was needed to brace oneself against the pitching of the carriage. Without warning, the sun slipped behind the canyon walls, and night seemed to flow out of the black clefts of shadow. The drivers raced the darkness, prodding their teams insistently. Some place between these slopes a stagecoach station waited. But with the haste, the carriage rocked from side to side as if being tumbled by two giant hands, back and forth, slower, then faster again with no rhythm, just a crazy frenzy of motion. As the tossing grew worse, Sister Praxedes gradually forgot about Sister Florence and Bishop Salpointe. She forgot who she was and why she was here. She forgot everything. Gripping the seat in front of her and fighting the threatening nausea within became her sole absorption. The sickening odor of wool and perspiration, the throbbing pressure of her veil pressing her damp-matted hair against her head made her feel that she was being smothered. Everything around her hammered her deeper and deeper within herself.

"It should be beyond this next turn," she heard a voice call. "Watch for light, Sisters."

Sister Praxedes could not steady her gaze to look for the light, but the thought seemed to give her strength to brace herself for the next few minutes.

Ahead, high against the canyon wall, a fleck of yellow marked the night. As they moved toward it, it receded, disappeared, and then reappeared, sometimes bright and sometimes only a hint. As the sky, turned indigo, fused with the dark canyon walls, the point of light took shape. What from a distance had been only a vague identity now formed an open campfire before which shadows wove a weird unrhythmic dance.

The shadows worried the Bishop. What if there weren't room for the sisters to sleep inside? The wagonload of men from Arizona were expecting to bunk out, and he and Father Bourgade were accustomed to sleeping under the stars, but he wanted the sisters to have a clean, indoor room to sleep in. Again his thoughts went to the letter in his pocket. One word kept bothering him. "Consumption," the letter said.

"Welcome, friends!" a voice called. "Looking for shelter?"

"Yes, we are, sir." The carriage jerked to a stop; but before it had stopped swaying, the Bishop had jumped to the ground.

As he walked away with the man, Sister Praxedes became conscious of a strange sensation in her ankles. Even before she leaned over to touch them, she knew that they were swollen.

"What do you Sisters think of the westward movement now?" Father Bourgade asked as he and young John joined them.

"I'll like it better after a night's sleep," was Sister Florence's opinion.

"What's the verdict?" Father Bourgade asked the bishop, who had finished his conversation with the stranger.

"We may use the fire to cook our supper. Then we'll figure out the sleeping arrangements. A friendly chap! He was here the last trip I made."

For the next half hour there was much traffic back and forth as the horses were unhitched and fed and supplies hauled from the wagons to the open fire. When Father Bourgade looked at Sister Praxedes' pale face, he suggested that the menfolks do the cooking for this meal so the two sisters could get a good look at a stagecoach stop.

The interior of the cliff dwelling consisted of two rooms about twelve by twelve, one sparsely furnished with a table and three chairs, and, in the far room, an old iron bedstead covered with blue calico. Several women from the other caravan had already made themselves comfortable by the time Sister Florence and Sister Praxedes arrived.

"We'll double up," a woman who introduced herself as Nell drawled cheerfully. "A bed's a bed."

"Is there any place where we could freshen up?" Sister Florence asked.

"Freshen up?" a corpulent woman wearing a pair of white-scarred dungarees questioned. "Oh, I know what you mean. Sure thing. I'll take this here bucket and fetch you ladies some water. There's a whole rain barrel full outside."

In a few minutes, the woman returned saying that she was sure sorry not to have some soap to offer them, but hers was out in the wagon under things. "I always saves my washing till I gets where I'm goin' to."

She left them with the assurance that they needn't worry about the menfolks coming in since it had been agreed that the inside belonged to the woman. "The trail has good manners about most things," she added.

"I can't stand myself any longer," Sister Florence said, taking off her veil. "I hate to shake it in here but I guess that's the only thing to do."

Sister Praxedes sank down on one of the chairs as Sister Florence poured water from the bucket into a tin basin she had placed on another chair.

"What's wrong? Losing your point of view?" Sister Florence teased. She splashed water on her face.

"Maybe so," Sister Praxedes said, with a strange seriousness.

"Wash your face. A little water does wonders!"

"Sister Florence, do you feel like yourself? I mean, do you feel like all this is happening to someone else?"

"No, but for a few hours this afternoon I was wishing it were."

The woman who had brought them the water poked her head in the doorway and called, "Those gentlemen of the ministry has supper about ready."

Sister Praxedes wanted to say something kind to her, but thinking was such trouble. Oh well, she was rough and probably would not care anyway. Immediately Sister Praxedes felt ashamed of her own thought. What was happening to her?

During their meal of dried meat, bread, and black coffee, Sister Praxedes revived slightly. Looking at the faces around the open fire, she forgot about herself momentarily, but then the firelight paled and once more she receded into herself, more sick perhaps in soul than in body.

Sometime during the night Sister Praxedes awoke with a sensation of pressure against her back. Crammed against the iron footpiece of the bed, she did not at first remember that she and Sister Florence were sleeping sardine fashion with the three women from the wagon train. When she tried to move, she realized that it was Sister Florence's arm pressing against her. Lying there unable to sleep, she longed to be back at Loretto, where the beds were clean and smooth, where one did not awaken with the hot weight of someone's arm on her back, where all was quiet and peaceful, where everything smelled sweet and holy and comfortable, where one could pray without men shouting in the background, where the food was not peppered with sand. The discord of sleep-weighted breathing seemed to mock her. "Where are You?" she prayed. "I am lost!" Drifting slowly back into an uneasy sleep, she seemed to be on a bit of winding road. "Moira?" she tried to say. "Lead me." And then she was asleep again.

The next morning as they were eating breakfast outside, Domingo came over and spoke to the Bishop in Spanish. They talked in low tones for a few moments, then the Bishop excused himself and followed the old Mexican.

"What's the trouble?" Father Bourgade asked on the Bishop's return.

"A gluttonous horse, I think."

"Too much corn?"

"Probably. The men are working on her now, but we can't get away for several hours."

"Good!" Father Bourgade said, rubbing his hands together. "Then we can celebrate."

"Celebrate? A sick horse?"

"No, of course not," he laughed. "Corpus Christi. Let's go up on the *mesa* and have a procession. There are thousands of flowers waiting to join us in giving glory to God. *Et vous, Jean?*" he said to the little boy with the toothless grin.

"*Oui, mon père.*" The child clapped his hands.

"What do you say, Sisters?" the Bishop asked.

Sister Florence consented with a smile, but Sister Praxedes held the tin cup to her lips, envying John's burst of enthusiasm. Somehow the very thought of walking, of even moving, was repugnant. Reaching down into the pockets of her once-abundant enthusiasm, she found herself a near pauper, robbed by fever. Once in the bright sunshine, knee-deep in prairie grass, she hoped she would revive a little. Gathering flowers, she hoped that no one would notice how slowly she moved.

"Let's sing some hymns and offer thanks to God for this lovely feast," Father suggested.

"And for the gluttonous horse that delayed us," Sister Praxedes added, with what sounded almost like bitterness.

Little John edged his way between the two sisters. In his right hand he clutched two limp daisies. He glanced first at Sister Florence and then at Sister Praxedes. Sister Praxedes knew he was there before she decided to give him any attention. Finally she looked down at him. He held out the flowers. Although she recognized the gesture of giving, she did not take them. Instead she gave him one of hers. His mouth made a thin line that failed as a smile. As soon as she gave the flower, she regretted her rejection of his. Oh well, she thought, he would have wanted them back in a few minutes. But in her heart, she knew that was not true.

Abruptly the procession ended with Domingo's call that the horse could take the trail again. They rushed back to the wagons and with one jolt felt any rest they may have thought to be theirs vanish as quickly as the dust rising behind the wagon wheels. As fatigue was stretched to exhaustion, and the roads became washboards of humps and gullies, Sister Praxedes grew desperately aware of her own weakness. She was sick, but why couldn't she fight it? Why couldn't she breathe in this suffering? Could one want to and yet not?

Just as she was going to ask the Bishop if they could stop, the sky blackened and hailstones, pecan-size, pelted them from every side. The wagons stopped and the men bounded out to restrain the horses. Blood appeared on knuckles and faces as the force of the storm lashed away. Bishop Salpointe called for help as he felt the reins slipping from his grasp. For ten minutes they all were panicky, fearing that the horses would stampede. Just as suddenly as it had begun, a shaft of sunlight escaped from the clouds and the storm ceased.

"You're shivering," Sister Florence said as she put her arms around Sister Praxedes' quivering shoulders.

The next thing Sister Praxedes was to remember was nightfall and a deserted cabin. That night, rolled up in a blanket on the dirt floor, she slept soundly. When she awoke, she realized that her whole body was itching. What was wrong? Bedbugs! She was covered with measlelike spots.

The next two nights and the day between they spent in Trinidad, Colorado, with the Sisters of Charity. After leaving there, the road was better until it wound up and up into the Raton Pass, where they reached the highest point of their journey. With the increase in altitude, Sister Praxedes' breathing became so labored that Sister Florence was alarmed. Suddenly Sister Praxedes grabbed Sister Florence's arm.

"Sister, I—" she gasped, then slumped against her.

"Domingo, stop!" the Bishop shouted. "Tell the wagons to pull up, Domingo. We can't go on."

Exactly what happened after that Sister Praxedes did not know. She only knew that, when she became conscious, she was looking up at a patch of sky encircled by faces. They were looking down at her. She saw the Bishop's lips move, but she did not know what he said. Then she closed her eyes.

The Bishop turned to Father Bourgade. "What do you think we should do, Father?"

"Where can we get a doctor?"

"I'm sure that there is one in Otero, but I wonder if we should risk moving her tonight?"

Father said, so only the Bishop could hear, "I don't think we should keep her in this altitude overnight. The sooner we get through the pass the better."

As the two men walked out of earshot of the others, the Bishop said, "I didn't want to frighten Sister Florence, but that little sister is very sick. Unless we get her to that doctor, I'm afraid she will never see Santa Fe."

"Her soul is suffering, too, Your Grace."

"Yes, I know; but if we get her to Santa Fe that might be fixed too."

In less than an hour the caravan was on the roll again. Sister Praxedes was not sleeping, but her eyes were closed as she tried to relax amid the awful rocking. She was trying more to shut out the murmuring within her than the roughness of the terrain. For days she had fought back the idea rising inside, but now she thought over and over again, "If I were asked again, I would say, 'No, I do not care to go to New Mexico. Let me go home, and let me be Susan Carty.'"

"The first time I made this trip," the Bishop's words caught her attention as she found herself listening, "was in '59. It took seventy-one days from the time we left Le Havre until we saw the adobes of Santa Fe. It seemed as if New Mexico were at the end of the earth."

"Did Father Bourgade come with you then?" Sister Florence asked.

The Bishop smiled as her question brought to mind the picture of eager, young Peter Bourgade, who had volunteered so wholeheartedly when Bishop Salpointe had returned to France in 1869 in an effort to obtain more priests for Bishop Lamy's far-flung diocese.

"No, Father came six years ago and he's been doing fine missionary work ever since. His parish is at San Elizario, Texas, now and," he smiled, "the day will come when he too will wear a bishop's ring. The Holy See is very much aware of the good work being done by the French missionaries in the Southwest as the conferring of the pallium on Bishop Lamy testifies."

He smiled with an honest pride in the revival of faith which the priests of his native France were fostering among the people in the wilderness of Colorado, Arizona, New Mexico, and the extensive territory of Texas.

As Sister Praxedes watched Bishop Salpointe's face brighten in speaking of his fellow missionaries in the part of America where she herself was going, her young heart, lonesome for so many things, grew ashamed. They left their beloved France and came across the world to find a strange place without any of the familiarity of home; and I, leaving one Loretto home, have another waiting to welcome me.

By nightfall the caravan had reached Otero, where the doctor was found. With his attention and a night's rest in a real bed, Sister Praxedes was soon feeling more like herself. With this problem at least partially relieved, Bishop Salpointe found himself faced with another problem as vexing. It had been only four days since the caravan was formed and began winding its way from Kit Carson, yet the food supply was quickly dwindling. Someone had inadvertently short-supplied them or had failed to recheck, but the fact remained that the food could not last to Santa Fe.

By the evening of June 1, besides feeling the pangs of hunger, the drivers burdened the Bishop with a frank admission that they must have taken a wrong turn at some time. They were lost.

"It's nearly nine o'clock," the Bishop was saying to his traveling companions. Then, looking out the carriage window, he remarked with a chuckle, "At least we're still going in the right direction if the moon hasn't lost its way."

"We can always depend on the good God, can't we, Your Grace," Sister Praxedes answered.

"Yes, Sister. And don't forget that when you get to the great city of Santa Fe."

"Your Grace." Sister Praxedes remembered the questions she had asked Sister Florence way back in Colorado. "I don't even know what the name Santa Fe means."

"Well that's not hard to answer. Santa Fe means Holy Faith. It is the city of Holy Faith. Some find faith there; some, I guess even lose it there—but no one can doubt that it is the city of the true Faith."

The carriage jerked and they all lurched forward. "Halt! Who are you?" A gruff voice shouted as the sound of men on horseback became evident to the Bishop and the nuns.

"Where are you going? Who's in charge here?"

"This is Bishop Salpointe's party headed for Santa Fe," one of the drivers called back.

"We think that we've lost the trail," the Bishop called as he jumped down to the sandy ground. "Could you tell us where we are?"

"Sure." The man laughed. "This is Cimarron. You scared us for a minute there. We're a company of soldiers from Arizona camped here for the night. Guess we're getting jumpy with all the Indian attacks lately."

Bishop Salpointe shook hands with the captain, introducing himself as Father Salpointe.

"Father, I think you'd better make camp here for the night. It's not safe for a slow-moving caravan to be traveling these parts after dark."

"Our supplies are running low and we want to make La Junta, where the Jesuit Fathers are expecting us."

"It'll be easy to find your way in the morning if you double back just a few miles toward Otero, but I wouldn't try it tonight. Anyway, we can let you have foodstuffs if that's all you need."

"That's good of you, sir. I'll have the men draw the wagons into a circle. You don't know how glad we are to have come across you."

"This is tricky country, Father. Anyone's liable to get off the trail. All you'd have to do to miss a place like Cimarron is to be a few feet on the other side of one of these sand dunes."

Early next morning, having bid good-by to the friendly captain who had been generous with food supplies, the caravan doubled back about three miles and picked up the trail.

From there to Las Vegas the road was firmly packed, and so with some care the drivers could avoid the worst holes and ruts. A rain storm delayed them for about an hour just before they reached

Las Vegas, but with no more unexpected incidents Bishop Salpointe decided that they could make it to Santa Fe without spending another night under the stars.

As the caravan drew to a stop in the midst of the frame and adobe dwellings of Las Vegas, New Mexico, the Bishop turned to the sisters.

"I think it is safe to send a wire message from here to Bishop Lamy so that they will be expecting us in Santa Fe tonight."

"We'll really be there tonight?"

"Unless something happens. We can stay here about an hour and then the next stop will be home."

The Bishop jumped into the dusty street and gave each of the sisters a hand as they jumped out of the carriage.

"You're getting good at this. Say, Father," he called to the young French priest who was coming toward them, "why don't you take the sisters over to the church? It's a real mission church," he said to them.

The sisters and Father Bourgade, followed by little John, crossed the almost deserted street. A few chickens scratching in the dirt by the mission seemed to be the only ones working in the town. Several men leaned against a hitching post in front of the frame hotel where Bishop Salpointe had gone.

As they entered at the rear of the narrow adobe church, Sister Praxedes caught her breath. Slender shafts of afternoon sunlight speared down from the high, narrow windows creating an aura of saffron yellow. The odor of wax was heavy on the air. From the door where they stood, except for one low step separating the body of the church from the sanctuary, the floor was a clean sweep of hard brown earth. There were no benches. And the altar seemed to quiver with bright red, paper roses and winking blue and red lights. The statue of Our Lady was in blue satin and lace.

Father Bourgade genuflected and walked slowly toward the step, where he and little John knelt to pray. Sister Praxedes turned to look at Sister Florence, who was still standing beside her. They smiled at each other.

"How did you like the church?" the Bishop asked as they all climbed back into the carriage.

"A little shocking at first, but you get used to it."

"Why do the statues wear real clothes?"

"Oh, that's Spanish. I suppose there are other explanations but I like to think that the saints are dressed up for heaven."

Sister Praxedes liked that idea. Looking down at the condition of her once black habit, she could appreciate being dressed up.

The trip from Las Vegas on was uneventful. It was also smoother because of the gradual ascent through rise after rise of conical-shaped hills, bare except for green-blue, bushlike piñon trees and dried swords of yucca pointing to the cloudless, royal-blue sky. Gradually the sky grew deeper and deeper and the last day of the journey was gone. As they moved along through the darkness with Santa Fe getting closer, the bishop and the two young nuns dozed.

As the occupants of the carriage slept, the drivers kept a steady vigil. From experience they knew that Santa Fe was not much farther. The road had broadened; the scattered adobe dwellings were closer together. Here and there the brilliance of blazing firelight marked an Indian encampment. Then at last, as the carriage made a sudden turn to the west, the orange dots of campfires, arching the perimeter of Santa Fe, marked their destination.

"Santa Fe, Santa Fe," rose like an incantation from the throats of the drivers. Each voice held the *San* almost reverently and then exploded the *ta Fe* as one word.

"Padre, Padre Salpointe," one driver called. "Santa Fe, Santa Fe!"

The Bishop was awake. Yes, there was no mistaking those lights. Those were the lights of Santa Fe.

"Are we here?" Sister Florence asked, shaking off her drowsiness.

"Almost. Look there to the left."

Sister Praxedes stirred. She wanted to open her eyes, but the lids were so heavy.

"Sister, look at the lights! We're here!"

Half incredulous, half wondering, Sister Praxedes squinted, trying to decide just what kind of lights they were. "Are those camp-fires?"

The Bishop chuckled. Apparently this was the reaction he had expected. "Those are the Indians who are camped on the mountain slopes on the other side of Santa Fe. Years ago they were required by law to leave the city at night; now those who come to town to sell their wares camp outside on the mountain slopes for want of places where they are welcome in the city. Neither the white man nor his Mexican brother has found heart enough—even when they accept each other—to accept the Indian also."

The Bishop grew silent with his own thoughts as the lights grew and multiplied themselves into clusters and broken chains linking unseen houses into the frontier town of Santa Fe. To the Bishop there was no mystery in the as yet invisible settlement. He knew the sound of Spanish voices and Indian dialects, the sight of crude carts and burros no longer surprised him, the very differentness of Santa Fe was its charm. He looked and was glad for the flicker of lights. Behind them, surrounding them, were people dear and important to him, people dear and important to his God.

Sister Florence saw something quite different in the pattern of light. The lights of Santa Fe marked a place to be investigated, an experience to be weighed, measured, and examined. Once before she had held an evaluation and she had thought she wanted what she saw, but for reasons she could not quite grasp she had been sent off to a situation she had not bargained for. But she would give it a try. If it did not turn out well, she knew what she would do.

The lights were signaling a challenge to Sister Praxedes, the youngest of the three. Now that the actuality of Santa Fe, the city of Holy Faith, lay within reach, her courage began to grow. She stared hard at the chimneys and flat roofs, which stepped from the blackness to greet her. She would try to forget the tiredness and the longings in her heart. God was here and she would find Him. "You will help me. I know You will. You just have to," she prayed.

The carriage began to ease along. Slower, slower, one sudden jerk, and they had stopped. In a moment the Bishop was out and on the ground; presently a small group of people carrying the golden glow of lanterns came toward him.

"Sister, we're here," Sister Florence said in an almost-whisper. "And I feel a little frightened."

"It will be all right," Sister Praxedes replied, patting her hand. "Come on. Let's see if the ground feels solid."

The two young nuns squinted. It was too dark to distinguish faces, but they could tell that a man, slightly shorter than Bishop Salpointe, and two sisters were greeting the Bishop with enthusiasm. Sister Florence and Sister Praxedes found themselves waiting near the carriage. It did not seem proper to go forward just yet.

"Where are the sisters?" a man's voice, evidently not Bishop Salpointe's, asked after a moment.

"Here they are," the taller of the sisters said kindly as she turned. Walking toward them, lantern in hand, she added, "You poor dears, did you think we had forgotten you?"

"This is Archbishop Lamy," Bishop Salpointe began, smiling to himself because this was the first time he had spoken the title *Archbishop* for his old friend.

"We are happy to have come at a time when you are being so honored by the Holy Father," Sister Florence said in her calm way.

"Thank you, my dear. How do you like God's country, Sisters?"

"It is very different, Your Grace. We don't know yet quite what to make of it," she answered frankly.

"Sisters, this is Mother Magdalen and Mother Francisca," Bishop Salpointe went on. "They have been much concerned about you."

"You poor dears," Mother Magdalen began in a voice vibrant for all her sixty-one years, "Loretto is such a long way. Come along inside. After such a trip you'll have forgotten the conveniences of the mother house and think we are quite stylish." She laughed. "We're plain but very happy out here in the West."

"We'll bid you good night, Sisters," the Archbishop said. "Father and I have many things to talk about."

"Good night, Your Grace. And thank you, Bishop Salpointe," Sister Praxedes replied.

Mother Francisca surprised Sister Praxedes by taking her hand and holding it between her own as they walked toward the light of the convent door. In the full light of the convent hall, Mother Francisca turned her dark penetrating gaze on Sister Praxedes.

"We are going to help you find health here, Sister. Just breathe in some of this good air. Nowhere in the world is there air like this. Smell the rich incense of burning piñon wood. It will get into you very soul. Breathe it in, breathe it *all* in, Sister Praxedes."

SANTA FE, NEW MEXICO—1875

Her hands folded, waiting for grace to be said, Sister Praxedes could not take her eyes off the black oilcloth covering on the refectory tables. How strange to have tables covered in black! After everyone had been seated, a voice pitched above the muffled sounds of passing dishes and clinking tableware began uttering those same sounds—explosive, unintelligible—that she had heard in the chapel. All the prayers had been in Spanish, and now the spiritual reading at table! She was in a world that neither spoke to her nor in which she could speak. This was a strange place of black oilcloth.

Seated on the opposite side of the room from the professed sisters and next to the until-yesterday youngest novice in the Santa Fe community, Sister Praxedes forced herself to take a spoonful of corn mush and then another. The stiffness in her muscles and the sensation of thirteen days in a pitching carriage did not add to her appetite.

Her deliberate movements were momentarily observed by two dark eyes on the other side of the refectory. Mother Francisca, the mistress of novices, was mentally noting that the young sister was paler than she had looked by lantern light and that she was thinner, too.

Mother Magdalen also had taken a closer look at Sister Praxedes this morning. As Superior of the Santa Fe community and as a person vitally concerned with the Church and education in the Southwest, Mother Magdalen's first responsibility was for the spiritual and physical welfare of her Loretto daughters. And now she could see that this young person could not stand the three days' journey down to Las Cruces, almost to the border of Mexico. She knew that Reverend Mother Elizabeth would agree. Already she was forming the words that would explain why she had decided to keep Sister Praxedes here.

"Sister," Mother Francisca whispered to Sister Praxedes as Sister passed on the way to chapel, "Come to my room immediately after prayers."

Kneeling in her place with the novices, Sister Praxedes was an empty shell of herself; all feeling was gone.

"Where are You?" she whispered, looking at the Tabernacle. "Where are You?"

All about her voices were praying, praying in Spanish. Everywhere it was Spanish.

"I can't even pray to You here," she thought.

Prayers were over and the sisters were leaving chapel before she realized it. How could she go to Mother now? Mother would know something was wrong, but if she asked, what would she say? She was not sure what was wrong. But the "immediately" rang in her ears. Getting up, Sister Praxedes stepped into the aisle and genuflected.

A very worried-looking little novice motioned to her and Sister Praxedes followed, sensing by the anxiety of her guide that Mother must have sent her to find the novice who did not understand the import of the mistress' "immediately." Mother's door was ajar. Barely pausing, the little novice rapped and indicated by a nod that Sister Praxedes should go in. The novice bowed in Mother's direction and was gone.

"Sister, I've been waiting," Mother Francisca said, her tone saying more than the words.

"I'm sorry, Mother," she said, lowering her eyes and fighting desperately to keep back the tears. She, who could count the times she had cried as a child, seemed repeatedly on the verge of tears since leaving Kentucky. What was wrong with her?

"Sit down, Sister. You found the trip here difficult? You find us strange."

"Mother, I—"

"No apologies, Sister. We all have to grow accustomed to the West. There is much to soul-saving that is beautiful, but it is beauty one has to search for often." She continued after a moment. "You are not well, I know. But you must be patient with yourself."

At this the young novice looked at Mother Francisca. There was more kindness in her eyes than Sister Praxedes had first perceived. She was younger, too, than Sister had expected. Sister Praxedes did not know, but Mother Francis was only thirty-two.

"Sister, the climate here will work wonders. God will give you back your health if He sees fit. Go now and report to the sister in the kitchen. I have told her to give you some light work in the garden. And Sister will also help you to learn Spanish. You cannot get along here unless you speak and understand the language of the people. As you work outside, Sister, breathe in our good air."

Sister Praxedes turned and left Mother Francisca, not knowing that she had not even begun to know the woman who would stand beside her in the great crisis of her life. That day Sister Praxedes was too absorbed in finding herself.

Sister had her first Spanish lesson that very day. It was not what she had expected—no grammarbook, but an improvised method of reading aloud and learning objects by the point-and-name system used by little children.

As Sister Praxedes weeded in the patch of garden behind the convent, she reviewed the "exercise book" of her surroundings. She glanced from the window, *la ventana*, to the door, *la puerta*, to the wall—wall? *Como se dice wall en español?* she would ask herself. Wall? If the weeds had taken her down to the edge of the garden nearest the kitchen door, she would ply her question where an answer could be found. If not, she would put "wall" aside while she went on to the other words that she could remember. Sometimes the task of learning a new language was a game, but most of the time it was a task that remained a task.

But even the Spanish had to be suspended for a few days as preparations for Bishop Lamy's great day drew near. In the process of learning her new home, Sister Praxedes had almost forgotten the pallium which Bishop Salpointe had carried over so many miles to confer on the aging prelate of Santa Fe. On June 16, just nine days after their arrival, the ceremony took place.

Long before 9 A.M., the time set for the procession to form in front of the cathedral, the celebration had begun. In fact, shortly after daybreak cannon salutes from Fort Marcy, on the north above the city, awakened the celebration. Small boys ran about lighting strings of firecrackers, which sent chickens and pigs, usual occupants of the winding streets, scurrying for shelter. No one would stay in bed today. Most of Santa Fe, from the humblest *peón* watering the oxen in the plaza to the territorial governor in his quarters in the ancient "Governor's Palace," hoped to witness the ceremony that would make John Baptiste Lamy an archbishop and would raise their diocese to an archdiocese.

As Sister Praxedes wove her way through the shifting crowd in the street between the convent and the cathedral steps, where the religious were to join the procession, she found herself being caught up in the excitement around her. She felt for a moment like a participant, not a mere onlooker in a kind of community of love. Who was this man whom Rome was honoring? Why would a churchman draw so many people and so much fanfare? Although not fully grasping the significance, she was a part of it, knowing that others around her appreciated what this moment meant both to Archbishop Lamy as a person and to Archbishop Lamy as the highest-ranking representative of the Roman Catholic Church in the Southwest.

Mother Magdalen, whom he had brought to Santa Fe in 1852, realized how extensive had been the work of this giant among men; Mother Francisca, his own niece, could appreciate the depth of humility which this honor was crowning. Both women knew John Baptiste Lamy not only as priest and bishop but as friend and consoler. As their hearts thrilled to the excitement of this day, it was in full awareness of the price he had paid.

When he had arrived in Santa Fe in 1851, in many ways unwanted by the clergy, he had found in ruins the churches and mission schools which the Spanish Franciscans had been forced to abandon twenty years earlier. Several priests, there were only nine altogether, were in ruins too. So long neglected because of their remoteness from the episcopal see, over a thousand miles away in Mexico, they—like the churches—had weakened and crumbled, falling into decay. Sister Praxedes could not know, as Mother Magdalen and Mother Francisca knew, how relentlessly Bishop Lamy had labored to rebuild his vast mountain-desert diocese. She had not waited and wondered with them during long weeks when he had taken to horseback to visit some remote adobe hut isolated by steep mountains. She had not known the winters of concern when they had longed for his return from Europe, where he had gone to recruit missionaries for his people. She only knew that now after twenty-five years Rome and Santa Fe had joined to express gratitude to a man named Lamy.

On the steps of the old cathedral, which sat like a prisoner within the partially built walls of the new, Sister Praxedes waited like the other sisters to take her place in the line as priests and city officials formed the procession that would march to El Colegio de San Miguel, the Christian Brothers' school for boys. Since so many people were expected for the pontifical Mass, the altar had been set up in the yard north of the college within the shadow of San Miguel, the old Franciscan mission. Once formed, the procession moved steadily down San Francisco Street past La Fonda, to the corner of the plaza, then turned left into the old Pecos Road, now College Street, passing between crowds of black-shawled *madres,* blanketed Pueblo Indians, and "Anglo" men and women wearing the latest in United States styles. As she passed the Loretto convent ground, Sister Praxedes looked above the heads to get a new view of the partially constructed Gothic chapel of the academy. This, like the new cathedral, was being built after the design of a French architect the new archbishop had brought from France. From there the marchers crossed the wood bridge which spanned the Santa Fe creek, then up the hill-like rise of the winding street in front of the old mission to the yard between it and the one-story adobe building that she knew must be *el colegio*. To Sister Praxedes both the adobe mission and the adobe school for boys looked more like giant mud structures left by some prehistoric children of an elephantine age than a church and a school.

Here the processors divided and took their places before the improvised altar. Down the narrow aisle between them came the new Archbishop and the prelates accompanying him. Sister Praxedes had seen him only briefly the night of her arrival. Now as she caught moving glimpses of him in the narrow openings between scarfs and veils and heads, she was surprised to see that his face was brown, almost like the richly weathered faces of the men she saw in the streets. Against the brilliance of his ecclesiastical robes, his deep color gave him a youthfulness that Sister Praxedes had not expected. On one side of him walked the familiar Bishop Salpointe, while on the other was a prelate who Sister Praxedes later learned was Bishop Macheboeuf, once Bishop Lamy's vicar, now the Bishop of Colorado.

As the pontifical Mass proceeded solemnly and reverently beneath the blueness of the morning sky, Sister Praxedes experienced conflicting feelings of revulsion and admiration for these strange dark people kneeling in the dust about her. She had not been completely prepared for so many dark-skinned, gaily-dressed people. And yet there was a pulsation in the crowd, a murmur that rose as the prayer in their hearts burst forth into audible praise. There was a reverence, even an awe; the awe of truly simple people. At Loretto, at the mother house in Kentucky, she had felt prayer going up and out like this; yet she had somehow been missing it these days while she knelt in Santa Fe's chapel trying to struggle with the words. Perhaps, she suddenly thought, in her concern for her threatened health and in her fumbling about in this strange new language, she had forgotten that she wanted to serve others. What had happened to the gold in her heart? Kneeling there, she caught the first breath of something she had lost. Grace seemed to come to her through kneeling in the dust with these simple people. And she started to be ashamed.

After Mass, a priest she did not know spoke in Spanish; then Bishop Salpointe spoke in English. It was impossible for her to hear all his words, but somehow she knew that no words would convey what he must be experiencing now as he took part in this celebration for the man who had brought him and so many others like him to this part of the world. Sister Praxedes had great admiration for these French priests. Hearing Bishop Salpointe speak in English, she realized for the first time that he could switch effortlessly from his native French to Spanish to English. Would she ever be able to use Spanish so facilely?

His address over, Bishop Salpointe performed the brief ceremony of placing the pallium over the head of his fellow missionary. Archbishop Lamy read his acceptance in Latin; next he turned to speak to the people who had flocked here to share in his great honor. A trace of emotion marked his voice as he spoke in grateful terms of all the people had done for him. His manner seemed to breathe love.

The celebration lasted late into the night. And although the sisters left the crowd and returned to the convent after the recessional, the revelry of music and laughter followed them deep into the night as the people took to dancing in the streets.

When Sister Praxedes and several other novices were leaving the chapel after night prayers, Mother Francisca motioned for them to follow her. In silence—for they did not ordinarily speak after night prayers—the young sisters followed, wondering what they were going to do. It had been such an exciting day and their young hearts were dancing to the sound of violins and guitars in the plaza only a block away.

Mother Francisca took them to a shuttered window on the second floor. "I want you to see the torches," she said softly. "The people are parading from the mission to the cathedral. This is a sight no one should miss." And she pushed aside the shutters.

Sister Praxedes gasped. Flames like bright luminous flowers moving, moving, hundreds of them forming a living line of light. And bonfires on the flat roofs of the houses!

"No place in the world do people use fire so well," Mother Francisca smiled.

Sister Praxedes watched the shadows play across Mother's face.

Her eyes were like a child's. She has a gay side, Sister Praxedes was thinking.

"I should like to think that we can spread God's love the way these torches light the darkness. Oh, Sisters, learn well the lesson of fire. It inflames only by contact. That is the great lesson that the dear Archbishop has given us. These are his people because he has become one of them. He gave the fire of his love to them. You must pray that we too can spread love as he has."

The next day the torches were gone and the touch of a sense of communion with the people was gone as well. But a spark was there; Sister Praxedes had brushed against a living spirit. Still her "problem"—that is what she started to call it—still her problem remained. The specific problem of the language assumed precise dimensions when Mother Francisca handed her a book, a book written completely in Spanish.

"Tomorrow at breakfast you will begin to read in the refectory, Sister. When you cannot pronounce a word," she added as encouragement, "just go and ask someone. The sisters won't mind, and you have to learn sometime."

Stunned, Sister Praxedes stood holding the book in her hand as she stared helplessly after Mother Francisca. Her first thought was that Mother had mistaken her for someone else; the next was to pursue the mistress of novices to explain that the Spanish lessons hadn't progressed far enough yet.

"My dear child," a soft voice said, "you look perplexed. Is anything wrong?"

"Anything wrong?" the soft voice repeated.

Sister Praxedes turned to find Mother Magdalen standing at her side.

"Well, Mother—" her own voice trailed off in mid-air.

Mother Magdalen had already noticed the book in Sister's hand, and she was fairly sure that Mother Francisca, whom she had seen going down the hall, had given the book to the young novice. This was the way readers were made.

"Well, Mother, I think Mother Francisca mistook me for someone else. She just gave me this book and said that I am to read in the refectory tomorrow. It's in Spanish!"

Mother Magdalen could not keep back the smile. "Well, my dear child, that isn't so bad. Let's see the book."

Mother took the book from the limp hand and opened it. "No, this won't be too difficult. Just remember two things: if the word ends in a vowel, the accent is on the next to the last syllable; if it ends in a consonant, put the accent on the last. You know the sounds of the vowels, don't you?"

"Sometimes, Mother."

"Well now, you read this over. It won't be too bad and it really is the fastest way to learn, Sister. Just forget about yourself and read."

No meal ever seemed as long as that breakfast. Struggling from vowel to vowel, from accent to accent, Sister Praxedes' hands wept perspiration. Twice she had to ask the nearest sister how to pronounce a word. By the time the meal was over, she had struggled through six pages, six pages of words, Spanish words! Had anyone understood what she read? It was a sure thing that Sister Praxedes had not.

By fall Sister Praxedes' physical condition, the doctor said, was such that there was no reason why she could not work with the little girls in the academy. It would be good for her, he said. Mother Francisca thought that it would be good too. Sister Praxedes needed to be busy, but even more she needed responsibility. She seemed so happy at times, but then, Mother sensed a holding back. She did not seem completely committed.

"So you think you will like working in the boarding school," Mother Francisca said to Sister Praxedes the day Mother called her to her office to tell her about her new assignment.

"Yes, Mother, you see I almost went to boarding school once myself. It was a great disappointment when I didn't."

"What happened?"

"My parents went back to Ireland and I couldn't go."

"Perhaps you did not miss as much as you think. I spent most of my childhood in boarding school in New Orleans. Boarding school isn't like home. I think you will learn that."

Gradually Sister Praxedes learned the routine of the boarding-school way of life. Teaching in a classroom was only one part of a work that included dressing the very small girls, caring for cut fingers, listening to childish cares, and making sure that the covers were tucked in at night.

The Academy of Our Lady of Light was already twenty-two years old. Most of the pupils lived in Santa Fe and so returned home at night, but those from towns like Albuquerque and Las Vegas boarded at the school. The majority of the girls were of mixed Spanish and Indian origin. Some were "Anglo," non-Mexican, whose parents were merchants in Santa Fe or whose fathers were officers with the United States garrison at Fort Marcy. Only a few were pure Indian since the Pueblo Indians of the area were not only terribly poor but they were also fearful that their daughters might grow away from the tribal way of life if they went to the sisters' school. Whatever the differences of national and racial background among the general population of Santa Fe, such did not exist in the school. Sister Praxedes slowly came to see that the common denominator of childhood has no room for such petty differences. Their problems were the problems of childhood and not the problems of Spaniards or Mexicans or Indians.

Early one Saturday morning late in October, she walked up one side and across the back of a classroom full of little girls who were supposed to be finishing their lessons.

"I'm afraid," she said, "that some of us will have to be working on our lessons while the rest are enjoying the hike to Tesuque."

Large eyes grew larger as the little girls listened to the words. Hermana Prajedes would not make them miss the day's outing at the Archbishop's *ranchito?* Or would she? Two or three girls wiggled nervously, realizing that perhaps they would be among the missing. All the heads went down again and the spirit of industry was somehow more productive. How long the day would be in the lonely academy with all the others, sisters and children, at the stone cottage four miles from town. But yet one pencil did not move, and one pair of shoulders drooped lower.

Sister Praxedes walked down the aisle between the desks and stood beside Elena. Elena, Sister believed, had not gotten any connection between numbers and reality. Perhaps numbers were a mystery quite as difficult for Elena to understand as keeping God's point of view seemed to be for Sister.

A roughly executed four-plus-two bearing the answer forty-two stared up from Elena's slate.

"Are you having trouble, Elena?" Sister asked of the seven-year-old.

"*Si*," she smiled with the ingratiating manner of one who even at seven has learned that to be sweet and helpless may have its own reward.

"What seems to be the trouble?"

Elena pointed not to the problem that was worked incorrectly but to the next which had no answer.

"Well, let's look at this one first," Sister said, indicating the four plus two. "Elena, what is four and two."

"Four and two," she repeated with precision. "Four and two is this," she said, pointing to the forty-two.

"Yes, I see what you mean, Elena, but when you put them together . . ." No, that wasn't the right way because apparently the child had put them together.

Elena looked up at Sister. "Do you want me to make them into one number?"

"Yes, Elena, put them into one number."

"Oh, that is easy." And she erased the forty-two and wrote a six.

Sister Praxedes sighed. Then wondering, she asked, "How do you know that that is right?"

Elena looked at her slyly. "I have fingers in my head and I count them."

"Oh," Sister Praxedes replied. "Do you think that I have fingers in my head, too?"

"Maybe, but I don't think so."

"You don't? Why not?"

"Because you keep your eyes open when you count. To see the fingers in your head, you must close your eyes. Your eyes are always open." She smiled.

"Which eyes, Elena?"

"Oh, hermana, those eyes," she laughed, pointing up into Sister's face.

As Sister Praxedes walked on down the aisle, she thought of something she had not remembered for a long time. Blind Moira had claimed that the good God did not keep everything from her eyes. She knew that she needed some of Moira's kind of sight. She needed to be led. How had she ever lost touch? A few months before, she shuddered to realize, she would have been indifferent to Elena. Even now she often failed to serve, to make contact with other human hearts. Was there, she wondered, some bond, some community of human love which she had broken or lost? All she knew for certain was that when she had led Moira, she had been happy and she had known love.

As June approached and with it the end of school, Sister Praxedes realized with a tinge of disappointment that there were only two more Sunday mornings of the school term left. Sunday morning had come to be a high point of the week, for then it was that she took her little charges, dressed in their best, to visit Archbishop Lamy. During the fall and spring the visits were in his garden, which he called "Cuba."

This particular morning as she crossed the wide yard behind the academy, followed by a silent but excited processional of little girls, she hoped that the Archbishop would not be occupied. Sometimes he had important visitors or he was called away before she and the children were ready to leave. But at other times, he spoke to them about Our Lord and all He had sacrificed for them and how He had served all men, or he asked them questions to see how much they had learned. Occasionally he told them about his boyhood in faraway France.

At Cathedral Place, the street that separated the grounds of Our Lady of Light from those of the cathedral and the Archbishop's residence, Sister Praxedes paused and told the two girls leading the line to stay together. "Don't hurry but walk quickly. When you get to the gate, wait for me."

Two by two the little girls smiled up at her and then stepped or jumped across the gully, trying to land gently so as not to get their highly polished shoes dusty. When the last two started across the street, Sister walked with them, lifting her long skirt. By the time Sister Praxedes reached the group that waited in the shadow of the wall which bordered the garden, some were giggling with excitement and others were whispering softly. One of the two at the gate was jumping up and down with anticipation.

"Shall we be a surprise this morning?" she asked. "Let's tiptoe in without a sound and then we can call surprise before His Grace sees us."

"Si," several chorused. Heads nodded and some shrugged their shoulders in delight.

"All right then. We'll have to be very quiet," Sister Praxedes warned.

Sister Praxedes turned the handle of the wooden door that opened into the garden. It yielded to her touch. According to custom, the first two girls held it open while Sister and the others entered.

The first sight of the garden, no matter how familiar, was always an exciting experience for Sister Praxedes. Here was a lush oasis in stark contrast to the sun-baked street which surrounded it. Here in *el jordín del obispo*, as Santa Feans termed it, grew every conceivable variety of tree and flower and plant.

Stealthily the silent army followed the gravel path, bordered by saucy orange poppies that shook their heads in silent protest against a swarm of honey stealers, to the first willow, whose trailing tresses of green could shelter them from view while they watched the Archbishop tossing bread crumbs on the surface of the sapphire pond.

"What are we doing?" one girl asked.

"We are watching His Grace feed the fish."

Although they could not see the crumbs being nibbled from the surface of the pond, they knew that every time the Archbishop's arm went forward with another handful, the fish were there. Many times he had let the girls throw crumbs, but somehow the fish never seemed to come in such numbers as when he did it.

"Does he know we're here?" whispered a black-eyed little Mexican girl.

"No, Angelica. Shall we tiptoe a little farther?"

Quietly they moved forward, lifting their feet high and placing them gently on the gravel path. Suddenly someone screamed, "A bee! A bee!" and the creeping army fell into disarray.

The Archbishop straightened, then he came forward, scattering the remnants of crumbs as he saw the girls running in all directions. One was clinging to Sister Praxedes' skirt.

"Has someone been hurt here?" he asked.

"Oh no, Your Grace, Angelica was frightened by a bee, but the bee is gone now."

"I didn't hear you come in, Sister. I must have been lost in thought."

"We meant to be a surprise."

"Oh, you were. Yes, indeed you were." Turning to the children who had gathered around, he said, "The bees will not bother you if you are kind to them. Now run about and enjoy yourselves."

The children skipped off in different directions, some crossing the small bridge to the miniature Swiss chalet on the island in the middle of the pond and others heading for the vegetable garden to see if the radishes were ready to be sampled.

"Come, sit down, Sister. The children will be all right," he said.

She did not demur but accepted without a word his invitation to sit on one of the rustic benches near the edge of the pond. This was going to be one of the rare occasions when he spoke to her alone.

John Baptiste Lamy had the sharply chiseled features of the French. His jaw was firm, his eyes penetrating, his whole bearing that of a general. The rugged life of a missionary to the Indian-roamed territory of the vanishing buffalo and the tenacious cactus had hardened him to trial, but it had not changed his native sensitiveness to beauty. If anything, it had sharpened it.

Sitting here in the garden which he had planted, listening to him talk, Sister Praxedes could not help but think that he was among men as his garden was in the midst of New Mexico's barrenness. As he had planted the beauty of trees and flowers where such had not grown before, so his life stood as an example of what the willing spirit can accomplish.

Again and again he had returned to his native France and inspired other priests to return with him to America. In 1852 he had brought the first Sisters of Loretto to Santa Fe, and later he had encouraged the Sisters of Charity of Cincinnati to start the hospital that was so badly needed. His zeal set fire to many hearts and to these hearts he had given the credit for the spread of the Church in the Southwest.

On this particular Sunday morning he seemed preoccupied with the garden, which was especially lovely in the golden light of the June sunshine. When he asked Sister Praxedes what she thought of the pear trees he had trained to grow like vines, she decided to ask some questions that had come to her as often as she had been here.

"Your Grace, where did you get so many different trees and plants?"

"It is a long story, Sister." He paused as he looked toward the straw-thatched chalet, where the children were playing. After a moment, he turned to her. "Over the years I have made many trips to Europe and to the States and each time I have brought back the beginnings of new life—some seeds, a few sprouts, and one time a hundred saplings."

"A hundred!"

"Yes, a hundred young elm trees came to Santa Fe in barrels. I brought them from St. Louis. Most of them are planted about the city. That's one over there and there's another. They thrive, Sister, just like those of us who were transplanted from another world, another way of life." He looked at her with a new sign of interest. "Where were you transplanted from?"

"Like the elms I came from St. Louis, but I am originally from Ireland."

"Ireland! A lovely place. Do you remember it?"

"Yes, Your Grace. The roof of your little house there," she indicated the Swiss chalet, "reminds me of the roofs there. I have sometimes wondered if my memory was correct or if I have just imagined that they looked like silver in the early morning. So many things of childhood turn out to be illusions."

"No, you are not mistaken. I have seen the same thing in France. In the early morning they are silver; at sunset they are bronze." He stopped. Changing his tone, he shifted his position. "But I do not like what you said about the things of childhood being illusions. What do you mean, Sister?"

"Oh, I wasn't thinking of anything in particular, Your Grace; but sometimes I wonder if life could ever be as magnificent as I thought it was when I was ten."

"It's all in your point of view, Sister." She started at the familiarity of the phrase. "If the ideas of childhood are true, then they are not illusions. God has made life a great adventure. Children seem to sense that, but many times in adulthood they lose the point of view of God. They forget that life is a great journey—magnificent, as you yourself called it."

He seemed to see her now for the first time. She was the one Mother Francisca had mentioned months ago, but he had thought that by this time she had grown accustomed to Santa Fe.

"Let me show you a bit of my childhood," he said. She walked beside him. "Part of that walnut tree there came all the way from my native Auvergne in France." Near the base of one of the lower branches, the Archbishop indicated what looked like a scar. "See that mark? This branch is a grafting from a tree in France. Strange enough, this is an English walnut tree; but of course the best English walnuts grow in France." He smiled.

"Archbishop Lamy, this garden must have cost a great deal."

"Yes, but it has produced a great deal, too, Sister. This garden is an investment. Once there was nothing here but a few piñons, some sage, and sand. Where that pond is a wild spring once flowed. Now instead there is order, beauty, fertility. This garden is my classroom, where I have learned and where I have tried to teach that work and faith and love can change the land. I learned that New Mexico's soil needs care, but it is not sterile. By late August those grape vines will produce clusters of grapes twelve inches long." And he motioned toward an apple tree blossoming near the wall. "Once she returned my care with an apple that weighed a full pound. This garden is even now in the process of growing a cathedral."

"Your cathedral?" she asked, looking across the garden to where the great walls rose like a fortress shell around the old St. Francis Cathedral.

"Yes. You see we give much of the fruit and vegetables to the poor, but much is sold, too. Grapes and cherries and English walnuts are helping to build Santa Fe's cathedral. When the harvest is great enough, we will have a cathedral church worthy of her."

Just then Angelica came running toward them, cupping a poppy in her small hands.

"Angelica, you know you are not to pick the flowers," Sister scolded.

"They are His Grace's flowers, aren't they?" she asked with seriousness large in her dark eyes.

"Yes, that is why we are not to pick them."

"But I have brought His Grace one of His Grace's flowers. Isn't that all right?"

Archbishop Lamy smiled at this and drew the little girl to him. "Angelica, that is the nicest thing anyone has done for me in a long time. I thank you for my flower," he said, taking it and holding it in his tanned hand, adding, "did the bees see you pick it?"

"Yes, Your Grace, but you said if we are kind, they will not hurt us, so I picked it kindly."

As quickly as she had come, Angelica smiled and ran back to her playmates.

The Archbishop looked at the flower for a moment and then

remarked, as if to himself, "I would carry poppy seeds half around the world to have one appreciated so."

As Sister Praxedes looked at the flaming poppy cradled in his strong, steady hand it seemed to mean something. Somehow, in its setting, through the Archbishop's words and spirit, through Angelica's simple kindness, it became more than a fragile flower.

Walking back to the convent with the little girls, she felt her heart beating wildly in a way it had not beat for many months. She glanced back to look at the Archbishop standing at the gate. He waved and she waved too. For one moment he was her father standing at the mill door. Her eyes looked up above the flat roof of his house to where the mountains went up to the sky. He had said that if the ideas of childhood are true, they are not illusions. As she walked, she thought of the poppy again, of Angelica being kind to the bees, of Mother Francisca telling her to breathe in all of this. How had she ever forgotten? When had she started to forget that serving God was serving others? She *must* serve others. That was God's point of view. She had always known that. Mother Dafrosa had said that that was the way to happiness. She knew she had forgotten about a bond of love, had forgotten to serve. If only she could forget herself instead.

After leaving the children with the sister in the study hall, Sister Praxedes went to the chapel. She must tell Him that now she understood this strange place of black oilcloth. She understood this strange language of the people. The only thing to understand was the point of view.

Now the days began to go faster and faster. June was gone, then July and August, and as September replaced August, Sister Praxedes looked forward to one day, Our Lady's birthday, September 8, the day set apart for her to pronounce her first vows. On September 8, 1876, fifteen months after her arrival in Santa Fe, she was to vow to God Poverty, Chastity, and Obedience.

When she knelt to speak the words of her consecration to God, it was before Archbishop Lamy, who stood at the altar holding the Host, which she would receive into her heart. The Archbishop stood motionless as he heard her strong brogue-tinged Spanish:

"Prostrada á vuestros piés, O Dios mio, y animada por el deseo de consagrarme entermente á vuestro divino servicio, yo, Hermana Maria Praxedes, os hago volo de Pobreza, de Castidad, y de Obediencia, en la Sociedad de Las 'Amigas de Maria al pié de la Cruz' según las Reglas de San Agustin y las Constituciones de la misma Sociedad."

In her adopted language she had pledged herself to belong to the society, the Friends of Mary at the Foot of the Cross. Now the embroidered hearts on her veil meant a great deal. As the Archbishop had said, life was a high adventure.

With the tools of good health, the Spanish language, and her vows, Sister Praxedes became a full-fledged member of the teaching staff of the academy. This left her little time for herself, but somehow this did not matter. She belonged here.

Whenever Sister Praxedes had a few minutes, and that was not often, she would stop to watch how the workmen were progressing on the new Gothic chapel that had been under construction since before she had come to Santa Fe. The dedication was being planned for April 25, but no one had yet been able to solve the problem of building a stairway to the choir.

"Señor Sanchez tells me that it is absolutely impossible to build a stairway to the choir," Mother Magdalen told the group seated around the community-room table.

"Why are they having so much trouble?" Sister Praxedes asked.

"Sister, there just isn't enough space for a regular stairway. Really, in this particular type of architecture, a choir loft in the rear of the church is unusual. Consequently, the architects did not plan one. Now they say that only a circular stairway would fit but there is nothing to support a stairway."

"Why can't they build a 'something' to hold it up?"

Mother Magdalen shrugged. "I don't know much about building, but I think that a support would have had to have been put in when the foundation and walls were going up. There's nothing to bear the weight."

"Do you mean that we won't have a choir then, Mother?" someone else asked.

"Not unless someone figures out a way to build a stairway. We must pray to St. Joseph. If anyone can figure out a way, he should be able to."

Mother Francisca leaned in Sister Praxedes' direction and whispered so no one else could hear, "Could I see you in my office when recreation is over? Bring your street veil, please."

"Street veil?" she repeated.

All the way upstairs then all the way downstairs to Mother's office, she tried to figure out why Mother Francisca would want to see her street veil at this time of night? It is a lovely street veil, she thought, as she peeped at the bare hallway through the sheer black. It was long and not too heavy. Mother Dafrosa had given it to her when she left Loretto. She loved it because she knew that it looked nice and felt nice as she walked along College Street to the cathedral on Sunday mornings. When she wore it, she always had the illusion that she was really dressed up.

When Sister Praxedes arrived at Mother's room, a sister whom Sister Praxedes had never seen before, probably the sister who had arrived from St. Louis that evening, she thought, was with Mother Francisca.

"Oh, fine, Sister. I told Sister that I knew you wouldn't mind letting her take your veil. Hers is so shabby. Let's see."

Sister Praxedes watched Mother drape her lovely, long, street veil over the sister's head.

"Yes, it will do nicely. A little long but it will do."

"But I hate to take Sister's," the nun was saying.

"Oh, Sister doesn't mind. She only has to take the girls over to the cathedral on Sundays. Here, Sister Praxedes, you take this one."

Sister Praxedes took the shorter, much-darned veil.

"Thank you, Sister," Mother Francisca said.

Out in the hall, Sister Praxedes fingered the veil. How will I ever be able to appear in *this?* she wondered. Then she smiled. Wouldn't Kitty love this? Oh my!

BERNALILLO, NEW MEXICO—1878

Brother Gabriel ran the tips of his fingers back and forth across his forehead as he looked pensively at the fat crocks of fruit before him. He plied his fingers vigorously as if trying to knead out the answer to Brother Vincent's question. Finally, Brother Gabriel put his hands into his well-worn pockets and looked at the brother cook.

"I think," he said slowly, "if you seal them with the same kind of clay, they ought to be all right." He paused and smiled doubtfully. "It's worth trying anyway."

Brother Vincent, a much older man, whose deep, chiseled wrinkles told of many years of hard work in God's service, went to his task immediately. For him there was no doubt. Whether the fruit would be preserved for use during the winter or whether the clay failed to seal, he was carrying out his Superior's instructions.

Brother Gabriel came in and out of the low-ceilinged kitchen several times during the process, gaining assurance from the enthusiasm with which the old brother worked.

"There," Brother Vincent said with a note of triumph in his voice. "There, they are finished."

"Good, good!" Brother Gabriel responded. "Let's carry them down to the cellar. No," he went on, motioning to the cook, "no, Brother, you go ahead and finish your work. I'll take them down."

Brother Vincent looked with kind eyes at his Superior. He knew what Brother Gabriel meant. This was his off-handed way of saving him any extra exertion. Their understanding and deep affection for one another spoke a wordless language.

After the jars had been stored away, Brother Gabriel promptly forgot about them as he turned his attention to other matters. For several days he had meant to call on the sisters. The children had told him, the women had told him, and even Mike Sullivan had told him that the sisters' new Superior had arrived. Thus far he had heard that she was tall, that she was young, and that she had already inquired how much it would cost to replace the muslin window-covering with glass.

Mike Sullivan had remarked just yesterday to Brother Gabriel that the new *hermana* was good for the town because she wasn't afraid of changing things. "She's brought a lot of ideas with her from Santa Fe—and it's a good thing," Mike had concluded.

Bernalillo in 1878 was a low, sprawling town of adobe and frame dwarfed by the vastness of the surrounding plains and the nearness of the towering Sandia Mountains. Untouched by the railroad, the town claimed a population for the most part Mexican and Indian who spoke no English. The "Anglo" seen on the streets might be a local merchant, professional man, or a rancher in town for supplies.

The native populace was Catholic, but their faith took some conflicting forms. The uninitiated in the ways of Southwestern Catholicism often saw only the demonstrations, the processions, the deep prostrations, and judged only the emotional surface of what they saw. True, for some, religion and life were as neatly separated as the church aisle and the street. Baptism, matrimony, a church burial—of course; but continence and confession, honesty and Sunday Mass? Well, perhaps these were for *las madres y los ninos*. And yet, in the midst of these people were the deeply spiritual, who had preserved the purity of the Faith brought early to their forefathers by the Franciscan friars. Theirs was a faith that held firm through poverty and the unscrupulous dealings of the white adventurer. Theirs was a truly inbred, ingrained faith that was basic to every decision. This was a town of contrasts—the ignorant and the inspired; the Anglo and the Mexican; the plains and the mountains. But the subtler contrasts in faith only the practiced eye could distinguish.

As Brother Gabriel walked the short distance from the Christian Brothers' school to the Loretto convent, he hoped that the new

Superior possessed the ability to laugh. Living in a small adobe convent with two other sisters and an array of wiggly, giggly little girls could prove trying for her. Living in this "foreign" town might prove even more trying since this sister seemed to have some rather "high-flying" ideas. As he walked, he reflected that he too had had many ideas when he first came to Bernalillo some years before. But he had found that soul-saving is not as much a matter of glass windows and wood floors as some missionaries think. He smiled to himself. "No, but it's a bit easier to understand God's love if with it comes a few comforts."

He looked up to find himself approaching the one-story adobe convent with its muslin windows staring blankly at the warm September morning. He could recall that three years before José Leandro Peréa, a typical example of the completely generous New Mexican, had gladly donated this house to the sisters for a convent. Just as Brother Gabriel was about to knock, he heard someone calling his name. He turned and there coming toward him in a half run was a panting Brother Vincent.

"Brother Gabriel! Brother, wait!" came the frantic call.

"Why, Brother, what's wrong? Brother Vincent," he said sternly as the older man came up to him, "you know you shouldn't run. It's bad for you."

"Yes, yes, but Brother—" he was so out of breath that he could not speak for a moment.

"Catch your breath first. It can't be so bad as all that."

"Yes, yes, it is. Oh, Brother, I am a poor old fool. An old fool, that's what I am."

"For running, yes, but for nothing else. What seems to be the matter?"

"The fruit, the fruit is ruined. Just after you left we heard such a loud noise and Brother Simeon rushed to the cellar and there the crocks were broken and apples and pears running all about. It is my fault, Brother. I am a fool!"

"Brother Vincent." The younger man laughed. "Brother Vincent!"

"Do not laugh. I am not joking, Brother. It is true. The fruit is all ruined and it is because I do not know how to make the clay seal."

Without the two brothers realizing it, the sisters had heard the commotion and the door now stood ajar. Not knowing what the excitement was all about, Sister Praxedes, Sister Loyola, and Sister Marianita waited patiently in the doorway. It was Brother Vincent who first became aware of the sisters' presence.

"Oh, Sisters, Sisters, good morning!" he said, not knowing what else to say.

At this the nuns stepped out into the warm air, Sister Loyola and Sister Marianita looking very grave and Sister Praxedes showing the hint of a smile.

"Sisters, you must excuse us for making so much noise on your doorstep. Brother Vincent has just come to report an explosion at our house," he chuckled.

"An explosion!" Sister Loyola exclaimed.

"Yes, it seems the fruit we canned the other day has decided not to stay canned so now the Christian Brothers have apples and pears running about in their cellar."

The sisters tried not to laugh, but Brother Gabriel was not so restrained. Brother Vincent managed only a meek little grin.

"Well, I suppose I should go home now," he said weakly. "If you will excuse me, I will return to see if I can salvage any of the fruit."

They watched the brother back away.

"I imagine that you are Brother Gabriel," Sister Praxedes said as Brother Gabriel turned to her.

"Yes, and you must be the new Superior I've been hearing about."

"Sister Loyola has been telling me how good you and the brothers have been to us here. It is consoling to know that we have such friends. Won't you come in, Brother?"

At this Sister Loyola and Sister Marianita excused themselves and Sister Praxedes showed her guest into the small room which served as parlor and community room.

"I'm rather interested in how Brother Vincent sealed his fruit to have it explode," Sister Praxedes said as they sat down.

"It is really my fault, Sister. We had no sealing wax so I suggested clay."

"Clay?"

"Yes, but evidently it isn't such a good idea."

"We've been experimenting, too, and as yet there haven't been any explosions. We didn't have the money for fresh wax so we used the ends of old candles."

"Leave it to the sisters. Why, we've got boxes of candle drippings. Candle wax! Now why didn't I think of that?"

At that a small gray kitten announced its presence with an almost sarcastic purr. Brother Gabriel smiled.

"I see the cats are still here."

"From what I've been told, they are part of the community. This little fellow even goes to prayers."

The kitten had crossed the bare dirt floor to where Sister Praxedes was sitting. Reaching down, she took the thin little animal in her hands.

Brother Gabriel noted the hands against the gray fur. They were young hands, slender hands that looked unaccustomed to work. He wondered how old she was. Maybe twenty-five, he thought.

Sensing that she was being scrutinized, Sister Praxedes put the kitten down and said almost abruptly, "Brother Gabriel, will you give me some advice?"

He blushed slightly, wondering if she had read his thoughts. "Why, if I can."

"Will you come with me to the patio? I suppose the hole in the middle of our house could be called that," she said, smiling.

Standing in the yard formed by the rectangular shape of the low adobe building, Sister Praxedes asked Brother Gabriel if he thought there was any way to put porches on the structure.

"This isn't a very ideal time of the year to start tearing things up, Sister."

"Oh, we couldn't do anything until spring, but if these walls can support porches, I want to find out the cost and try to have the sum put away by the time it can be done."

"You'll have to experiment as we did with the pears and apples." He laughed. "But seriously, I think it could be done. Adobe walls are stronger than they look."

After Brother Gabriel had left, Sister Praxedes went into the warm little kitchen, where she knew she'd find the other two sisters.

"What do you think of Brother Gabriel?" Sister Loyola asked before she could say anything.

"He is very pleasant, isn't he? But I had the feeling that he was trying to guess my age."

The two sisters looked at each other and laughed. "That's just what we were trying to do," Sister Loyola admitted.

"Let's have open confession then. I'll tell my age if you tell yours," Sister Praxedes said as she took up the knife she had been using to peel potatoes before Brother Gabriel's arrival.

Sister Marianita blushed.

"She's only seventeen," Sister Loyola volunteered.

"Seventeen? Why, you're not much older than Delia, my youngest sister! Only seventeen, Sister?"

Sister Marianita turned scarlet. She had tried so hard to seem older. Why had they ever started talking about age?

"I'm nineteen—but I'll be twenty before long," Sister Loyola went on.

"Then I really am the old lady," Sister Praxedes said.

The two sisters waited for more, but Sister Praxedes went right on peeling potatoes.

"Aren't you going to finish the agreement?"

"All right. I'm twenty-four, but I feel as capable as fourteen so don't you two abandon me."

They all laughed. Sister Praxedes did not add that she had not made her final profession yet, but for that matter neither had they.

The three sisters divided their time between teaching and the endless tasks attached to the domestic side of the school and convent.

Since no trains came into Bernalillo, much of their food had to be grown. Remembering Archbishop Lamy's fruitful garden in Santa Fe, Sister Praxedes tried her skill with planting and hoeing. The soil was good, and with kindly attention it yielded fine tomatoes and beans for the table.

When Mike Sullivan, one of Bernalillo's few Irishmen, found out that Sister Praxedes was gardening, he made it his business to show up at the proper time. It was worth any amount of work just to come to the convent and hear "a bit of Ireland" in her talk.

"*Dónde está Hermana Prajedes?*" asked Mike Sullivan in his Irish-tinged Spanish.

The little boy to whom the question was addressed looked up from his job of feeding the three gray cats and the very thin kitten to point toward the kitchen. "*Allá,*" was all he could be bothered saying.

Mike tucked his ancient straw sombrero under one arm and strode across the yard in the direction of the kitchen.

"I should have known," he mumbled to himself. "Smells like something's cookin'."

Through the doorway Mike caught sight of the familiar blue apron. With a big ladle in her hand, her face flushed from the heat of the stove, Sister Praxedes was stirring something in a large kettle.

"Smells tasty, Sister," Mike called, waiting for an invitation to step into the kitchen.

"I'm trying to make a little apple butter from those apples we canned last fall. I promised the children a treat and they won't let me forget. Come on in, Mike. What can I do for you?"

"Well, I've been meanin' to stop by sooner. I was wonderin' who it is that's goin' to plow up the ground for your garden. It's time the tomato plants were in, Sister. Who's goin' to do it for you?"

"*¿Quién sabe?*" she said seriously, her eyes smiling a different answer.

"Well, I'll be over in the mornin' then," he answered, and was out the door before she could thank him.

"Mike!" she called.

As he turned she walked to the door, ladle in hand, saying with all the Irish brogue she could muster, "God be good to you, Mike!"

In the evening the three sisters, with the small children who boarded at the school, gathered in one room. Recreation was far from a time of idleness. It was then that the little girls learned to darn by working on their own poor garments, and when that grew tiresome, for it seldom was a task that was finished, the sisters taught them how to weave baskets, which could be sold to help earn a little money for the poor community.

Looking about her at the children crouched cross-legged on the smooth dirt floor, all busy, Sister Praxedes knew that God was blessing their work here in New Mexico. If they were poor in all else, love was in abundance.

"Adela, why aren't you sewing? You have been sitting there staring into the candlelight since recreation began," Sister Loyola was saying to a very black-eyed little girl not more than eight years old.

"No, no," she said, her lips making a pout.

"Adela, answer me. Why aren't you sewing?"

"No sew," she repeated in her few English words.

And pushing aside the little cardboard box in which she had two very-much-darned stockings, she hopped up and put her arms around Sister Loyola.

"No," she begged.

"Very well," Sister Loyola said in a soft voice, patting the child's firm cheek. "But sit down and be good."

The child smiled and was just starting to return to her place when Sister Praxedes' voice caused her to stop.

"Adela, will you bring me your box?"

The child's dark eyes grew very serious, but without a word she picked up the disarrayed darning, and, looking back at Sister Loyola, who was already busy helping another little girl, walked to Sister Praxedes.

"Adela, why don't you want to darn?" she asked kindly but with no indication of softness.

"No sew, Hermana." She began to pout again.

"But, Adela, you will have no nice stockings to wear tomorrow and tomorrow is Sunday."

"No sew," was all she would say.

Sister Praxedes looked at her very solemnly for a moment, then taking one of the stockings pushed her hand carefully through it until she came to a hole in the toe. Sticking out one finger, she wiggled it at the child, and said almost severely, "Adela, you darn this hole so you can wear them to Mass tomorrow."

The child looked up at her. No, Sister Praxedes was not smiling as she did when she gave them apple butter on large slices of bread. Sister Praxedes meant that the stockings were to be darned, and that they should be darned right now. The child took the stocking in her hand as Sister drew a piece of thread through a large needle.

"Sew?" Adela asked. Her eyes were very large and the pouting mouth had disappeared.

"Yes, Adela, sew."

A few minutes later Sister Praxedes glanced up. It is difficult to be strict and kind at the same time, she was thinking.

One day after she had been in Bernalillo nearly two years, Don Benigna, a young man with a family of six small children, came to her for work.

"*Hermana,*" he began almost apologetically, and continuing in Spanish he explained that there would be no work in the fields for several months and that his children would not eat unless he was able to do some work until harvesttime. "We have another baby this summer," he told her.

"How good God is to send you many children, and how good He is to send you to me when I need the convent walls white-washed. Will you do that for me?"

"Si, si," he smiled eagerly.

Don Benigna swung the wide brush in even sweeps up and down the adobe wall, humming as he worked. He is happy, Sister Praxedes thought. He likes working for his family. I wonder how he would be at carpentry.

"Don Benigna, I have another bit of work which I think you could do. We need a porch around the patio so the sisters can get out for some air in the daytime without suffering from the heat. Finally I have saved enough from selling canned vegetables and needlework; so if I order the lumber, will you have time to build it before harvest?"

Don Benigna smiled. "Si, *hermana*, I finish it or I do not go to the harvest."

So Sister Praxedes ordered the lumber. When it arrived by wagon from Las Vegas, she told Don Benigna, "I will be home from the Santa Fe retreat on August 25. By that time you will probably have all these other jobs finished and you can start building the porches. Will you need help?"

"Si, *hermana*, but you no worry. I fix."

As she rode the stagecoach from Bernalillo up to Santa Fe that August morning in 1880, she wondered whether it was her imagination that made this road seem smoother than the road (much like it) which she had traveled five years before from Las Vegas into Santa Fe on her arrival in the West. How different was this trip! She who had never known the feel of returning as a woman to her native Bawnboy, she who had not felt the thrill of reunion with her family on Pine Street, she who had not yet ridden along the pike for a homecoming in Kentucky, experienced the excitement of going back to a place that was home—going to Santa Fe was like going home.

Looking through the open window as the stage rumbled along the road that gradually climbs for sixty miles from the floor of the desert between Albuquerque and Bernalillo to the top of the foothills of Santa Fe, she closed her eyes again and again to open them on this no longer strange, rolling New Mexican desert. For miles, except for a rare isolated hut, there was no sign of human life. It was one of those days when a plane of scudding white cloud divides the atmosphere into the clear sunlit blue above and a changing pattern of sun and shadow below. As the clouds rode easily above, trailing shadow prints across the brown hills dotted with blue-green scrub piñon, the sand hills, chameleon-like, turned red-brown, then green and brown again. There was a living quality to this response of earth to the depth or shallowness of its ceiling of cloud. To Sister Praxedes this was nature's lesson of easy adaptability. The earth was firm, was sure; but it responded to a moving beauty above it. That was the way she dreamed of being.

When the coach reached the crest of the road from which they would gradually wend their way into Santa Fe, it seemed to pause and draw breath as she did. There it was! There was Santa Fe! First she saw it all at a glance—a city made miniature by the immensity of mountains behind it. Then the mountains were forgotten as her eyes caught the focal point, the angular lines of the cathedral, with all the streets forming a winding, fanlike pattern spreading out and out to the hills. She could see the pencil-like steeple of Loretto's spire pointing above the cluster of tree tops around it. And then the coach moved down the road and in among the brown adobes and the wooden fences and there were low doorways, flashes of tamarisk, children's faces staring, rough carts. She was back in her Santa Fe.

Mother Francisca would be there! And Mother Magdalen. And the Archbishop! She must go to the garden to see him. Would she ever forget that day in his garden? How lost she had been until he had helped her see the way.

The coach swung along the south end of the plaza, trembled to a stop. Stepping down, she waited for the driver to hand her small, black valise from the top of the coach. She glanced around. Santa Fe! Fine dark faces, smiling. People hurrying across the plaza. The "Governor's Palace" on one side and shops shadowed by covered walks on the other three sides. And there were the gas street lights she had heard about! Santa Fe was going modern.

"*Gracias, mi amigo*," she sang out to the driver as she took her bag.

Just down the boardwalk in front of the La Fonda and she'd be there. Walking along the street alone, she had the desire to call out to the people she passed, "I'm home. I'm back!" Wasn't life strange? Five years. Five years ago she had seen this same place and yet had not seen it. We have eyes but see not, she thought.

A man doffed his hat. She nodded. "*Buenos días!*" Everyone was happy today.

As she crossed Canal Street and saw the convent, she smiled. They would probably be surprised to see her. It was good to arrive this way—alone. She looked around at the stragglers on the street and she felt very close to them. She could stop and breathe it all in. Mother Francisca had been right; Santa Fe had good air. It got inside. It got inside one's soul.

As she opened the iron gate and went up the two brick steps to the walk, someone came out onto the porch. Because of the shadows the veil cast on the sister's face, Sister Praxedes didn't recognize the nun.

"There she is!" she heard the sister say to someone behind her in the hall.

It was Mother Francisca herself!

"I just said to Mother Magdalen that we ought to walk over to see if the coach had come in. Here, let me have your bag."

Mother Francisca met Sister Praxedes at the porch steps. Mother Magdelan stood in the doorway. How like and yet how unlike that first meeting five years before!

"Oh, it is wonderful to be home again," Sister Praxedes said, smiling.

"Yes, and we are happy to have you. After retreat we must have a long visit," Mother Francisca told her.

"Oh, we must. If I didn't have to return to Bernalillo to get Don Benigna started on the porches, I think I'd stay a few days after retreat."

The spacious stillness of the French Gothic chapel at Santa Fe closed around Sister Praxedes as the retreat began. The August before she had made her final profession here, but even the retreat prior to that had not seemed so permeated with peace and love. Even the usual urgent sweep of a large community at prayer seemed relaxed and quiet now. Over and over she thanked God for the depth of happiness He had granted to her. Five years before she had come to this strangely different New Mexico ill, fearful, wondering; now vigorous, trusting, sure, she knew a love for a land and a people that somehow answered an unasked question of her childhood. She had never understood how her mother could have returned to Ireland, leaving her children behind. But now although she still could not fully understand, she could understand how love of a place could coerce one's reason. Why should her mother have longed for hills and valleys and people of a particular spot? Why should she herself now care for this contradictory land of mountains and sand and dark-skinned people? Was it perhaps a natural desire for security, a desire to belong to a place, to have a home? As she thanked God for the ability to love and to make a wider world a home, she asked not to love too much. "I have the same heart as she. I too could love a place beyond reason, hurting perhaps even You."

Thoughts of others came in the spaces of quiet between formal prayer and spiritual conferences. She remembered with sorrow Sister Florence, who had not found this place a home and had abandoned her religious life. She looked at the winding curve of the chapel's stairway and wondered about the man who had come suddenly, worked quickly, and left unpaid. Had he been St. Joseph? Surely he had at least been sent by the saint whose patronage the sisters had sought. Positively the man had been an artist who worked by inspiration. Nothing so beautiful could be made by an uninspired man. She heard the muffled sounds of the town outside and wondered where Angelica of the poppies had gone. Was she safe from the temptations and the evils that skip little children only to return when they are grown? She thought of the Archbishop, who was growing old now and whose health had begun to decline. She pictured Mike Sullivan and Brother Gabriel and Don Benigna. And all of these, the errant nun, the genius carpenter, the former pupil, the elderly Bishop, and the faithful friends, she wrapped in prayer. Life was so full of blessings, but the greatest of these were the persons He asked that she love in His place. During this retreat words that she had so often heard grew more meaningful. "Whatsoever you do to the least of these my brethren, you do unto Me." We serve God when we serve others.

Sooner than she realized, the thoughts that had come easily during the quiet moments of the retreat were to be challenged. The day before the retreat ended, August 20, a conversation in a distant corner of the convent at Santa Fe moved toward her.

"I cannot believe that Sister Ignatia would have allowed the girl to have any contact with Father Rouault if she had had the slightest reason to mistrust him," Mother Magdalen was saying to Mother Francisca.

"Nor do I, but with people gossiping and saying that it is her fault, she will be made miserable. And if the report is true that they have returned to live in the town, Sister will find it very awkward since she knew both of them so well."

"But who will you send? There is so much to do there—a building half finished, a debt, a school to run, novices. Why it is a job for two women!"

"I know, Mother, but we can't send two women." Mother Francisca paused. All day she had been wondering what Mother would say about sending Sister Praxedes, since she knew that Mother Magdalen had an almost protective attitude toward the young sister.

"What about someone from Socorro?" Mother Magdalen went on. "Isn't there anyone there?"

"I've been up and down the list at least a dozen times today, Mother. I have only one suggestion and you may not agree with me."

"Yes?"

"What about Sister Praxedes?"

"Sister Praxedes? That child! Why, Mother Francisca!"

Mother Francisca waited. Then since Mother Magdalen did not actually disagree, Mother Francisca decided to pursue the matter.

"Although she is still rather young, she has had two years managing a school. She is a good religious and she knows how to get along with people. And she seems to thrive on adversity. Right now we need someone who can win the respect of people."

"She will be very disappointed not to be going back to Bernalillo."

"I know, but she has learned to handle disappointment well."

Since Mother Magdalen made no further objections, Mother Francisca went on. "Do you feel able to make the trip to Cruces with Sister? I would like a first-hand report on the whole situation."

On the morning of August 24, Mother Francisca asked Sister Praxedes to come to her office.

"Every time I was ever summoned here, it meant a sacrifice," Sister Praxedes bantered.

Mother Francisca was so struck by the comment that she could not bring herself to the subject of the interview immediately. Instead she asked Sister to tell her about the porches she was planning for the convent in Bernalillo.

"It is really one porch to go around the inside walls of the quadrangle. We do so much of our canning out there, that we really need protection from the heat and glare of the sun."

"That sounds like a very practical addition." She paused and then added, "But I'm afraid that someone else will have to oversee the work, Sister. Here comes another sacrifice."

Not too sure what Mother Francisca was trying to say, Sister Praxedes explained, "The lumber is already in the yard. Don Benigna knows exactly what is to be done. In fact, he may have started already."

"That is fine. You see, Sister, I have had to make a few changes, and instead of returning to Bernalillo, you are going to Visitation Academy in Las Cruces, New Mexico. You will find some building to do there, too; more than one kind of building. It will not be quite so simple as a porch."

As Mother Francisca paused, Sister Praxedes did not attempt to speak. She was too stunned to know just what to say.

"There is much more that I would like to tell you. Mother Magdalen is going with you so she will give you more information on the way. I do think that you should know that this change has been caused by a very unfortunate situation. There is a scandal there which you will have to handle as you see fit."

"May I ask what happened?"

"Yes, you should know, but actually we have gotten only the sketchiest report and I do not know how much of it is true. You see, Sister Ignatia, who has been Superior there, was here in Santa Fe when the difficulty occurred so my information is by letter from one of the sisters there. This much is certain: one of the novices, a Margarita Garcia, left one night without anyone's knowledge. We are certain that she went off with a priest from the area. Rumor has it, if it can be believed, that they have gotten married. The reason we do not want Sister Ignatia to return is because the people have somehow gotten the idea that she was a party to the intrigue since she seemed to be so conveniently out of town. That of course is ridiculous since I myself sent for her on other matters."

"How could anyone blame her?"

"I don't know. How do any of us get false ideas? The fact remains that it is a very bad situation and you will have to be extremely careful. The sisters are upset and the whole place is in a rather shaky condition because of the building and the debt. If the people turn against us, we cannot expect to finish the building. In fact, what use would it be? So you can see that this is not a very pleasant situation."

"When are we to leave?"

"I am afraid that you will have to take a carriage to Albuquerque today. There is an early train from there to Socorro in the morning."

"I'm rather stunned by all this, Mother Francisca. I had no idea that I might be changed from Bernalillo."

"No, none of us did. I had no such plan when you came, but situations change quite suddenly sometimes."

"Is there anything more I should know?"

"I will tell you that I am very worried about Las Cruces. I fear that if this scandal has gone too far, we may have to withdraw from the town. If, after you are there for a while, you think that is so, I want you to let me know."

"Maybe everyone was excited at first. Perhaps they will forget about it."

"Perhaps."

"I think I had better get my things together if we must leave today."

"Yes, you do that. I will see you before you leave, but I am sure that you know that we will be praying for you. I am sorry that we cannot keep you a few days. The Archbishop, too, will be disappointed."

For the first lap of the journey, to Albuquerque, Sister Praxedes was in a daze; but the abrupt reality of getting up at 3 A.M. the next morning to make a work train jarred her into consciousness. When the train chugged through Bernalillo at dawn, she leaned hard on some of that consolation she had experienced during retreat. How she wanted to get off and go back to her safe little convent! At noon the train reached the end of the line at Socorro, where they waited until 2:50 for a stage going south. The only other passenger was a Negro soldier, who chose to ride on top with the driver.

As they started on the most difficult phase of the trip to Las Cruces, Mother Magdalen turned the conversation to the country they were going through.

"I've heard some wild tales about this stretch of country," Sister Praxedes said.

"Wild is right. We may even have some to tell. See through the stage window there?" Mother indicated the mountains approximately twenty miles in the distance. "There are Indians up there. And not very polite ones either. The only reason the San Carlos ever take anyone alive is to torture them."

"You mean those stories about the *jornada* are true!"

"Of course they're true, but this isn't called the *jornada del muerte* just because of Indians. The Spanish explorers named it because up until about twenty-five years ago this was a ninety-mile stretch of desert without water. Now Martin's Well breaks the trip; but in those days if anything happened to delay a party crossing this piece, it was sure death. If you watch carefully every few miles, you'll notice grave mounds. I guess this could just as well be called the graveyard of New Mexico."

They rode along in silence for some time. Watching for one of the graves, Sister Praxedes could not keep from glancing suspiciously at the mountains. What would happen if Indians descended upon them? She thought of the driver and the Negro soldier sitting on top of the stage in full view.

"Do you think anything will happen?" she asked Mother Magdalen.

"Yes, I do, but it will probably not be more than a few disconnected joints. Up a few miles farther the trail is terrible. I wish there were some other passengers to weight us down. It isn't so bad in a full stage."

Mother Magdalen's description of the bouncing had been mild. They tossed from side to side, hitting first one side of the stage and then the other. Sister Praxedes felt her stomach churning. But she had to think of the older woman, who could not brace herself as easily.

"Mother, maybe if I put my arms around you and you leaned against me neither of us would be thrown around so much."

Without further questioning, Sister Praxedes took advantage of a few feet of smooth road and shifted to the other seat. Then bracing herself with her feet against the other seat and her back flat against the back of the carriage, she put her arms around Mother Magdalen and steadied them both.

For hours they jogged along in this position. About the time that Sister Praxedes thought she could not stand the ache in her arms and the numbness in her feet, she noticed that they were slowing down. At first she was relieved; then she remembered the Indians.

"This must be Martin's Well," came the answer to her unspoken question.

The stage jerked, then gradually stopped swaying, and Sister Praxedes relaxed her hold on Mother Magdalen.

"Whew, what a trip! I'd be battered to insensibility if you hadn't thought to do that. You must be stiffer than a cactus needle." She laughed, using the expression she had heard the driver use.

"That was murder up there!" the soldier was saying as he shook his head and mopped his brow. "I'm for riding the rest of the way inside."

"Why don't you?" Sister Praxedes said. "Maybe it would balance the inside better."

When the coach reloaded, several more persons joined them. A seedy-looking prospector who said he was from Oregon volunteered to perch on the top with the driver; so the two sisters, the soldier, and an elderly couple lugging a large wicker basket, a coffee mill, and a bed roll all squeezed into the two seats inside.

"You ladies better ride straight ahead," the old man said to Mother Magdalen.

"Why don't you?" Sister Praxedes said to her. "Sit across from me, Mother."

Mother Magdalen shifted to the place next to the window directly across from Sister.

"What about you, ma'am?"

"I don't mind riding backward." She smiled. For some strange reason she expected him to comment on her remark, but he did not. For years and years she had not thought about Mr. Shawn, but something about this man and her own remark about going backward reminded her of him. Mr. Shawn had said she would never get anywhere going backward. She smiled inside, she was not too sure that she wanted to get anywhere today.

"I think I'll put this here roll under your feet, Mama," he was saying to his wife. She smiled sweetly but said nothing.

"Now you sit there, boy." He indicated the place next to Sister Praxedes for the soldier.

Sister Praxedes wanted to smile as she watched the old man arrange the basket and the coffee mill on the seat next to the soldier.

"Everyone comfy?" he asked looking around. "Now we'll have no smoking, drinking or cussing on this trip," he chuckled as he sat back and took a bite off a stick of chewing tobacco. He held it out to the soldier, but the young man shook his head.

"Now, Matt." His wife blushed. "He's always joking," she said in Sister Praxedes' direction.

"That weren't no joke, Mama. Why anyone knows them soldier boys from Fort Union has some mighty rough ways. Ain't that right, boy?" He patted the young Negro on the knee.

"Yes, sir, some sure does." The young man gave him a broad smile.

"You folks all set in there?" the driver asked.

"Sure am, mister," the old man answered for all of them.

The driver slammed the coach door. As he climbed up to his place, the stage sagged slightly.

"Heavy feller," the old man chuckled.

A full coach promised an easier ride for the rest of their trip to Las Cruces; but before they had gone two miles, rain began to fall and they had to drop the canvas flaps over the windows. Gradually the air became saturated with the odor of perspiration, coffee, and chewing tobacco. This, together with the water splashing in through the cracks and windows, caused the travelers to drift from a semiconscious state of drowsiness to moments of sudden alarm when cold rain hit a hand or cheek. The trip lasted far into the night. At 2 A.M. the driver stopped the stage, bounded to the ground, and called in to the sleepy passengers, "This is where you sisters get off."

The soldier had to step outside to make room for them to crawl out. The prospector handed their bags down from the top of the stage, and the driver climbed back into his place.

"Thank you for bringing us right to the door," Mother Magdalen called.

"It's nothing," came his reply.

"I hear there's some gambling in this town, so you ladies beware," the old man said, sticking his head through the stagecoach window.

"Thank you. We will." Sister Praxedes laughed.

The stage rumbled away, leaving Mother Magdalen and Sister Praxedes in front of the darkened convent. What a strange sight it was! At one end was a half-constructed section; at the other, stacks of lumber and piles of something, probably sand or cement. It was impossible to tell in the dark.

Mother Magdalen motioned toward a door that was apparently the entrance to the original building. Sister Praxedes followed her. Just before Mother Magdalen rapped on the door, she turned to Sister. "I meant to tell you on the way," she said, "but we were in such close quarters. Here at Cruces you will assume a new title, *Mother* Praxedes." Then she knocked hard on the door.

"Surely they heard the stage and the men talking so loud. They must be deaf," Mother Magdalen said as she pounded harder.

Sister Praxedes was glad for the delay. She had a strangely wild idea that the sisters on the other side of the door were waiting for her to try on her new title. She said the name, Mother Praxedes, to herself. She had never thought of herself ever being called anything but Sister Praxedes.

"I think they're coming," she said.

A voice from behind the door called out in Spanish, "Who's there?"

"Mother Magdalen from Santa Fe, Sister."

They waited while someone inside fumbled with a bunch of keys. After another few seconds, the lock clicked and the door edged open to reveal two wide-eyed sisters attired in nightgowns, shawls, and veils, staring over the top of an oil lamp, which they both seemed to be holding.

"Oh, Mother Magdalen, we thought it was the sheriff or someone trying to force his way in."

"My gracious, child, no one with any sense would be pounding on a convent door at two A.M."

"Hah, you don't know Las Cruces!"

Sister Praxedes smiled, but Mother Magdalen frowned just a little.

"Mother, but we have been so on edge. Come in. You must be weary."

"We are. The stage was late because we ran into rain."

The sister who was carrying the lamp took Mother Magdalen's valise while the other closed the door and locked it again.

"This is Mother Praxedes from Bernalillo. This is Sister Vestina and Sister Clotilde," Mother said.

Everyone seemed to nod and smile and then Sister Vestina asked, "Are you hungry?"

"Only hungry for sleep," Mother Magdalen answered. "Let's all get to bed."

The next morning after Mass, Mother Magdalen introduced Sister Praxedes to her new community. At first surprised by the size of the group—six sisters, four novices, and four postulants—she did not know just what to say. The sisters were more stunned since they did not know that they were to have a new Superior.

"Mother Praxedes will need everyone's help in getting acquainted and I know that you will be good to her."

Sister Praxedes turned to Mother Magdalen and, without realizing that she spoke in Spanish, said, "I am the one who should be good to them."

Everyone smiled.

During the morning Sister Vestina, who kept the accounts, showed Sister Praxedes the empty cashbox and informed her that the debt was $5000.

"How do we raise money here?"

"I don't know. We've never had a debt before."

By noon Sister Praxedes had a fair picture of the proportions of her new assignment. She had found that the novice's elopement was more serious than she had thought. Margarita and Father Rouault had been married by a justice of the peace and were now living in town. Besides this sad situation, Sister Praxedes was faced with an unfinished building, no money, and a small novitiate to handle. In two weeks school was scheduled to start and there was some talk that people were not going to allow their daughters to go to a school where such intrigues could happen right under the sisters' eyes.

After dinner Mother Magdalen told Sister Praxedes that she wanted to return to Santa Fe the next day.

"Aren't you going to stay to see Bishop Salpointe? Sister Vestina said that he wrote that he would be here."

"Oh, I guess I should. Mother Francisca will want to know what he thinks about this scandal. I guess he intends visiting Father."

Mother Magdalen reached into her voluminous pocket and drew out a well-worn leather pouch. "You take this. It isn't much but it is something to start with."

Sister Praxedes took it and edged her fingers between the folds of the opening and looked inside.

"It's only nine dollars," Mother Magdalen said.

"It sounds like a fortune. Do you know that the sisters—I should say, *we*—have no money? The sisters have been getting food on credit."

Sister Vestina came hurrying down the hall with a newspaper in her hand. "Look what Señor Ascarate just brought. He said that you should read a letter that's been printed in today's paper."

"Oh, dear, I hope it isn't from some unreasonable citizen condemning us," Mother Magdalen said, taking the paper. She could see that a pencil line encircled a section of print. "Mother Praxedes, you read it to us."

Sister Praxedes took the paper and began to read:

> Sir: Charges of a damaging character having been made against the Sisters of Loretto, in connection with my marriage with a late inmate of the convent in this place, I want to inform the public that such charges have not me for authority. On the contrary, I took occasion, soon after my return to Las Cruces (on the 13 inst) to state in the presence of Messrs. Eugene Van Patten, Francisco Ascarate, and Domingo Luguini that the Sisters knew nothing of my relations with Margarita Garcia, my present wife, prior to her

leaving the convent. And I now repeat, and with greater emphasis the expression of my belief that the Sisters had not the slightest suspicion of my designs, or that Margarita Garcia intended to leave the convent. This statement will, I hope be broad enough to meet and utterly refute the allegation which appeared in the Mesilla *News*, namely, that the Mother Superior was forced by a sense of guilt, or led by a desire to facilitate my plans, to be conveniently absent from her post at the time those plans were to be executed. It is within the scope of my certain knowledge that she left Las Cruces to go to Santa Fe just when she did in obedience to a telegram requiring her presence at the latter place.

Sister Praxedes paused. "You mean something against Sister Ignatia was printed in the newspaper?"

"Oh yes," Sister Vestina answered.

"No wonder everyone is worried about the people. But we have to admit that Father is trying to be fair with the sisters."

"Oh, but isn't it a sad thing to have all this paraded in the papers. If they ever have any desire to repent, what will they do after all this publicity," Mother Magdalen lamented. "Is there any more to the letter?"

Sister Praxedes began reading again:

In what I have done, no one is responsible but myself. I meditated no harm to any one, and I regret that my action in this matter should have led to reflections upon the Sisters of Loretto. My intention was to leave the cassock and be married. This I have done; and for it I have no regret. As for the statement attributed to me that intrigues between the priests and young ladies of this convent are common, I unqualifiedly disclaim it. If it is a matter of any interest to the public, I will state that the buggy which conveyed Miss Garcia and myself from the convent, on the occasion referred to, was stationed at the northeast corner of the convent garden from 9 until 10:30 P.M.

"And then his name is signed," she said. She turned to Sister Vestina. "When did the sisters know that Margarita was gone?"

"It wasn't until the next morning when one of the other novices saw her habit hanging in the dormitory with a note pinned to it. She must have gone out after everyone else had gone to bed."

"I can't understand how they could have had enough opportunity to get to know each other," Mother Magdalen said.

"Oh, Mother, Margarita knew him a long time. When she was in school here, she was in the choir that Father directed. It seems that at the same time she was being courted by a young man from Juarez, Mexico. In fact, plans were underway for her marriage when suddenly she decided to ask for admission to the novitiate. Maybe even at that time Father Rouault thought he was advising her correctly or perhaps he was already interested in her for himself. I remember last spring seeing Father stop by the gate to talk to her when she was presiding with the children. No one thought anything of it because he had been her adviser; however, I remember Sister Ignatia going out one time and asking him if he wanted something because he had been there so long. If anyone had thought that they were planning such a thing, she would have been asked to leave and the Archbishop would have been notified."

"The poor girl! I guess I should say the poor priest. We'll have to storm heaven for them," Sister Praxedes said.

The next day Bishop Salpointe visited the convent after having called on the couple. He was visibly sad as he told about the cold refusal he had met.

"He always was difficult to talk to, but we had had pleasant relationships," the aging prelate said, shaking his head.

"We will pray for them every day and make reparation that the good God will show them their mistake," Sister Praxedes told him.

At last she hoped to get him to talk about more pleasant things by suggesting that perhaps he and Mother Magdalen would like to have a visit alone.

After Sister had excused herself, the Bishop looked at Mother Magdalen gravely. "This is a nasty situation for such a young woman."

"I know, Your Grace, but what were we to do? Frankly, I think that Sister will do as well as anyone could. If the people continue to believe that the sisters were at fault, then no one will be able to do anything. If this passes over, Sister Praxedes is capable of handling the school and I think she will even manage to finish the building. She has a lot of energy and gets along well in difficult situations."

"Oh, but she was pretty sick a few years back when we brought her West. Do you think her health will stand up?"

"Oh, it will, Your Grace. She is just fine now. I think that was God's way of getting her out here to us." Mother smiled.

"Well, I hope you're right. She has a nice way about her. Maybe she'll win the people." He paused for a moment. "How was your trip down, Mother?"

"No Indians this time, which was one thing to be grateful for."

"I hear the San Carlos Indians are warring about something again. Things will never settle down until Chief Victorio is gone."

"Well, we saw no Indians, but until we got to Martin's Well it was a rough ride."

"Don't tell me that an old pioneer like you minds a bounding stage?"

"You must remember, Your Grace, I'm not as young as I once was. Even the trip back in '52 nearly killed me and I was young then."

"My, the Sisters of Loretto have been in New Mexico a long time."

"Twenty-eight years the twenty-sixth of September. This is God's chosen land!"

"And sometimes God's forsaken land."

"Yes, but when we think of the progress the Church has made here since Archbishop Lamy came in 1850, we know it isn't. The number of priests from your own country is remarkable, Bishop Salpointe. Why thirty years ago it was as hard to find a priest in the Southwest as it was to find a drinking well and when one could be found, he might not be the right sort after all."

"Ah, but, Mother, we can't count progress in religion by counting priests!"

"No, not entirely, but more priests mean more frequent visits to the missions; more sacraments mean more grace."

"But there is still such a strange mixture of paganism and superstition among the people in the remote areas. I am not sure that we have found the way to make Christianity meaningful to the lives of the Indians, for example."

"If the white, so-called Christian continues to rob the Indians of their rights, we can't expect them to understand Christianity at all," Mother Magdalen said.

"At least the priests no longer rob the poor by taking the best of their products as was true of some before His Grace came. But we have still not found a way to erase their ignorance and abolish their hunger. Hungry people can be hungry and holy, but most often, I think, they are only hungry."

"You seem pessimistic, Your Grace," Mother Magdalen said.

"Oh, perhaps it is the day. I always get discouraged when one of our men does as this priest has. It can undo so many years of work. But no more sad talk, Mother. When you return to Santa Fe, remember me to the Archbishop and Mother Francisca. I hope to see them both before winter sets in, but with the Indians acting up, I don't know whether I'll make it. A lone horseman makes easy prey."

"I wouldn't want to be doing it." She smiled.

"Well, I've kept you long enough, Mother," he said as he rose to go. "I'm happy to have seen you again."

"Thank you, Your Grace. If you do get up to Santa Fe, come over to visit us. You'll be pleased with our chapel. Have you been there since it was completed?"

"Yes, it is very lovely indeed. I told the Archbishop that the architects gave the gem to Loretto and the rock to Santa Fe. I don't think he liked it. The cathedral is his gem. By the way, how did you ever solve the problem of a stairway to the choir loft?"

"You'll have to see it, Your Grace. It was an answer to prayer. If you're a skeptic, you won't believe this, but St. Joseph built it for us."

"He's a good one to pray to in the carpentry line."

"No, I don't mean just praying to him. He actually came and put it up for us."

"Now, Mother," Bishop Salpointe said with a wrinkle of his brow.

"One morning a man came to the door and wanted to know if there was anything he could do around the place. When he heard about our not being able to get to the choir because the architect had neglected to plan a space for a stairway, he offered to build one. He went to work and made a circular staircase, and the reason I know it was St. Joseph is that when I went to pay him for his work, he was nowhere to be found and we've never seen him to this day. What do you think of that?"

"Well, Mother," was all he answered, his tone indicating disbelief.

"You just come over the next time you're in Santa Fe and I'll show it to you."

"I wish I had the faith you sisters have," he remarked as he left.

Very early the next morning, the sisters gathered outside to say good-by to Mother Magdalen, who was returning to Santa Fe.

"You have a big job here, child," Mother Magdalen said to Sister Praxedes. "But you can do anything if you rely on the good God."

"Thank you, Mother Magdalen, for everything. May God go with you to Santa Fe."

Sister Praxedes watched the buggy that was taking Mother Magdalen to the stagecoach office pull away. She wished that she could be as strong and sure as this woman. As she stood there, scarcely able to see the road for the dust the horse and buggy had raised, she remembered something. Somehow this had all happened before. Why was that? Then she remembered. Stooping down, Sister Praxedes picked up a pebble to throw into the dust flurry. "Moira," she thought. Moira riding away with Padriac: someone must throw the pebble to chase the fairies away. For a second she was young again, standing on a hillside in Ireland. She was the Susan who was going to find a new world. She was Susan who led the blind. She hoped she could still lead them; and be herself led.

"Mother, Mother Praxedes." She heard a voice behind her. It was Sister Vestina. "Mother, is anything wrong?"

"Oh no. Nothing is wrong. I was just thinking about something."

"About Mother Magdalen?"

"Yes and no. I was really thinking about an old friend who was blind. Sister Vestina, do you think that I'm blind?"

"Blind? I'm afraid I don't understand."

"No, of course you don't, and I'm not too sure that I do. Sister, what do we need the most?"

Sister Vestina got a mischievous look in her eyes. "Some food in the house."

"You mean we haven't any?"

"That's just about right. And Pascual refuses to go again and ask for credit. He said he's afraid the storekeepers will throw him out if he comes again without money."

"Where's the market?"

"I'm not too sure."

"Haven't you ever gone to any store here?"

"Never."

"Then this will have to be the first time. As soon as I get that purse Mother Magdalen gave me, we are going shopping."

"But the people will stare, Mother. We've never gone to a store here."

"Then they'll just have to stare. Perhaps if they realize that we are human beings and have to eat, they'll extend our credit. *¿Quien sabe?* Maybe they'll even help us finish the building."

"Mother, maybe we ought to ask someone to take us to the right places. There are some stores that respectable ladies don't go to."

"Maybe then we can make them respectable by going." She laughed. "Do you know anyone we can ask?"

"Mrs. Duper, whose husband owns the hotel, has always been very nice to us. She told us that she'd always be glad to do anything if we'd just let her know."

"Fine. Then we'll go to see Mrs. Duper first. I'd like to meet some of the people anyway."

When the two sisters walked into the small lobby of the town's only hotel, several men standing near the entrance did turn to stare as Sister Vestina had predicted. Another man came from behind a desk at the far end of the room, where he had been talking to a woman.

"Say, Sister Vestina, what brings you here? Anything wrong?"

"No, nothing is wrong, Mr. Duper. This is Mother Praxedes, the new Superior at the convent; we were looking for your wife."

"I'm glad to make your acquaintance, Mother. Why don't you both come on upstairs?"

"No, thank you, we will wait here if you don't mind. We wanted Mrs. Duper to tell us where she does her shopping."

"Shopping?" He looked puzzled. "Oh, sure. I'll go get her."

The three men had started to talk softly, glancing now and then at the two sisters.

"I guess we do look rather odd standing here," Sister Praxedes said.

"This will give them something different to talk about."

"Maybe it will just confirm the bad impression they have when they see our skinny little figures and our sour faces," Sister Praxedes added with a half smile.

"Oh, Sisters, I'm so glad to see you," a small plumpish woman bubbled as she came bustling down the stairs. "I thought Mr. Duper was joking when he said you were here. This is the best surprise. Won't you come upstairs?"

"No, we really can't. Mrs. Duper, this is Mother Praxedes, who came from Santa Fe a few days ago to replace Sister Ignatia. Mother wants to do some shopping and I told her that you would know all about the stores in town."

"I'm very glad to know you, Mother. I hope you'll like Cruces. Just what kind of shopping did you have in mind?"

"I am mainly interested in getting acquainted with the merchants. I do want to purchase food, of course, but I would like to meet the people."

"Oh, all right. Then if you will wait just a minute, I'll go with you."

Mrs. Duper could not help but overhear Mother Praxedes' conversation with various storekeepers. As the shopping tour progressed, she became keenly aware that the sisters were in grave need of help. When she left the two sisters at the convent door, she said, "Mother Praxedes, if you don't mind, I would like to tell a few very fine people in town just how much you need help. I wouldn't want to embarrass you but I think that you can well afford assistance from some of the people."

Before a week was out a delegation made up of the Dupers and the Ascarates, the Amadors and the Stephensons visited young Mother Praxedes to ask what they could do to help.

"You can help organize a bazaar," she told them. "If we hurry, we can have one this fall, and maybe—most of all—we can help some of the poor people in the town. It's hard, you know, to be holy when you're hungry."

"That's a splendid idea, Mother," Mr. Stephenson, who was county probate clerk said. "Why the crew of men working on the railroad will be pleased as parrots. Ever since they got to town, they've been asking why we don't have some kind of church social. And they've got money to spend, too."

"Is there anything you need for the convent right now?" Mrs. Stephenson wanted to know.

"Just the support of the people. If you can help them forget this summer's trouble, we won't have to worry."

The people who came to the convent were not the ones who worried Mother Praxedes. From what the sisters said, these people had always been loyal. It was those who turned on the street and stared who concerned her.

Whether or not people thought that the sisters could have prevented the elopement by more vigilance, Mother Praxedes was inclined to think that the physical arrangements of the Las Cruces convent were not suitable for a novitiate. Although a novitiate was not meant to keep those who wished to leave locked away from freedom, it had to have a certain privacy and remoteness from the traffic of everyday life in order to allow the young women there the opportunity to find out in peace if the religious life were their vocation. The untrained had to have seclusion if they were to grow spiritually. Deciding whether this was a good place for novices was not to be ascertained by the fact that one had run away—she could have more easily have said she was going and have gone. Some novices leave every novitiate. The decision must be based on those who had stayed. Were they developing into religious or were they simple girls, wearing nuns' habits, busy with convent tasks? If they were able to study and to meditate and to love and thus to grow in this place, fine; if they were not, something would have to be done. Mother Praxedes would reserve judgment until she had seen more of the situation, but already she knew that the physical setup was far from ideal.

"Mother, do we have a final count on the boarders?" Sister Vestina asked as she stood beside the desk in the front of the room which served as Mother Praxedes' office as well as her classroom.

"Yes, according to the numbers from each class, there are a hundred and five. If all pay the two hundred dollars tuition and board, we should be able to manage," Mother Praxedes said.

"Oh, but only about half paid the full amount last year. The others will give us flour or potatoes or maybe eggs from time to time. It gets the accounts so mixed up."

"Why don't you credit them with the value of what they bring? Maybe in some cases people are paying too much or in others too little."

"I could do that now that I have some idea of prices."

Picking up a list of names lying on the desk, Mother Praxedes changed the subject.

"Sister Vestina, something will have to be done about the presiding. Both yesterday and today Sister Josefina was not at morning meditation, so today I asked her when she gets her meditation in and she said that yesterday she did not find time and today she made part of it while the boarders were getting dressed and the other part just before supper. A novice who hasn't even learned to make a meditation can't be having her prayers broken up like that. It would be a hardship on a mature religious, but for a beginner it might mean that she'll lose all desire to meditate. The religious who does not pray is not a religious. I've gone over the list and I can't see who could take that time, so I'll awaken the boarders myself, but something must be done about these other situations. Sister Clotilde is in the kitchen during examen and during spiritual reading every day. Other sisters will have to take those times."

"I just followed the schedule we used last spring, Mother."

"I know you did and it isn't your fault, but we have to find some way to get the novices and postulants into a definite routine where they will be at spiritual exercises with the community."

Sister Vestina could appreciate Mother Praxedes' concern because she, like Mother Praxedes, had spent her postulancy and part of her novitiate at the mother house in Kentucky, where regularity was as set as the bricks in the buildings. Then she had had two years in Santa Fe. She was aware that the young religious here were at a disadvantage, but with so many things to be done and so few of them to do it, nothing else, she assumed, could be done.

"Sister, aren't there some older girls who could get the children up and put them to bed at night? I think one of the sisters should be available but I don't think that novices should be doing that."

"Oh, I think several of the senior girls would like some responsibility."

Another thing bothered Mother Praxedes. She had very little time to give the novices and postulants any kind of guidance. She had a class to teach and when she wasn't engaged with that she had to check on the men working on the building. She also wanted to start a garden so that they could grow some of the vegetables and fruits they needed. She hoped, too, that they could put in a few poppy seeds.

After much trial and error, Mother Praxedes came to a decision. The novices just could not stay here under the present conditions. In late September she wrote to Mother Francisca stating the situation as she saw it and suggesting that the four novices and four postulants be admitted to the novitiate in Santa Fe, where they would have a better chance of becoming good religious.

"If Mother Francisca takes them, how are we going to manage?" Sister Vestina asked.

"We'll re-do the whole schedule. With the responsibility of these young people out of the way, I think we will all be able to arrange our time better. Six sisters ought to be able to handle a hundred and five boarders, especially if the older girls help with the presiding. I also think that the children could do more in the way of helping. Why can't they wash and dry dishes? Sweep the floor and set the table? There are a lot of things they could be doing."

Mother Francisca replied immediately that she would be glad to take the eight novices. She told Mother Praxedes if she would bring them as far as Socorro on October 9 she would meet them there and take them the rest of the way to Santa Fe.

Mother Praxedes sighed deeply. It was only a month since the retreat had ended in Santa Fe; and yet, it seemed eons ago. In all the rush and urgency of this month, she had not even had time to wonder how the porches were coming in Bernalillo.

LAS CRUCES, NEW MEXICO—1887

Mother Praxedes sighed, gave one last chop with the hoe, and drew up to her full height.

"There!"

One hand on the hoe, the other raised to shade her eyes from the sun, she looked across the garden. Row on row of tiny green sprouts, and beyond, the orchard in full bloom, were evidence not only of a few weeks work but of six years careful gardening. Sometimes she wondered what the Archbishop would say if he knew.

Standing there in the warm March sunshine, Mother Praxedes fancied she saw the canned beans and apples, which would bring a good price in the fall. The list of entries in her receipt book would be a parade of flowers and fruit, melons and needlework. Just yesterday she had received thirty-two dollars for embroidered scarfs and pillowcases. Every little bit was added assurance that she would be able to meet the bills and have something to lend Father for the church fund. At this thought, she sighed.

Father Lassaigne and Mother Praxedes had become good friends since he came to Las Cruces five years ago, but the building of St. Genevieve's Church had made their relationship somewhat strained of late. He had always been pessimistic where money was concerned and now he was despairing. When he said that the responsibility for the project was hers, she could not deny it. The new church had been her suggestion. Even when he told her of the difficulties he had had in erecting the parish church at Tularosa, she had assured him that Las Cruces would be different.

Her thoughts were interrupted by an unfamiliar sound. She listened. Was someone crying? The staccato of sobs grew louder. Mother Praxedes looked toward the orchard. Her eyes searched systematically from tree to tree. No one was visible, yet the sound was clearly coming from that direction. Hanging the hoe on the picket fence, she walked slowly, listening as she went.

As suddenly as the sound had begun, it ceased. But Mother Praxedes had already spied a dark head pillowed against a young peach branch. There, just above a fork in the tree, two patched trouser legs were supporting an evidently very sad child. He had also noticed her and was trying to edge further up into the tree to hide himself. Without a word, Mother walked to the tree and put out both hands to the child, who was just even with her shoulders.

"Raoul," she said, "mavourneen, come." And then the tears began again. Almost frenzied with unhappiness, his whole body shook with convulsive sobbing. She lifted him from his tree perch, and kneeling down beside him, put a strong arm about his quivering shoulders.

"Raoul, have you come to water the orchard for me?" She smiled tenderly.

There was no comfort for the little boy. Whatever was troubling his six-year-old heart was, to him, troubling indeed. She said no more, but wiping his cheeks with her handkerchief, stood up and took him by the hand.

"Come along, Raoul. You will have to help me or I won't finish by dinner."

She chatted to him about the garden and told him how much she had been hoping for someone to help her. There were some tiny weeds between the melon plants which she simply could not get. One needed small hands just like Raoul's for such difficult work. She wondered if Raoul would be kind enough to help her since she needed him so much.

"There, Raoul! See between those two plants? Will you please pull that weed for me?"

Without a word he stooped down and with one steady tug freed the scrubby weed and turned triumphantly to her.

"*Aquí*," he said, thrusting it into her hand. Then he threw his brown arms about her in a momentary hug and ran away.

Half surprised, half delighted, she stood there holding the limp little weed with the feel of Raoul's arms still around her.

"Raoul," she called, but he was gone.

"Poor little Raoul," she thought. "Poor shy, black-eyed sweet little Mexican." Raoul had no father or mother; but Doña Apalonia, a good Indian woman who washed and scrubbed for a living, had taken him in. Doña Apalonia fed and clothed Raoul as she did several other orphaned children.

As Mother Praxedes thought of Doña Apalonia and Raoul, she sent God a silent reminder to keep sending people to buy her canned fruit and vegetables so that the school could remain open. She saw little hope of raising children like Raoul from their spiritual poverty unless they could rise from their physical poverty as well. Teaching them resignation to their state of misery was one thing, but using religion as a salve to quiet the inner desires for moral and intellectual dignity was another. The hunger of the body could devour the hunger of the soul, and of the mind, and then all would be lost. There was so much to be done here.

It was strange how much things had changed here in Las Cruces since that day six and a half years ago when Mother Magdalen left her here with nine dollars, a debt, and no food in the house. She smiled to herself as she took the hoe again and went back to work. She thought of the bazaar they had given in desperation that fall. It was like a fairy tale. Men working on the railroad tracks outside the town heard about the bazaar and donated a yoke of oxen for them to raffle. That started a flood of donations that included everything from tortillas to hand-woven sombreros.

"Six years!" Mother Praxedes stopped for just a moment as if to assure herself that the building was really there. Many times, even after that first successful bazaar, she had doubted that she would be able to pay off the five thousand dollars; but it had been paid. And how many things had happened since then that seemed as vexing and impossible!

Always there was the shadow of the ex-priest and his wife living in the town. Their children were a painful reminder that vigilance is necessary for those who would stay close to God. But as she prayed for their return to Him, she prayed, too, for grace to remember her own weakness, which before God might be as culpable. How easy it was to take success to herself! When she had moved the novices from Las Cruces to Santa Fe, she had doubted her wisdom; but when the fever epidemic hit the town two years later, she had felt great satisfaction in her own foresight. How easy it was to forget that God did these things, not she. Success as well as adversity had its pitfalls.

Nearing the convent, she saw Sister Vestina in the doorway, apparently looking for someone. When Sister saw Mother, she hurried out to meet her.

Before Sister Vestina could speak, Mother asked, "Do I smell chicken frying?"

"Chicken?" Sister Vestina pretended to sniff the air. "Oh, I think not, Mother."

"I was sure that I smelled chicken frying. Perhaps it's next door at Armijo's."

"Perhaps," Sister Vestina remarked. "Mother, Father Lassaigne is here."

"Oh," came a half sigh. "How does he look?"

"As if he needs his spirits lifted." Sister Vestina smiled.

The two nuns walked toward the door. Neither spoke. There was no need for words; both sensed the situation.

As they walked, Mother Praxedes thought of the thirty-two dollars she had received yesterday. No, she would not feel right in giving that to Father. The sisters had worked so hard on the needlework and she had promised that the next money she received would buy material for new aprons and underskirts. Sister Vestina's was so patched that none of the original material was there at all. Sister Febronia and Sister Marianita needed material too.

"Mother, I think Father needs some money," Sister Vestina whispered, not so much to inform Mother of what the latter already knew, but to let her know that she understood.

"We'll see. Sister Vestina, why don't you go to the chapel while I speak to Father?"

Sister smiled knowingly and started in that direction as Mother entered the small room where Father was waiting.

"Good morning, Father," she began, making a mental note that the priest looked worried.

"Mother, I'm sorry to come at this time. Sister said that you were in the garden. I won't stay but a minute."

"Be seated, Father. You didn't disturb my work, I was coming in as Sister came looking for me."

"Mother, I want to ask a favor of you." He cleared his throat nervously.

Mother Praxedes smiled as pleasantly as she could, mentally taking another look at Sister Vestina's patched apron.

"I'll be happy to assist you, Father," she answered, adding, "if I can."

"Well, Mother, I . . ." he hesitated.

It had never taken him this long to get around to the point of money before.

"Yes, Father."

"Well, I want you to do something for me, that is, something for St. Genevieve's Church."

"Yes, Father," was all the answer that would come as Mother Praxedes saw her thirty-two dollars being marked down under the heading BUILDING FUND.

"I hate to ask you again, Mother Praxedes, but . . ." The sisters must not be deprived of the things they need again, Mother was thinking. ". . . but Señor Perea wants a Solemn High Mass sung tomorrow. I told him that I just cannot find any man in the parish who will sing the Gospel. I told him that I would ask you again, but that I would not blame you if you refused."

Mother Praxedes smiled. She was not exactly sure whether it was a smile of relief or because of the incongruity of her being Father Lassaigne's deacon.

"I know this is late to ask, Mother, but what am I to do?"

"I do not mind, Father. If the congregation can bear to listen to me, I suppose I shouldn't mind singing."

The priest looked relieved; Mother Praxedes was relieved. She still had the thirty-two dollars.

As soon as Father Lassaigne was out the door, Mother went to the chapel. Sister Vestina was still kneeling there. Sister Vestina looked at her, and then followed her out.

"Sister, get the list, get the catalog. He didn't want money!"

"He didn't!"

"Sister, don't stand there. Where is the catalog?"

"The catalog, Mother?"

"Yes, I'm going to order that material this minute."

"Oh, the catalog. Yes, I'll get it!"

Mother followed Sister Vestina to a cupboard in the hall where everything imaginable was kept, all filed according to Sister Vestina's own particular system.

"Here it is, Mother."

"Sister, you'll never guess what Father wanted. A deacon for tomorrow's High Mass."

"And you . . . oh, Mother, you didn't say you would!"

"I did just that, and I wanted to add that I'd sing the whole Mass myself as long as he didn't want our precious needlework money."

"I marked the page the last time we looked, Mother. Here it is."

"Thank you. I'll write the letter today."

"Did you ask Father how the church is coming along?" Sister Vestina inquired.

"Yes, I did. Don Perea gave Father a generous offering when he came to have the Mass said."

"Mother, have you ever regretted that you promised to go security for the debt?"

"No, Sister. Las Cruces needs a new church and after six and a half years with these people, I'm sure of their charity. The church will be ready for Christmas and I won't have to pay the debt either. But I'm afraid I really didn't have the right to offer security."

"If we're in there by Christmas, it will be because your name appeared at the head of the subscription list last December."

"And because the sisters worked so hard to raise that five hundred dollars which put my name there," Mother hastened to add.

"We wouldn't know how to act if we weren't raising money for something."

Sister Vestina noticed that Mother did not seem to be listening to her last remark.

"Sister, I know I smell chicken frying."

The sound of the hand bell put a period after the word "frying," as it called them to examen. Sister Vestina gave a sigh of relief. In a few minutes the surprise would be known and then the suspense of trying to keep a secret would be over. Evidently Mother Praxedes had forgotten that this was her birthday. "For once she'll be surprised," Sister Vestina thought.

As the sisters filed into the refectory after examen, even Sister Vestina could not have denied that they were having fried chicken, for there it was in the center of the table.

Mother Praxedes asked the blessing as all the sisters stood with clasped hands and bowed heads. The prayer concluded, Mother looked at the array of good things to eat, then continued seriously. "For some reason chicken has found its way to our table. Therefore, we will rejoice in the Lord as we enjoy it."

A chorus of "Happy Birthday, Mother," came in reply.

"Thank you, thank you." She smiled. "I thought that for once I would add a year without anyone knowing."

"Isn't this a delicious-looking dinner," someone remarked.

"Sister Febronia, take a bow," Mother said.

Sister looked pleased as the sisters began passing the bowls. As the conversation ebbed and flowed, going from one thing to another, it finally lapped on the shore of the past.

Sister Vestina, who had been in Las Cruces during the whole of Mother Praxedes' six and a half years, looked at Mother with a glint of mischief in her eyes. "Mother, why don't you tell the sisters about the time you made Our Lady stand in the rain?"

"You make me sound like a villain."

Sister Vestina only laughed.

"Well, Sister Vestina, since you recall the incident so well, why don't you entertain the sisters." Mother turned the tale over to her friend with a slight gesture of her slender hands.

"When the addition was nearly finished, Pancho Isles, who was in charge, told us that the beams which were supporting the roof were too heavy for the walls. He wanted to know what to do so Mother said calmly, 'I suppose the only thing to do is to take the roof off and replace the beams.'"

"So far, so good," Mother said, smiling.

"It seems the clouds were just waiting for the men to get the roof off because in no time the rain began. Some of the men got a large tarpaulin and spread it over the opening. That worked all right until the tarpaulin couldn't hold any more water, and then the excess started leaking through at the edges, bringing some of the adobe from the walls with it. There was a regular waterfall of muddy water coming down the stairway. It was heartbreaking."

"You can't imagine how we felt seeing our beautiful furnishings standing in that dirty water," Mother added.

"What about the Blessed Mother?" Sister Marianita asked.

"That's your part of the story, Mother," Sister Vestina said.

"There really isn't very much to it. I just asked Sister Vestina to help me carry the statue of the Blessed Mother from the chapel to the yard. I thought that if Our Lady realized how hard it was raining, she'd do something about it."

"Did she?"

"No, Sister, she didn't. It rained all the harder."

"What did you do?"

Mother chuckled in reply.

Sister Vastina took up the story. "Finally, Mother looked at me and said, 'Oh, bring her in. She must be displeased.' So we dashed out in the rain and brought the poor wet statue back inside."

"But Mary did answer our prayers," Mother said. "After the

water was mopped up, there were just a few marks on things we expected to be completely ruined."

Turning to Sister Vestina, Mother Praxedes said, "Now, Sister, since you have told a story on me, why don't you tell one on yourself?"

"Which one?" she asked skeptically. There were stories and there were stories. She and Mother Praxedes had learned a lot about each other in their years together.

"Tell them about the blanket. I know some of the sisters have not heard it."

Sister Vestina felt the pinkness of excitement mounting in her cheeks. She did not mind telling *that* story.

Everyone turned to listen. Somehow more interesting things had happened to her than to all of them put together.

"I really should get the blanket to show you, but I'll do that later. As you may know, while I was still a novice, I was sent from the mother house in Kentucky to Sante Fe. When I got to Denver, I was told that I would have to make the rest of the trip alone because there was no one to go with me. I was too young to let that worry me. I was sixteen. Well, anyway, I got into the stagecoach and then an old man got in, and then several more men, and finally the coach was filled and I was the only woman. It didn't bother me at first but one by one the men looked me over and several of them made remarks that I didn't quite understand.

"Everything went along all right, but as night approached, I began to wonder where we were going to stop. I didn't ask any questions. Finally we stopped right in the middle of the prairie and the men started making a campfire and fixing food for supper. I have never felt so left out in all my life. I stayed in the stage, where I ate the lunch I had. When I was about finished one of the men brought me a tin cup full of coffee.

"At last the driver came over to tell me that the men would roll up in blankets by the fire and that I could have the coach to myself for the night. At first I was comfortable, but as the night wore on I got colder and colder. Finally I was sure that I was going to freeze to death and the fire looked so inviting that I decided to get out of the coach. Several men were sitting in blankets by the fire. I looked at them and then asked one who looked rather kind if I could sit by the fire because I was so cold.

" 'Sure,' he said. 'Why I'll be glad to share my blanket with you, miss.' The other men looked at him and one nudged the other. My heart stood up in my throat. I couldn't say a word. But right away the man pulled off his blanket and handed it to me. 'Here you are. I'll crawl in with someone else,' he said.

"As fast as I could, I took the blanket, thanked him, and went back to the stage. After a while I got warm and went to sleep. In the morning I looked for the man to return the blanket but I could not find him. The driver insisted that no one had left the party but none of the men knew who the blanket belonged to. If I hadn't had the blanket, I would have thought that I imagined the whole thing."

"I want to see the blanket," someone said.

"I have seen it and it certainly would be good for a cold night on the desert."

"Who do you think he was?"

"I don't know who you think he was, but he was St. Joseph to me," Sister Vestina answered.

"I hate to end a lovely dinner," Mother Praxedes said, "but these dishes won't wash themselves, you know."

"Mother," Sister Marianita said as she came in from the kitchen, "one of Doña Apalonia's boys is at the back door to see you."

"Timed perfectly to get out of the dishes," Sister Vestina teased. "Shall we wait to do the dishes?"

"Oh, I wouldn't think of having you wait. You won't miss me," Mother laughed.

"Since it is your birthday, Mother, it will be all right," Sister Febronia offered.

"You are all so sweet. Let's say grace and then you can do dishes."

When grace was finished, Mother went to see what the boy wanted.

"Juan," she said. "Did you want me?"

"Madre Prajedes, Doña Apalonia hurt her leg. Could you come? Please?"

"Is it broken?"

The boy, who could not have been more than ten, shrugged his shoulders. He did not know.

"I will come. Just a minute."

The boy shifted impatiently from one foot to the other as he waited for Mother. In just a moment she returned and they were walking across the yard to the side gate.

Doña Apalonia's little two-room *casa* was not far. Mother had been there before with vegetables for her.

"When did this happen?" Mother asked.

"Yesterday she fell. Today she cannot walk. Her leg is big."

"Oh, Juan, you should have told me yesterday."

"No, she said she was not hurt. She would not let me come."

Mother Praxedes hurried along the side street. Children, dogs, chickens, all seemed to be trailing her.

"Did your mother get the washing done today, Juan?"

"No, *madre*, she did not walk today at all."

Juan ran ahead now, announcing in a loud voice that *La Madre* was coming. From around the low adobe house came more boys and more dogs, all prancing and shouting. There was Raoul, his patched trousers covered with dirt, and Tony and Dionicio. It was always hard to tell which were Doña Apalonia's and which were the neighbors.

Mother had to step around the makeshift wagon and a broken chair that the children had been playing with in the bare little dooryard.

At the door of the house, Juan waited for Mother, where by this time a small crowd of seven or eight youngsters were greeting her with wide grins.

"Well, Raoul, I see the storm is over," she said as she patted his round firm cheek. She smiled at each child individually. They were more to her than just a crowd of children.

Juan pushed open the heavy wood door and Mother stepped up

and over the doorsill. Inside, the bare dirt floor was immaculate. The low, *vega* ceiling slanted toward the rear of the room, where long strings of red chili hung like necklaces from the beams. The few pieces of squatty wood furniture showed an orderliness which always seemed to exist here.

"Now, children, you wait outside for me," Mother said as the crowd tried to push in behind her.

Obediently they edged backward through the door, which she shut. Juan led her across the room to a doorway covered with a ruglike curtain, which he drew aside. This room was larger than the other, but its furnishings, too, were simple. Six low pallets lined the three walls. On one in the far corner beneath the room's only window, with its cheesecloth covering, lay Doña Apalonia, fully clothed and with a thin blanket over her.

"Oh, Mother, why did Juan bother you when you were so busy?" the Indian woman asked in a voice that was soft and gentle, a voice of great dignity.

"Juan, get a chair for Mother."

"Juan should have called me sooner. How is your leg?"

"Oh, it is just my ankle, Mother. Yesterday I was carrying in some clean clothes and I tripped over the children's wagon."

Juan was offering Mother a low stool, which she took. "Let me see your ankle."

Docilely, almost like a child, the woman put her bare foot from beneath the blanket. The ankle was swollen, her brown toes were puffy.

"Oh, Doña Apalonia, we must bathe this in warm water. I will heat some."

"No, no, Juan can heat the water, Mother. He is a very helpful boy."

"Yes, I will make the water warm," he answered. And that fast he had left the room.

"What about the washing today, Doña Apalonia?"

"Today I do not have so much. Tomorrow is the heavy day, but I will send Juan to say that I cannot do the washing."

"But you need the money, Doña Apalonia. Do not send word.

Have the boys collect the clothes. We will wash them at the convent."

"Oh, no, no, no, Mother!"

"Here is the water, Mother."

"So soon, Juan?" Mother tried it with her hand. "Juan, I will use this, but make some more a little warmer."

Doña Apalonia sat on the edge of the pallet. "Mother, I can do it. You must not," she apologized.

"I am very good at this, Doña Apalonia. Just put your foot in and I will move the water over your ankle. When I come back this evening, I will bring some salt to put in the water and that will be even better."

In the latter part of June, Father Lassaigne was beginning the prayers after Mass as Mother Praxedes quietly left her place in the chapel. Putting one hand into her pocket, she felt to make sure that the envelope was there. He will be pleased she told herself, as she genuflected and went out the door onto the porch.

The stillness of the air predicted another hot day; and yet it was good to get out and breathe what freshness there was. The chapel had been stuffy. Going along the side of the chapel to the door which led from the porch to the sacristy, Mother noted that the garden was weathering the heat better than she was. "If Pancho gets the tomatoes picked, we can start canning today."

The sacristy door was closed. Rapping softly, Mother Praxedes pushed it open. The odor of burning wax weighted the air, giving her the momentary feeling of suffocation. Father was approaching the sacristy from the sanctuary as Mother caught her breath.

Mother did not speak. She waited for Father to put down the sacred vessel.

"Good morning, Mother."

"I won't keep you, Father. I just thought you might be happy to have this." She extended her right hand, which held the envelope.

He took it and peeked inside as a small boy might cautiously peer into a deserted house. When he saw what it contained, he smiled.

"You are always giving me money for the church. How much this time, Mother?"

"One hundred ten dollars, Father. You see, God is providing."

"Yes, yes," he said in his matter-of-fact way. "But still I was a fool letting you talk me into building this church."

"Father," she said kindly, "my mother once chided me for taking over God's worries, as she called them. 'What's God to do if you do all His worrying for Him,' she would say. I often think of that, Father. If God wants a new St. Genevieve's Church, He's going to have it."

"Yes, but, Mother, don't you think He expects us to be prudent?"

"Yes, but more confident than prudent, Father. However, we can't refuse any opportunity which presents itself, and an opportunity is presenting itself now."

"What's that, Mother?"

"You know what a difficult time the people attending the county fair always have in finding a place to eat when they are here?"

"Yes, I do, but how is that an opportunity?"

"I was thinking that a group of ladies from the parish could serve dinner. I'm sure they would be glad to do it. If the parishioners donate vegetables and chickens, everything we make will be profit for the church building."

"It sounds fine when you say it, Mother, but the whole plan for the new church sounded fine last December, too."

"Father, if you give your consent, I'll get some of the ladies together this afternoon."

"Go ahead, Mother Praxedes. Who am I to stop you now? You've raised most of the money already."

"Remember, Father, I promised to go security for this project, and I haven't any money in case you come asking me to make my promise good." She smiled.

It did not take Mother Praxedes long to organize a group of

ladies for the county-fair dinners. Women like Mrs. Stephenson and Mrs. Duper, the hotel owner's wife, were willing to donate supplies and money, while poorer women like Doña Apalonia could contribute labor in cooking and serving the meals.

The idea happened to be a timely one as most people came prepared to do without a regular meal until they reached home in the evening. The sum of money presented to Father Lassaigne eased his anxiety considerably. Then within a short time several large donations came to him and by late fall it was evident that St. Genevieve's Church would be completed before Christmas, as Mother Praxedes had predicted.

Mother Praxedes heaved a sigh of relief as she and the sisters joined the congregation gathered for the first Mass. It was apparent that Father Lassaigne was pleased to know that the cause of so much worry was now a reality of floor and roof and tabernacle.

At the end of the Gospel, Father Lassaigne turned to the people, and, with a few words of appreciation to all, descended the steps from the altar, took the collection basket, and announced to the congregation, "La Madre Praxedes will take up the collection."

The church became a lonely canyon in the dead of night where a thousand unseen eyes stared wonderingly at her. Inside she could feel the blood throbbing through her temples as her heart quickened and color mounted to her cheeks. Had she heard correctly? Must she stand up before them all? Must she go from the front to the back, pushing the collection basket in front of the Dupers and the Amadors and the Ascarates and the Stephensons? The long slender handle of the collection basket pointed threateningly at her. She was the one. Yes, he had said she would. Putting her missal down on the seat, she realized that her hands were wet with perspiration. With a shiver of excitement, she rose. She had the feeling that she was watching herself move, stretch out her hand, take the handle. This could not be happening and yet to the amazement of all, Mother Praxedes began passing the basket from person to person.

Later Mother shook a finger at Father as she said, "Father Lassaigne, whatever prompted you to do such a thing?"

"Well, Mother, the church by right belongs to you since it was your idea and you did more than anyone else toward its realization, so I thought that you should have the pleasure of making the first collection."

"Father, I'll never forget this," she said, then smiled. She had paid in full for her promise of security.

"I wonder if we'll have any snow," Sister Vestina queried, shifting her bundle to the other arm.

"I doubt it. We've already had snow twice this winter," was Mother Praxedes' reply.

They walked along side by side for some time without talking. Not many people were out. It was early, and with the sudden drop in temperature most of the town's people were staying indoors.

As they came to the church, the two nuns turned and stepped inside for a short visit. The plain rectangular interior breathed the newness of fresh paint and varnish. The light from the stained-glass window on either side of the sanctuary threw an aura of soft color on the altar. What an improvement over the dilapidated adobe structure of the past, Sister Vestina was thinking.

Outside again, Mother Praxedes remarked as if to herself, "The church needs a statue of the Sacred Heart."

Before Sister Vestina could comment on this, Mother had stopped dead still and was looking at the pile of lumber and odd bits of building material which were strewn about on both sides of the church. When was Father going to get someone to haul it away? For two months the work had been finished!

Mother did not say a word, but after a moment of survey she turned and walked on, Sister Vestina beside her.

The two nuns hurried on their way and in a few minutes were at the convent gate. Two little girls came running around the side of the convent calling to let them carry the bundles.

"Here you are, Letitia," Mother said, handing a package to the older girl, who must have been about ten, "and one for Olga, too," giving the smaller child a bag.

Olga smiled a minus-two-teeth smile and the children walked beside the sisters.

"We waited such a long time for you," Letitia said.

"And Sister Marianita said we couldn't go down the street but had to wait 'til you was coming."

"'Were,' Olga," Sister Vestina corrected.

"Until you *were* coming," the child said, correcting herself.

"That's right, Olga. You must do what Sister says but Sister and I do appreciate your wanting to help."

"It's fun," Letitia answered.

Once inside, the children scampered off to other duties that meant Saturday morning in a boarding school. Mother Praxedes went to see what the morning mail had brought.

Flipping through it hurriedly at first to see if there was anything of importance, Mother stopped at the sight of a familiar but rarely seen handwriting. Carefully, in the absence of a proper letter opener, she ran one finger under the flap.

Her eyes went quickly from the heading, "Santa Fe, January 24, 1888," to the news of the first paragraph. Her face grew grave as she read. After a few moments Mother Praxedes stood looking into space, the letter still in her hand.

Archbishop Lamy is very ill, Mother Magdalen said. She spoke lovingly of her old friend as she told Mother Praxedes that Father Jouvenceau had brought the Archbishop into Santa Fe from the *ranchito* on January 7. His Grace had received Extreme Unction and Viaticum. The sisters were taking turns staying with him.

Putting the letter back into the envelope, Mother Praxedes went to the chapel to pray for the Archbishop. She could still see him holding the poppy in his hand, the fragile poppy Angelica had brought to him one morning in his garden. What was it he had said to Angelica about being willing to bring poppy seeds half around the world? That poppy in his brown hands had somehow brought back all her desire for giving. The gift of love to others was like the poppy had been—just a tiny seed; but returned, it was a flaming, full-blown blossom. Love given was the only love that one ever really possessed. Don't ever let me forget, she prayed.

Her prayer finished, Mother Praxedes left the chapel to return to her duties, yet she was unable to take her thoughts from the dying prelate.

That afternoon as a group of parish ladies gathered in one of the classrooms for their monthly meeting over which Mother Praxedes presided, Mrs. Stephenson, one of Mother's good friends, sensed that Mother was preoccupied.

"Mother Praxedes," she said, "you look worried. Is there anything I could do to assist you?"

"Yes, Mrs. Stephenson, there will be plenty to do. Just wait."

The meeting was slow in starting, but when they finally got to the matter of forming a League of the Sacred Heart in the parish, everyone had something to say. At last Mrs. Stephenson could see that most of the ladies were in favor of the idea but were simply re-saying what others had said, so she decided they'd have a League of the Sacred Heart. Then she asked Mother to say a few words. Mother told the ladies that she would like to see a statue of the Sacred Heart in St. Genevieve's Church. She intended to take up the collection herself. If she had done it once, why not again? She asked only that the ladies back her venture. This was her own special project.

"But I have a project for you, too," she said, smiling.

Everyone looked at her eagerly. Mrs. Stephenson had already surmised that another church supper or bazaar was in the offing. Similar thoughts were registering in the minds of some of Mother's faithful helpers.

"Ladies, there is a very disreputable looking pile of debris beside the church. It has been there for some time. I suggest that since nothing has been done about it, we, the ladies of the parish, arm ourselves with shovels and the like and clean it away."

"That is a fine idea, Mother. It is a disgrace to see it there ruining the appearance of the new church."

"When shall we do this?" one lady asked.

"The sooner the better," Mother replied, adding, "why not tomorrow after the eight o'clock Mass?"

After discussing who would help and what each would bring,

the group gradually disbanded and Mother went to chapel again to pray for Archbishop Lamy.

The next morning, as had been planned, the women grouped together outside the church after Mass, anticipating a grand cleaning of the churchyard.

"Mother Praxedes, I don't think we are going to clean the debris away, after all," Mrs. Stephenson said, as she approached Mother.

"Mother, someone has already started our job," Mrs. Duper put in.

"Well, look at that," Mother said as she saw what the ladies had just discovered. There were at least ten men with shovels and wheelbarrows at work on the quickly diminishing pile of debris.

"Someone has turned traitor," Mother said, with a lift of her eyebrows. "Who told our plans?"

Everyone claimed innocence.

"Well, we got the yard cleaned up," one lady remarked.

"Yes, and Mother, you were right. It didn't take long."

The duties of the next few days were punctuated by thoughts and comments on the part of all the sisters concerning Archbishop Lamy, but as often happens, when days group into weeks, the thoughts came more seldom. Finally on the fifteenth of February, Mother Praxedes received word that the Archbishop had died two days before and that he was to be buried on the sixteenth, the following day.

"Are you going to Santa Fe for the funeral?" Sister Vestina asked Mother.

"Yes, if I can make the afternoon train."

"We'll see that you make it!"

Late that afternoon Mother Praxedes boarded the train for Santa Fe. Just a few years before, it would have been impossible to get to Santa Fe overnight, but now railroad travel had shortened the time considerably.

Mother Praxedes left the train at Lamy Junction, the nearest railroad stop to Santa Fe. Several of the sisters from the Santa Fe community met her and they went immediately to the cathedral for the solemn Requiem Mass.

As they rode along to the cathedral, Sister Euphrosine, who had been with the Archbishop during the last hours, said simply, "His passing was so serene. We hardly knew just when he died."

A hushed throng filled the young cathedral whose inspiration had been born of the man now lying still in the taper-lighted coffin near the altar. Down a side aisle, between the pews of curious and devoted, sad and sorrowing, the group of sisters followed a kindly old man who showed them to a pew near the front.

Just as they moved into their places, the throng rose in one sudden rush of movement. The clergy were entering the sanctuary to begin the Office of the Dead. Waiting to kneel again, Mother Praxedes felt for her beads and found that her hands were trembling. All knelt and then she could see above the heads about her to where Archbishop Salpointe knelt, his white head bent in prayer. Near him, straight and solemn, was Bishop Macheboeuf, Lamy's closest friend. Looking at him, a man of deep emotion, so apparently serene, Mother Praxedes caught her breath. These three, Macheboeuf, Salpointe, and Lamy had been seminary friends in France, had come as youthful missionaries to America, and had, as young priests, found God where others had feared to look. Little more than ten years ago—when she herself had just come to the Southwest—the three had knelt together as Archbishop Lamy had received the pallium. As the threnody of the Latin chant swelled to fill the wide expanse of the cathedral that Archbishop Lamy had watched rise as a guardian church of Santa Fe, Mother Praxedes realized that the priests gathered near the altar were a greater tribute to his memory than even this cathedral. And perhaps even greater were the hundreds of poor Indians and Mexicans and Anglos who had found in him a loving father. Love had made the difference. He had loved them. He had loved them enough to lash out with excommunication against the priests who would not give up their sinful living for the good of the people. He had loved them enough to ride thousands of miles on horseback to eat with them and pray with them. He had defied the government that would rob defenseless Indians of their rights to land. He had loved them enough to fight for their temporal as well as their eternal needs. He had been a loving father. This indeed, she thought, was greater than his cathedral. Cathedrals were meaningless without a priest who could carry Christ from it into the streets. Locked in a cathedral He might be known; but held in the heart He could be understood. Archbishop Lamy had made Christ lovable because like Christ he had gone about the country doing good.

The choir was responding, "Christe, eleison"—Christ, have mercy. "Oh, Christ will ever have mercy on the kind," she thought. "You do not need to even ask." Blessed are the merciful . . . Christ had said that, and the Archbishop holding the poppy had indeed been merciful to her.

"Dominus vobiscum," chanted the celebrant: the Lord be with you. It was then that her thoughts joined the priests kneeling there in the sanctuary. There gathered about the altar were the men Lamy had rallied to the cause of Christ in the wide Southwest. When these men, real missionaries, lay dead like their captain, would the flame of zeal flicker and die? Would the sacrificing spirit of these pioneers live on in others? Now that the West was coming of age, would there be others who would carry on in their generosity? Would men come, and women, too, to be merciful? Who would take time to feed fish and be kind to little children? Lamy was great not for his cathedral or his garden or for the fire he had lighted in the hearts of missionaries; he was great because all these things were loving God. Would others come who could serve God in little things, who could be small and not trivial, great and not gigantic?

The Mass, the sacrifice of Christ, the whole oblation of the Son to the Father, proceeded with the voices of the choir responding to the "Oremus." Mingled with their chant were the tears of tired old Mexican women who knew the Archbishop as a friend, the Aves of little Indians to whom he was their "padrecito." Caught up with the prayers of the Mass was the filial gratitude of Lamy's spiritual sons whom he had ordained and guided in the first days of priesthood. To all this wealth of love and heart-made prayer was added a memory. She remembered a priest in black soutane, an Archbishop with a red poppy in his hand who looked at her and said, "I would carry poppy seeds half around the world to have one appreciated so." Giving of self—planting seeds of love —is worth any price—even the price of going half around the world.

After the funeral services were over, Mother Praxedes, with the other sisters, threaded her way through the crowd and across the street to the convent. Inside the gateway, she stepped aside to wait for Mother Francisca, who was near the end of the group. A tiny woman with dark eyes and an ordinarily serious expression, Mother Francisca looked almost austere in her sorrow. Mother Praxedes put out her hand to take Mother Francisca's arm as the latter passed her. Knowing that Mother Francisca was a woman of keen emotion, whose feelings were well hidden by a serene exterior, Mother Praxedes met her on her own ground.

"Mother Francisca," was all she said.

"Mother Praxedes, how kind of you to come. During the Mass I thought of how much he always liked having the children in his garden on Sunday mornings. You were one of the first sisters who took the children to see him. I think he missed those visits very much when he retired to the ranchito."

They left the group and walked alone through the garden. They were an utter contrast in size and temperament, the tall, distinctly Irish, and the petite, definitely French.

"It's strange," Mother Praxedes said, looking off toward the mountain behind the Archbishop's house.

"What is strange?" Mother Francisca asked almost the same words had been forming in her mind, too.

They walked on a few steps more, then hesitated, stopped, and faced one another.

"You'll be surprised, Mother," came the reply.

"I don't think I will. I've ceased to be surprised by you, Mother Praxedes," and there was a sad smile in her dark eyes at this.

She was scarcely aware of what she had said. Her heart was still heavy.

"I was thinking that ten years make a great difference in some things. Ten years ago I was a novice and you were my Mistress. I found you as staunch as that mountain and feared you in a way. Today I am grateful for things staunch."

"Is that so?" Mother Francisca said reflectively. "If you had called me 'cold' I would not have been surprised. You are more kind than others. I remember once when I was young, just a girl, and the Archbishop came to see me in New Orleans, where I was in school. He said to me, 'You must learn not to show your feelings to the world.' Then later on when I came out here and wanted to become a nun, he chided me on my high temper and willfulness. I decided then to conquer it and I think sometimes I missed the *via media*. I seem cold sometimes even to myself. But, tell me, Mother, have you tired yet of Las Cruces?"

They began to walk again as Mother Praxedes' voice took on its familiar gaiety.

"I'll never tire of Cruces, Mother. Father Lassaigne is an interesting person, the people are dear. I love every square inch of Cruces, every brick of the convent, every breath of air. I think God made me for the adobes, Mother, and how glad I am."

"Now, Mother Praxedes . . ." Mother Francisca said.

And Mother Praxedes was glad to see her smile at last. She was forgetting just a bit.

"You must have a visit with Mother Magdalen before you leave. Although her arthritis is very bad, she never complains. She feels the same way about Santa Fe as you do about Cruces. All she does is praise God for the years she's had here."

"She must feel the Archbishop's death keenly. He brought her here, didn't he?"

"Yes, he did. They worked together so long in days when things depended much upon one's fellow laborers. He had nothing but praise for her. I remember the last time I went up to the ranchito to see him, he sent her a flowering cactus, and told me to tell her that it was like their life out here, 'thorny but beautiful.'"

The next day Mother Praxedes was on her way back to Las Cruces, where her daily duties again enveloped her. The roof had sprung a leak while she was away and two of the boarders had gone home with measles. The project for a statue of the Sacred Heart had to be launched. This, however, took less time than the roof or the measles, because all she had to do was voice her desire and her friends went to work.

"La Madre Prajedes" or "La Madre Grande," as she was called, passed from mouth to mouth and it was no time before the statue was enthroned in St. Genevieve's Church. This, too, took a surprising turn when one morning after Sunday Mass several persons accosted Mother with the request that she bless their Sacred Heart badges.

"But I cannot bless such things," she insisted kindly in her now very precise Spanish.

"Oh, you must," they continued. "Father Lassaigne said to bring them to you."

After repeating several times that it would not be a real blessing as the priest imparts, she consented to make the Sign of the Cross over the articles.

Instead of continuing on her way to the convent she turned, walked up to the church entrance, where the priest was standing. Seeing her, he turned to go inside.

"Father Lassaigne," she said, narrowing her eyes meaningfully, "I want to see you, Father."

"Very well, let me have it," he said, hanging his head in anticipation of a scolding.

"Father Lassaigne, you mustn't send people to me for blessings. You know I can't do such things."

"But it makes them happy, Mother Praxedes. They are not happy when I bless their articles."

"What will I do with you?" She smiled; but there was a shadow in her smile.

FLORISSANT, MISSOURI—1893

On a day in early September of 1893, Mrs. Horace Stephenson, a respected citizen and wife of the probate clerk of Doña Ana County, New Mexico, sat in her sitting room trying to compose a letter. Her words had to be well chosen for upon them hung the possibility that Mother Praxedes would be allowed to resume her work in Las Cruces, which after thirteen years had been brought to an abrupt end by her transfer to Missouri.

Mrs. Stephenson was writing not only as a personal friend of Mother Praxedes but as an influential citizen petitioning in behalf of her community. At last her pen formed the first words. "To the Mother Superior of the Convent of Loretto in Marion County, Kentucky." Mrs. Stephenson had never been to Kentucky. As she wrote, it seemed a great distance away, and the words "Mother Superior" carried no representation of the person for whom they were intended. If only she knew whose eyes would scan these words, her task would be easier.

This letter, formulated in Las Cruces, went to Loretto and thence to Bardstown, Kentucky, to the Ecclesiastical Superior, the Very Reverend C. J. O'Connell. Father O'Connell carefully read the letter which he could see was written with great love and a full understanding of Las Cruces' indebtedness to Mother Praxedes. He read and reread the words that stated, "The Convent here has greatly prospered, and is now in a most gratifying condition, under her guidance and direction. She has the unbounded confidence and respect of all businessmen."

Mrs. Stephenson would never know that it was these very qualities of which she spoke that had been the basis for Mother Praxedes' new appointment. Father O'Connell and Mother Catherine, the Mother Superior, had decided upon sending Mother Praxedes to Loretto Academy, Florissant, where just such a person was needed. Mrs. Stephenson's words pleased the priest who read them.

"Her knowledge of the habits and customs of the New Mexicans is invaluable," the letter continued, "and her sincerity, kindly demeanor and firmness of character have won for her the love and admiration of Catholics and Protestants alike." Father O'Connell scanned the list of signatures, mostly Spanish names, which followed Mrs. Stephenson's. Then he formulated a reply to the letter.

Bardstown Kentucky
Sept. 14, 1893

Mrs. H. F. Stephenson

Dear Madam,

Your much esteemed favor of the 9th inst. was received by me yesterday morning. I greatly appreciated your kindly feeling and the kindly feeling of all those good Ladies, signers of the paper you sent me, towards Sister Praxedes. I am sure it will be grateful news to the good Sister to know that those among whom she is beloved have such a high estimate of her worth. And though we should be pleased to respond to your very kind wishes we feel ourselves obliged to say that Sister is needed where she now is at the head of a very large Community and it would be impossible to replace her. I may also add that Sister Rosine who takes Sister Praxedes' place is a most worthy and amiable religious whom you will learn to respect and venerate.

Most respectfully in D.
C. J. O'Connell, Ecc. Sup.

In the meantime, Mother Praxedes was already in Missouri, where she had assumed her duties as Superior of one of the largest and most thriving academies under the care of the Sisters of Loretto. Located about fourteen miles west of St. Louis, on a rise of land that overlooked the town of Florissant, Loretto Academy was at this time educating its third generation of young women from some of St. Louis' most prominent families.

Late one afternoon in early October, Mother Praxedes stood at her office window in the academy building, looking out on the lawn, which was beginning to show the first signs of fall. An early frost the week before had nipped the trees and shrubbery. Now hints of yellow and red were on the leaves. Mother was thinking that it had been a long time since she had seen an autumn in the Midwest. The last she had known in this part of the country was at Loretto when she was still a novice. That had been in 1874, nineteen years before.

Almost twenty years since I left Missouri? she thought. What had become of all those days and hours and minutes? What had happened to the Susan Carty who had wanted to serve God by serving others? Where was the girl who had disliked the name Praxedes? And where was the young nun who, in trying to find health, had almost lost her desire to serve? Here I am, back in Missouri; she smiled. And I'm still trying to keep God's point of view—but not doing very well, I'm afraid.

As she stood at the window, she could see a group of eight or nine girls in black uniforms coming up the broad sidewalk. Apparently they had been to town, for several of them carried parcels. Mother Praxedes felt a pang of homesickness for her children in Las Cruces. Had these been they, she could have called them all by name and seen at the same time a line of sisters and brothers to whom they belonged. These young ladies were sweet and polite. They spoke to her in the halls, but they were still strangers. Somehow they lacked the effusiveness of Westerners. She had to smile at herself. In such a few years she had forgotten that young people can clothe their feelings with reserve. She would have to get accustomed to their sophistication. Above all, she must love *them*, too.

As she thought of Las Cruces, she thought too of the day in August when she had received word to leave for Missouri. The whole community had spent the day in the Organ mountains. They had all shouted and laughed themselves hoarse making the mountains play back in echoes. How unsuspectingly they had returned to the convent in the evening. With gaiety she had opened the letter, never dreaming that it would end her thirteen happy years in Las Cruces. Santa Fe and Bernalillo and Las Cruces had come in words from persons who had sensed her feelings; Florissant was a letter written by a stranger; and yet, it had to be equally the will of God.

Returning to her desk, she started to put some of the papers and letters into order. One letter caught her attention. It was from Mother Cecilia, who recently had been assigned as Superior of Cedar Grove Academy in Louisville. Somehow when Mother Praxedes thought the name, she saw again a pretty young sister hurrying down to the wharf in Cape Girardeau. She heard a soft voice explaining about the hearts which the sisters wore on their habits. All these years Mother Cecilia had gone from place to place, had grown older, had declined in health; and yet, she had remained the same in Mother Praxedes' mind. She was still Sister Cecilia, a gentle, holy woman, an inspiration. Until a month ago she had been at the mother house in the capacity of general treasurer of the society.

Mother Praxedes picked up the letter, which had been written after Mother Cecilia left Loretto. A tone of concern ran through it. From what Mother Cecilia had written, it was clear that the past year had been a hard one. There seemed to be something seriously wrong at the mother house. Everyone knew that Mother Dafrosa, the same Mother Dafrosa who had been mistress of novices when Mother Praxedes went to Loretto, had resigned as Mother Superior. But now Mother Praxedes found herself wondering if ill health and old age, the reasons given for her resignation, were the whole story. Mother Felicitas, the Secretary General, had suddenly been deposed by Bishop McCloskey, the Bishop of Louisville. But why? When Mother Cecilia said that Loretto's future hung by the thread of one man's whim, evidently she meant him. Mother Praxedes realized that Mother Cecilia had to be discreet in what she said, but frankly she wished she had explained more. Mother Praxedes did not know the newly elected Mother Catherine, but she hoped that she was a strong woman if more difficulties lay ahead.

A gentle rap on the door took her attention from the letter as a young sister hurried into the room.

"Mother," she began, before she was across the room, "what am I to do? Anna Lucille did not know her music lesson for Sister this morning; she left her bed most untidily made; and just now when I asked her as she left the study hall if her homework was finished, she said, 'no,' just no."

Mother Praxedes repressed her desire to smile. True, Anna Lucille seemed to be a bit disorganized, but were an untidy bed and an unlearned music lesson as tragic as this? Restraining her desire to make light of the matter, Mother looked at the young sister.

"Sister, sit down a moment."

"Yes, Mother," she said taking a deep breath.

"You have been running again," Mother began, deciding to take a serious view of the running to make a point with Sister.

"Yes," the young sister said meekly.

"Sister, there is no recollection in haste."

"No, Mother."

"And you took the stairs two at a time?"

"Yes, Mother."

"I am afraid that you are *my* Anna Lucille."

The young sister looked at Mother incredulously. "I do try, Mother, but there are so many things to do and so little time in which to do them."

"Perhaps that is Anna Lucille's trouble, too."

"Pardon me, Mother?"

"I was merely suggesting that perhaps Anna Lucille has somewhat the same problem as you yourself."

Really, did Mother know what it was to deal with a disobedient child? One who never did as she was told?

"You will have to learn, Sister, that human nature is given to forgetting. You forget to walk instead of run. I forget to rely upon God instead of worry. All of us need grace—both the grace of God and the grace of man—which is kindness and understanding, if we are to keep our point of view."

"But, Mother, I have tried being kind. I have spoken to that child as kindly as I would speak to my own little sister. She does not respond to kindness."

"Sister, everyone who comes under our care is sent to us that we, by our teaching and example, may bring him to knowledge and love of God. Unless you are patient with this child, you will not be able to teach her these things. Be firm and see that your instructions are carried out; but be kind, too. I think if you would try to understand why this child does what she does, you would have more success. Do you pray for her? Do you ask the good God to give her grace to be good?"

"Maybe I haven't prayed for her; but, Mother, I thought that perhaps you could say something to her. She will do what *you* say, I know."

"Sister, I could do that, but that would not be helping you. And perhaps not helping the child either. You do as I say. Don't forget that you have a far better helper than I. Ask Him."

As Sister left, Mother hoped that she had not seemed too preachy. It was, she knew, too easy to hand young people platitudes.

Picking up the postcard on her desk, she smiled. It was from Kitty. Kit and Delia would be out on the electric car in the morning. She made a mental note to send the surrey to meet them.

Kitty, a plump little woman in her late forties, was the first to step from the surrey. "Susie, darlin'," she exclaimed as she hugged her sister. Delia, whose golden hair looked reddish in the sunlight, gave Mother a peck on one cheek.

The three sisters chatted as they crossed the lawn to several benches near a circular flower bed that already wore its winter protection of gunny sacking.

"My, Susie, but this is a beautiful school you have," Kitty remarked as she surveyed the sweep of landscaped lawn and the broad expanse of the four-story academy.

"It must be nice for you here," Delia added.

Mother Praxedes smiled. The tone of voice indicated that they measured her success by the size of the place, but fine buildings and lawns did not constitute her world. She would trade all of this for one black-eyed Mexican and a stretch of raw mountains; and yet, she quickly told herself, she would trade neither for the will of God.

"Now tell me all about everything. How are *you*, Kitty?"

"Too fat and too lazy." She laughed. "With Delia and David gone all day I have nothing to do but play with pussy."

"Don't believe her, Susie, she's always taking on something new. The latest is sewing for the nieces. You should have seen the sweet dress she sent to Jenny's little girl."

"How does Jenny like Memphis?"

"Just fine. She claims that it's no hotter there in the summer than in St. Louis, but I can't believe that."

Mother laughed. "And, Delia, how's the Providence Chemical Company?"

"Oh, they couldn't exist without me," Delia answered.

Mother smiled. "I'm glad you like it still."

"It is a very nice place to work as long as a person must work."

Mother looked at Kitty. "You look chilled," she said, patting Kitty's hand. "Let's go inside."

"All right. It is a little cool sitting here."

"Tell me. How is David?"

"As big a tease as ever," Delia said.

Mother smiled. David Roden would always have a special place in her heart. "I can still remember David the time he and Maria took me to the Cape." She paused as she thought that that trip had really been the beginning of all this. Like so many things in life, it had served a purpose not grasped at the time.

"Remember how he teased when you told the family that you were going to the convent? 'You with your love of dancing and fine clothes.'"

"Now, Kitty, I think you were the one who said that," Mother corrected.

"Oh, I'm sure I couldn't have said that, Susie. You know I always had the greatest confidence in your ability to do whatever you wanted."

They ascended the white flagstone steps to the main entrance. Mother opened the door and ushered her sisters inside to the highly polished entrance hall, which opened into a parlor to the right.

"This will be better."

"My, this is lovely!" Kit exclaimed.

When they were seated, Kitty continued. "Susie, you'll never guess who I heard from." She opened her purse to take out an envelope.

"Let me guess. You only smile that way for one person. It must be from your favorite nephew Frank."

"No, you're wrong—but remind me to tell you about Frank. You know he bought a house in St. Paul." Kitty smiled with satisfaction. "But here's the letter."

"Oh, it's from Mother Cecilia!"

Mother scanned the short letter and smiled at several remarks. "It's like her, isn't it? When I heard from her last Christmas, she said that she will be so glad to get to heaven because she won't have to bother St. Peter to find out the price of pork or whether the supply of coal will last out the winter."

"I think Mother Cecilia's duties at Cedar Grove must be very pressing," Kitty offered.

"She hasn't been well, but she has the grace to be thankful for her crosses. She knows how to use suffering. I'm sure she's dear to God."

"But we've been going on and on about everyone else, but tell us about you, Susie. You like it here, I know."

"Oh yes. It is a beautiful place," Mother said in a tone purposely chosen to reveal none of her inner loneliness for Las Cruces. "This place has quite an interesting history. You remember, I think, when Pat asked about sending Agnes to school here, I told him that I really didn't know too much about it. I know she loved it here and until I came that was my only acquaintance with it. But a few weeks ago a Father Stuntebeck, a Jesuit, visited here and he had so many interesting stories to tell. When he was a novice over at St. Stanislaus Novitiate, which is just a short distance from here, he used to walk over here with baskets of vegetables for the sisters. He said that sometimes that was all the community here would have for the next day. They were very poor."

"Really!" Kitty found it hard to believe that this had ever been a poor place.

"For years the sisters had a hard time here. The Jesuits were very good to them. The story of how we happen to be here is interesting too. It seems that the religious of the Sacred Heart had a school here from 1820 to 1844, when they had to close it. At that time Father Van Aashe, S.J., whom Father Nerinckx, our founder, had brought to America, was pastor here at St. Ferdinand's parish and he asked the Sisters of Loretto to open a school. Six of them came from Kentucky in 1847."

"My, that was a long time ago," Delia said.

The following May, when Mother Praxedes received word from Kitty that Mother Cecilia was at the academy on Pine Street in St. Louis, Mother recalled the conversation she had had with her sisters. Now Kitty wrote that Mother Cecilia's health had declined so rapidly that she had been relieved of all work.

"But she doesn't seem to be getting any better," the letter added.

Mother Praxedes had planned to go to St. Louis to see Mother Cecilia; but, before the commencement exercises, it had been impossible to get away; and, by the time the busiest days were over, word came that Mother Cecilia had died.

It was hard to realize that Mother Cecilia was gone because in Mother Praxedes' mind she had never grown old. Her letters had always been full of that same youthful simplicity and that quiet sense of service that Mother Praxedes had sensed as a child. Why just this past Christmas Mother Cecilia had written, "No one will torment us up there for a new set of teeth or to have her lungs examined, and if any of our sisters should cough through sheer habit, we shall ask the Angels to take them out riding."

Two days after Mother Cecilia's death, Mother Praxedes' quiet interlude at Florissant came to an end. If she had thought that she would not soon return to the West, she was wrong; for on June 25, 1894, twenty years after she had first left Missouri, she was appointed to Loretto Heights Academy in Denver, Colorado.

She read the letter over several times. She had seen the Heights only once, but that must have been three, maybe four years ago. From her memory she recalled someone in the group saying, "Someday you will be the Superior here." She remembered what she had answered, too. "I belong in the adobe houses of the Southwest; my work is there."

It was hard to say where one's work was if one was working for God. Yet she felt apprehensive about this appointment. The financial panic through which the country was passing had affected many of the society's schools, and there had even been, she knew, talk of selling the Heights. She looked at the letter again. Yes, it said Loretto Heights.

DENVER, COLORADO—1894

Suddenly the sun disappeared behind the mountains. Lost in the shadows of a rapidly approaching night, Mother Praxedes sat motionless and alone. On the desk before her were copies of the two mortgages and the stub of a railroad ticket, the only remnant of a fruitless trip to Mexico. In addition to these she now had a letter, bearing a Milwaukee postmark. Within her, beyond the serenity of dark and shadow, raged a fury of conflicting emotions. Three weeks at Loretto Heights, three weeks of inquiry and discussion interrupted by a mad dash to Mexico, had chipped away all vagueness and left her problem starkly clear. But what was she to do?

The indebtedness of Loretto Heights Academy ran into figures almost beyond her comprehension. She had dealt in improvements, had helped finance a parish church. She had built and borrowed, but six-figure bargaining was another proposition.

The shadows lengthened into darkness. Mother Praxedes, head in hands, pondered the hopeless situation. The market for Colorado's silver had disintegrated with the repeal of the Sherman Silver Purchase Act. The whole state, in fact, the entire silver-producing West, was in the throes of panic. Property was rapidly depreciating and the company holding the mortgages in favor of the Heights was eager to salvage what it could before the market hit bottom. One thing was certain: there was no money to pay the mortgage and, as conditions stood, none could be borrowed. A loan could be obtained in Mexico, but the low exchange value of the currency made such an escape impractical.

Mother Praxedes sighed. For a woman who believed in action, this imposed delay was stifling. She walked to the window and looked to the black outline of mountains against the red-stained sky. "Mountains," she said audibly. Why was it that man could change hills and valleys, but mountains he left untouched? They are too big, too powerful, she was thinking.

A question was forming in her mind. Why couldn't Loretto be like those mountains? Strong, steady, impregnable. A union of houses and hearts could form a towering mountain, a mountain capable of weathering the storms of depression. How could any company refuse to wait out the foul weather if all Loretto's property were mounted together? She wondered. As things were, the Heights was isolated.

She did not know how long she had been trying to steady her thoughts in order to form some conclusion when she finally became aware that it was already night. Only the light of the evening star penetrated the blackness.

The next day and the week that followed carried more discoveries. She was learning legal terms and twists of finance which she had never had occasion to need before. Forming in her mind was the conclusion she had been unknowingly approaching for some time. The first step would have to be a personal interview with the men holding the mortgage. Letters and telegrams were unsatisfactory. There was nothing to do but make a trip to Milwaukee, to the Northwestern Mutual Life Insurance Company.

Having reached this decision, she sat down at her desk to write the words that would ask Mother Catherine for permission to make the trip.

"Dear Mother," she began. "Conditions here at the Heights being what they are, I feel that—" she paused. For a moment she sat as if waiting for the next words to shape themselves. Then she wrote, "I feel that only a personal interview with the men holding the mortgage will bring us to an understanding." She went on, stating her reasons for believing that this was the only answer.

When the letter was worded and written, she read it over. If the answer was affirmative, a task of diplomacy and tact would be hers. Somehow she did not let herself think beyond the last stroke of her pen. The future was too burdened to bear surmising.

Still seated at her desk, she was putting her signature on the letter when a knock on the door caused her to put the pen aside. "Come in," she said.

"It's the mail, Mother." And quickly Sister Jovita crossed the room and handed a large bundle of letters to her superior.

"Thank you, Sister. How is the work on the fence coming?"

"Fine, Mother. Joe says that they will finish by the day after tomorrow."

"Good! I think I'll go out to see it later today."

Sister Jovita left; Mother glanced at the stack of letters. On top was one from the mother house. Running the opener under the flap, Mother drew out the letter and began to read. It was from Mother Catherine. As Mother Praxedes read, her face did not betray her feelings. Her eyes paused on the words, "It was decided that the Loretto Heights property should be sold."

A meeting had been held at the mother house on September 21 and the decision of the council and Father O'Connell, the Ecclesiastical Superior, was that the debt was beyond their power to finance. But why hadn't they at least warned her? Couldn't she have been consulted? There they were in Kentucky, half a continent away, disposing of property that could never be replaced. A touch of anger, and maybe some hurt pride, welled up within her.

Beneath her hands that held the council's decision, Mother Praxedes could see her own letter. Her eyes went from one to the other, "should be sold," "a personal interview." There is a way out, she thought. I'm sure that there is a way. Sell this gigantic new academy? Give up the possibility of educating thousands of young women in the West? Ten years from now a school like this will cost twice the debt, and we will have no more means of financing it then than we do now if we just sit back. We can't give up every time we have more bills than we can pay. Isn't sharing God's truth more valuable than paid bills?

Her blood began to surge in her veins. Her fighting spirit was coming back when it seemed she had almost lost it. "Loretto will never be chiseled from that tower," she said with grim determination. "Not if I have to go all the way to New York on my knees."

As suddenly as she had been aroused, she once more became calm. She wondered if in the light of this decision, she should silence the thoughts that were pulsing in her mind. Was this God's answer? She had prayed. Wasn't this, then, what He wanted? Wasn't her role simply to obey? To breathe in the suffering of defeat? To submit? But this wasn't for herself! Loretto Heights wasn't hers! It was theirs! It was Loretto's! It was His. She couldn't let it go without a fight and He would have to help her.

Pushing aside the letter she had written, she took a fresh piece of paper. Without hesitation, her pen began to glide, the words flowing as she wrote. She would ask for a reconsideration. Halfway through she paused. If she asked for time and then did not succeed, would the society perhaps lose more? She could not think of that. She must try, no matter.

That afternoon after the letter was posted, Mother Praxedes left the academy by a side entrance and crossed the lawn, headed for the pasture where a new fence was being put up. She breathed deeply. Good air, fresh and crisp. The sun was brilliant. Her vigorous pace disclosed a determination consonant with her frame of mind.

No one was around when she arrived at the partially finished fence. Sister Jovita had been right. It was a good job and quite near completion.

Mother noted that the posts were well spaced and the wire was heavy. Then for a moment she stood facing the mountains. Those magnificent Rockies! Turning, she walked back the way she had come. "We won't give you up," she said to the red sandstone academy.

The days which linked Mother Praxedes' letter to Mother Catherine's answer were days with wide stretches of doubt and periods of confidence. But even as times of waiting always pass, so, too, did this interlude. The answer came.

Mother Catherine commented on the unusualness of the request since a vote had already been taken on the matter; but a special meeting had been called, she said. It was the desire of each one of the council members, as it was the desire of the whole

Society, to keep the Heights if at all possible. After much discussion, it was decided to give Mother Praxedes the opportunity she was seeking. Yes, she could go to Milwaukee.

Permission was all she needed. She glanced at the clock. Yes, she could make today's train if she didn't delay. With the letter in her hand, she went to the chapel. You have to help me convince the brokers to wait. After her visit to the Blessed Sacrament, she went to her office. She would need her street veil, shawl, gloves, and her purse. She picked up the timetable which she had gotten just in case the permission came.

Meeting Sister Lavialle in the hall, Mother said, "Sister, get your street veil and shawl and meet me at the front door as soon as you can."

Without any question, Sister Lavialle hastened to her room to get her street accessories and returned to the front door, where Mother Praxedes was already waiting.

"You didn't waste any time, Sister." Together they hurried down the broad, stone steps and into the waiting carriage.

"Where are we going, Mother?" Sister asked.

"To Milwaukee."

Sister Lavialle blinked and turned to her Superior with a perplexed expression. "Milwaukee, Wisconsin?"

"Yes," Mother said, rather enjoying the reaction she was getting.

"Why, Mother, I have scarcely more than a handkerchief with me."

"It's the same with me, but we'll manage. We may be back tomorrow."

Arriving at the Union Station, Mother bought their tickets and they boarded the train.

"I only took time to do one thing." Mother smiled as she sat back in the coach seat.

"What was that?"

"I left word at the desk that we were going out of town."

As the train made its way toward Chicago, where they would catch another train for Milwaukee, Mother explained to Sister Lavialle why they were making the trip.

"Pray, Sister," she said. "Only God will be able to keep those men from foreclosing. They've been patient for two long years. I just hope we get there before they decide to take the academy."

"What would they do with it anyway?"

"I don't want to give them a chance to think of a use for it."

The next morning, as the train pulled into the terminal in Chicago, the two sisters were feeling the full measure of weariness after their long afternoon and longer night in the stuffy, stiff-seated coach. An hour between trains gave them time to relieve their tired backs with a little walking, but it did not help them to feel any cleaner. Wrinkled, dirty, tired, they boarded the train for Milwaukee. When Mother realized that it would be only 10 A.M. when they arrived, she decided that they wouldn't look for a place to stay since they might be able to conclude their business and get a late afternoon train back to Chicago.

"We'll go right to the insurance office," she said. "There's no use waiting until tomorrow."

Glancing hurriedly at the sign which identified the Northwestern Mutual Life Insurance Company, the two sisters entered the office building. A young man with glasses looked up from his work and asked, "May I help you?"

"I am Mother Praxedes from Loretto Heights in Denver," she answered. "I would like to speak to the president of your company."

"I'm sorry," the young man answered with a bit of a grin, "but the board of directors is having a meeting. He won't be free for about an hour."

Could it be possible, she wondered, that they would be discussing the Heights? Even if they weren't, this was an opportunity to lay her request before the deciding powers of the company. "May I go into that meeting?" Mother asked.

The young man lifted his spectacles, pushing them further up on his nose, and replied, "That is rather irregular—but if you come with me, I'll ask."

Mother Praxedes motioned for Sister Lavialle to follow her.

As the young clerk knocked gently on a door near the end of the hall, he glanced uneasily at the two sisters.

A gray-haired man opened the door, whereupon the directors in view of the door rose to their feet.

"This is Mother Praxedes from Denver," the young man began.

"Why, Mother, won't you come in?" the older man said, and the clerk stepped aside to let the sisters enter the large meeting room.

"This is Mother Praxedes from Denver. Mother is in charge of the property we have been discussing, gentlemen," he announced as he showed the two sisters to places at the long table around which the directors were gathered.

Resuming his place, the president went on. "In fact, Mother, we have just about come to the decision that we can no longer defer foreclosure on the St. Mary's property which was originally mortgaged in favor of the Heights. But perhaps you have come to make some payment?" He smiled, trying to be kind in his manner.

"May I please speak to the board?" Mother asked.

"Why certainly."

Mother Praxedes rose to her feet. She began to speak words that sounded to her as another's voice. All the hours of prayer, mingled with the great desire in her heart that Loretto might keep its property in Denver, formulated into one petition; these men must trust that they would not lose one penny of the money they had loaned or the interest accruing therefrom. She had come to assure them of that.

"St. Mary's and Loretto Heights are not two isolated houses," she said. "The Sisters of Loretto are a large community with houses all over the Middle West and Southwest. Surely all of these places should have sufficient assets to assure you that your loan is safe. Just give us time, gentlemen."

At this Mother Praxedes sat down. The chairman looked from one man to another and said, "Gentlemen, if there are any questions you would care to ask Mother Praxedes, I'm sure she would happy to reply."

For what seemed like an eternity, one director after another asked for clarification of various points.

"How is your group governed?" one man asked.

"Our Society has a central governing body similar to yours, which resides at our mother house in Kentucky. This group of officers is in charge of all our many houses over the country. None of our institutions is independent, but all form one united group."

"But would your sisters be willing to pledge all the property they own as security for this debt?" came the final query.

"I believe I am safe in saying that they would," Mother answered, praying in her heart that this was not going too far with the permission she had been granted.

With this the members of the board talked among themselves for several minutes and finally, the chairman, seeing that the board was still reluctant to grant an extension, said, "Mother Praxedes, we appreciate your graciousness in answering so many questions; but I feel that it is still the opinion of the gentlemen here that we will have to foreclose."

"Gentlemen, if you take the house," she said, "you will have to take the sisters with it."

Two or three of the board members laughed slightly, but most of them scowled. The chairman cleared his throat uneasily.

"Mother, it is already late," he said, glancing at the clock above the door. "The board will have to discuss this privately after dinner. If you care to return at three o'clock, I think we can give you final word."

Mother's heart pounded. She had not convinced them. "Yes, certainly, gentlemen, I shall be very happy to return at three."

Silently the sisters left the room. Mother Praxedes' head was throbbing. She should not have asked to do this. Obviously it had been a wild chance and it had not worked. Had they intended extending the time, they would not have put her off.

"I thought for a while that they were going to give in." Sister Lavialle tried to sound encouraging as they reached the sidewalk outside.

"They asked so many questions that I didn't even know what I was saying."

"You did beautifully, Mother. A few times I almost waved my rosary in applause."

"Maybe you should have. It's clear that I didn't move them. What shall we do until three?"

"There's a restaurant across the street. Maybe a little food would help."

Mother Praxedes and Sister Lavialle crossed the street and entered the small restaurant, where they found a table near the back.

"Everywhere I look I see dollar signs." Mother Praxedes smiled, picking up the menu.

Neither of them could eat very much. By 1:15 they were leaving the restaurant with almost two hours left to wait. After walking several blocks without finding a church where they could say their prayers, they decided to go back to the insurance office.

"If I weren't so worried, I'd go into some of these stores and price material," Mother Praxedes said. "Sometimes I get curious to know the price of silk and ribbon."

Sister Lavialle looked at her. Maybe the worry *was* too much for her.

As Mother Praxedes walked, she could not help wondering about her own motives in this matter of the loan. Was she really fighting an unselfish battle? Was this purely for God and the Society? How much did she want to be successful for herself? She had wanted to serve others; and yet, after all these years, she still seemed to be getting more than she was giving. Was she perhaps seeking some personal triumph in this? But it isn't for myself, she argued. Don't let any selfish interest of mine jeopardize this work. Loretto needs the Heights. Do anything You want with me, but don't let us lose it.

At 2:15 the same young man adjusted his spectacles as he saw the sisters entering the office again. "The meeting is still in session," he offered.

"They certainly are taking a long time," Sister Lavialle whispered to Mother.

The minutes dragged on. Mother Praxedes tried to say her rosary and then she opened her prayer book, but her thoughts kept going back to the room where she had faced the members of the board. She saw them staring at her. She heard their questions and her answers. She had presumed a great deal in offering the Society as security. Had she perhaps presumed too much?

Suddenly the men started coming down the hall in two's and three's, talking softly. Group after group passed them without any recognition. None seemed to notice them.

"Cheer up," a man's voice said; and looking up, Mother Praxedes saw the chairman standing in front of her. Taking her hand, he whispered, "You have won. We will reconsider the matter and grant you more time."

The mail had piled up on Mother's desk while she was away. On seeing it, her first impulse was to leave it just as it was since, as she remarked to Sister Xavier, it contained nothing but bills and she already had too many of those.

"Oh, I had better see if anything needs attention," she relented. She flipped through all the bills, the usual advertisements and circulars, a letter from Kitty and another from Delia, which she put into her pocket to read later, and a plain white envelope, which she recognized as a death notice.

The postmark was Santa Fe. And the name? Sliding the card from the envelope, she saw written in precise letters *Mother Magdalen Hayden*. "Bless her," Mother whispered. No more rheumatism; no more frightening trips across New Mexico. Mother Praxedes knew that Mother Francisca would miss Mother Magdalen. Although the dear old sister had been crippled with rheumatism for over ten years, she had been there to guide and to encourage Mother Francisca in the vast cares that belonged to her as Superior of the Santa Fe community and supervisor-at-large over the convents in the Southwest.

"Mother, is something wrong?" Sister Xavier, the directress of the academy, asked as she entered Mother's office.

Mother handed the death notice to Sister. "Mother Magdalen was a dear old lady. Did you know her?"

"No, I heard about her but I don't think I ever saw her."

"Probably not. She seems to have been in Santa Fe as long as either of us would remember. She was a great woman. Archbishop Lamy thought a lot of her. Anyone who knew her could never forget her. She was of that Irish stock that decide everything on faith and their own native horse sense. She was fearless. And somehow she made others feel that way too. I remember when she took me to Cruces. She was at least seventy-five then, and suffering intensely from arthritis and reheumatism; but as cheerful and as peppy as a person half her age—more filled with God's joy, certainly, than I was. She gave me nine dollars when she left to return to Santa Fe. She would have loved hearing about the trip to Milwaukee."

Sister Xavier returned the card to Mother. She almost said that Mother herself seemed a bit like Mother Magdalen, but she decided against it.

"I'm sorry, Sister," Mother said. "Did you want to see me about something? I am not thinking this morning."

"I just wanted to tell you that the girls are quite excited about the current-events contest. If their enthusiasm is any indication, you are going to have a hard time picking the winner."

"What do you mean, I am? That part is up to you. I'll give the silk scarf, but I'll leave the literary judgment up to you. We may have a small school, but we want no second-rate essays winning the contest," she said, smiling.

"All right, Mother; but you have to present the prize."

"That I can do."

When Sister was gone, Mother Praxedes looked at the card again. As soon as she could collect her thoughts, she would write Mother Francisca a letter. Losing Mother Magdalen would be like losing a mother. All of Mother Francisca's adult life had been lived in Santa Fe, working with Mother Magdalen.

Putting the card down, slowly she became aware of the room around her, the letters on the desk, the sunshine on the floor. So much seemed to have happened since she opened the envelope. Gradually she remembered the rest of the mail on her desk. She had not noticed the other letter postmarked *Loretto*. She ran a letter opener under the flap. She smiled to herself. Maybe Sister Vestina had been right; maybe she was a fanatic on opening letters neatly. "Don't you ever want to rip a letter open?" she used to tease.

When she got the envelope open, she realized that it was a circular letter, one addressed to all the sisters. A Father Thomas Gambon had been appointed by Bishop McCloskey as Ecclesiastical Superior to replace Father O'Connell.

I hope this is a good appointment, she thought. Poor Mother Catherine has had so much trouble in this year and a half in office. Mother Praxedes still did not know much about it, but it was evident that there was a difference of opinion on the subject of authority. She did know, however, that before Mother Dafrosa resigned as Mother Superior she had appealed to Rome to have the Rule clarified on certain points of authority, but that Bishop McCloskey, the bishop of the diocese of Louisville in which the mother house was located, had forced her to recall the request. But more than this, Mother Praxedes did not know.

Before the week was out, another letter arrived from Kentucky. Mother knew that this would be Mother Catherine's reply to her letter about the successful trip to Milwaukee. She wondered how the board had taken the good news.

She unfolded the long, typewritten letter. She read it hurriedly at first. Then she read it over again carefully, trying to catch the tone. Several phrases flashed from the page. Wasn't it enough that St. Mary's Academy had been mortgaged in favor of the Heights? What had possessed her to offer the property of the Society as security? If the Bishop of Louisville heard of this, which he was bound to, they would all be in serious trouble. Actually, she had not told the insurance company executives the whole truth. All Loretto's property was not legally liable as security for any one piece of property, unless Mother Praxedes' word had itself legally bound the Society.

Mother Praxedes paced the room with the letter dangling from one hand. What other reaction could she have expected? She had, after all, made a wild promise. How was Mother Catherine to appreciate those hours of anxiety in Milwaukee?

As she walked up and down, she tried to repress her disappointment. There was no word of gratitude that she had gotten a two-year extension, which would give them time to figure out how to keep the property. From the tone of the letter, she visualized a fearful woman as its author. Gradually Mother Praxedes began to realize that perhaps she herself had not appreciated the position this may have imposed on her Superior. This is my way, she thought, to think of my own interest and consider the consequences later. Well, one thing was certain: she would have to make every possible effort to pay more than just the interest during the next two years.

The winter passed and although the financial straits of the house did not improve appreciably, the prospects for the future seemed better. At least the country was over the first shock of depression, and the sisters still had a roof over their heads. Perhaps before the loan came up for renewal, the country would be on its feet again and the Northwestern Mutual would be better able to sustain the loan.

In late spring Mother Praxedes received word from Mother Rosine, her successor at Las Cruces, that a group of people from El Paso and Las Cruces were planning a pilgrimage to the shrine of Our Lady of Guadalupe and that they wanted Mother Rosine and Mother Praxedes to accompany them.

"Oh, I couldn't think of it!" she said aloud. Sister Lavialle, who happening to be passing Mother in the hall, stopped. "Yes, Mother?"

"Oh, Sister, I was muttering to myself. Guess what that Mother Rosine wants me to do? Go on a pilgrimage to Mexico!"

"Wonderful! When?"

"The end of July. It's very tempting, I'll admit, but I couldn't think of it."

"And why not? It would be good for you."

"But I've already been to Mexico."

"You mean that hurried trip you took last fall? That was a nightmare. You weren't in Mexico two days and running from one bank to another. This would be a chance to relax."

Mother Praxedes thought about the trip, about seeing her friends again, about the chance for spiritual renewal; but she had just about decided that it was out of the question when another letter from Mother Rosine pleaded that she join them. The Amadors, who had offered to pay all expenses, were anxious for her to go, and Mother Rosine wouldn't go unless she went. Maybe she should go. It would be good to return for a while to the talk of old friends. At times she felt more like a businessman than a nun. Her companions had become dull papers and cold statistics, all the trappings of the business world. It had been a long time since she had sat down and listened to the human talk about children and everyday domestic affairs. A person could lose touch so easily, could forget so soon that other worlds continued to revolve, worlds as important in their way as was hers. Maybe she should go. Maybe kneeling with real people before the shrine of a real Mother, she could evaluate her own place in the community of love. Yes, she would go. She'd tuck a small American flag into her purse in case she needed to have Old Glory to prove her citizenship, and she'd join the Las Cruces pilgrimage to Mexico.

While Mother Praxedes was heading south for Mexico, Mother Catherine's problems in Kentucky were mounting, problems which were to affect Mother Praxedes more than she could ever have dreamed. As early as July 27, Mother Catherine had written to the Bishop, Bishop McCloskey, inviting him or a delegate appointed by him to confer the habit on the postulants at the end of their retreat on August 15. The retreat started on August 6 and since no word had been received from the Bishop by then, in desperation Mother Catherine wrote to Cardinal Satolli, the

Apostolic Delegate in Washington, D.C., asking him to appoint someone.

"If we get no word by the fifteenth, I'll ask the retreat master to conduct the reception," Mother Catherine told the worried mistress of novices, who knew that the parents of the postulants would not know what to think if they arrived and had to be told there would be no reception.

In the mail on August 14, the mistress of novices herself received a letter from the Bishop, who was in French Lick, Indiana. Since he would not be back in Louisville until the end of the week, the Bishop said, he wished the reception postponed until August 22.

"Why didn't he just appoint the retreat master? What will we tell the people?"

"We will tell them nothing," Mother Catherine decided. "Many have come a great distance at much expense. They cannot wait here until the twenty-second and some of them will not be able to return. I am going to assume that Cardinal Satolli will give permission for the retreat master to conduct the reception."

"What will you do if you don't hear from him?"

Mother Catherine shook her head. Whatever she did, she would have a problem.

"Why do you think the Cardinal hasn't answered?"

Again she shook her head. She had stopped trying to figure out some things. So much of it was beyond her.

While Mother Catherine was trying to handle this problem, which in comparison to others was minor, Mother Praxedes and Mother Rosine were visiting the Castle of Chapultepec, the summer home of the president of Mexico. Doña Carmelita, the charming wife of President Diaz, received them and told them that they were welcome to see whatever they found of interest at this historic place.

"You must see the tree of Montezuma on the east side of the hill," she told them. "He is said to have wept there after his defeat. Even great men find defeat hard."

Their visit to the solitary Virgin of Guadalupe, with her star-studded mantle of azure, was crowded between their visit to the Cathedral of Chihuahua, whose huge dome they could see against the purple hills for miles before they reached it, and their stay in Mexico City, where they were given official permits to visit government schools and prisons.

"Did you see any evidence of persecution?" everyone wanted to know when they returned.

"No, but the Father Superior of the Vincentians thought we were very daring to appear in Mexico City in our religious habits. We told him that we would pull out our American flags if anyone dared to lay a hand on us."

"For us it was safe, but not for many Catholic Mexicans."

On their return to the United States, Mother Rosine traveled as far as Denver with Mother Praxedes, and then went on to her new mission at Colorado Springs.

At the Heights, Mother Praxedes found everyone in the midst of preschool activity. The enrollment had increased, but best of all, Sister Pancratia had returned as directress of the academy. Sister Pancratia was really the foundress of Loretto Heights, for it was she who had chosen the site seven years before and supervised the erection of the academy only to be transferred in the spring of '92 just prior to the first graduation. Sister Pancratia's return was encouraging to Mother Praxedes.

October brought news from the mother house that the Holy Father, Leo XIII, through Francis Cardinal Satolli, the Apostolic Delegate in Washington, had appointed Bishop Thomas S. Byrne of Nashville, Tennessee, to investigate the disciplinary and financial affairs of the Sisters of Loretto. Puzzled by this new development, Mother Praxedes had no way of knowing that on August 16 Mother Catherine herself had requested Cardinal Satolli to send an impartial judge to settle matters between herself and Bishop McCloskey. Shortly after receiving this word, Mother Praxedes received another letter from Bishop Byrne asking about the financial status of the Heights. Immediately she wrote to assure him that the indebtedness was not hopeless. In fact, she said, Bishop Matz of Denver had given her permission to hold a bazaar, which she hoped would net enough to pay off some of the principal.

During the next few months letters from first one convent and then another told of Bishop Byrne's expected arrival or his recent departure. Some writers seemed mystified; others were sure that this was a portent of some change in the Society.

Late in January of 1896 word came to the Heights that Francis Cardinal Satolli, the Apostolic Delegate himself, would be in Denver in early March to visit the community. Naturally curious as to what his visit implied and yet more immediately concerned with the protocol such a visit entailed, Mother Praxedes started making plans.

"Sister Pancratia, will you take care of planning all the meals?" Mother Praxedes asked.

"May I consult Baur's about the menu!"

"Anything. You handle that part any way you like. I will be too busy to know whether anyone eats or not."

Before the week was out everyone in the community was assigned some part in the preparations.

The closer the time came, the more intense the preparations become. The air was electric; everyone felt that *something* was brewing.

"Sister, you polish the best silver. . . . I'll ask Sister Eustachia and Sister Mary Linus to come out from St. Mary's to help with the serving. . . . Where did I put that list? . . . Sister Aurelia, will you sing? . . . Sister Lavialle plays the harp beautifully. . . . Perhaps I could borrow those lovely hand-painted dishes. . . . Sister Arsenia will bring the Cardinal to breakfast. . . ." Back and forth, checking and rechecking, the buzz of preparations included everything from oysters for the Cardinal's breakfast to the purple throne in the sanctuary. The papal colors, gold and white, decked the main hallway. Finally, the morning of March 6 dawned. The community was ready!

As the Cardinal celebrated Mass, students and sisters made the whole house vibrate with their singing. Almost all of the Denver clergy were present. Mother Praxedes smiled. Second only to the privilege of having the Cardinal at the Heights, was the happiness she felt at the spirit of cooperation everyone had shown in preparing for this occasion.

When the breakfast was ready, Mother told Sister Arsenia to go to the sacristy with a cup of coffee for the Cardinal. After his coffee, Sister should bring him to breakfast.

Mother Praxedes took one last look at the table. It was a picture. The lovely hand-painted, gold dishes glistened, the arrangement of flowers in the center of the table was as perfect as the artistic hands of Sister Pancratia could make it.

"Everything is lovely, Sisters," Mother Praxedes said as she looked with satisfaction at the Cardinal's breakfast.

The four priests who had been invited to eat with the Cardinal came into the dining room quietly as Sister Mary Linus showed each to his place. All were in hushed excitement as they waited patiently for the arrival of the Apostolic Delegate.

Sister Mary Linus and Sister Eustachia were ready to serve. They had rehearsed exactly the way things should be done. Nothing had been forgotten.

Everyone waited. And they waited. Where was the Cardinal? It seemed the other guests had waited hours when finally the rustle of Sister Arsenia's beads caused Mother Praxedes to sigh with relief. The Cardinal was coming.

Sister Arsenia hurried up to Mother Praxedes. The Cardinal was not with her.

"Mother, Cardinal Satolli said to tell you that he will be ready to interview the sisters in ten minutes. And that the guests should go ahead and eat breakfast."

"Eat breakfast!" Mother exclaimed, perplexed.

"He has already eaten in the sacristy," Sister Arsenia replied. "When I went to take His Eminence the cup of coffee as you suggested, he asked for a slice of bread. I returned with that, then he told me to tell you that he would see the sisters in ten minutes. I asked what about breakfast and he said that the coffee and bread was his breakfast."

"Didn't you explain that we had breakfast waiting for him here?"

"Yes, Mother, I did, but he said to tell the others to eat; that he would be with them for dinner."

"Thank you, Sister," Mother said.

After the Cardinal had spoken to the sisters in a group, Mother Praxedes saw him privately in the parlor. As they seated themselves, Mother Praxedes noticed that the Cardinal grew more grave. He looked at her for a moment, and then said, choosing his words carefully, "This is a most grandiose academy, Mother Praxedes. In speaking to Bishop Byrne, I learned that its financing —is that the way you call it, financing?—has been a credit to you."

"It is still far from secure, Your Eminence. However, I am happy you have mentioned it. Since you have appointed Bishop Byrne to look over the financial condition of the Society, I am sure you would be interested to know that, in trying to find backing for the Heights, I became aware of one major problem. Our Society, though owning much property, does not have it in the name of the corporation. Consequently, it forms no large holding which is representative enough to back large property ventures."

"Yes, that is something which other religious groups likewise face. And I think, too, that Bishop Byrne is aware of that fact. However, I shall convey the knowledge to him. It is noteworthy. Yes, noteworthy."

Thus the brief interview came to an end.

Almost before the Cardinal had been escorted down the broad stairs of the academy, Bishop Byrne of Nashville, Tennessee, was being shown up them. It was now apparent to Mother Praxedes that, while she had been steeped in the problem of Loretto Heights, graver problems were seething elsewhere.

"Mother," the bishop said, "I have come in the interest of the Loretto Society. I have been asked, as you know, by Cardinal Satolli to investigate financial conditions in the Society and make some suggestions. I am most interested in the way you have handled the financial straits of this institution. I learned at Loretto and from the Cardinal that you secured an extension on the existing loan by promising the whole Loretto Society as security. You know, of course, that had the company challenged you on that, there would have been no way to show them in black and white that such security exists."

"Yes, I know that it does not exist on paper; but it could."

"It was fortunate they didn't challenge you. However, you showed foresight if not prudence. I am convinced that the Sisters of Loretto will have to consolidate their property. It is the only intelligent thing to do as economic conditions are. And every day it becomes more urgent."

With a shocking suddenness, almost before Bishop Byrne could have reached the mother house in Kentucky, Mother Praxedes received a letter asking her to make a trip to Loretto.

"I suppose Bishop Byrne wants to decide what to do about our loan before it comes due again. He didn't care much for my shaky way of promising security for it the last time," she said, laughing.

"When will you be back?" asked Sister Pancratia.

"I'm not sure. If I'm not back in ten days you had better look after the graduation invitations and the programs. Whatever you decide will be all right."

"Mother, are you sure you're coming back?"

"I'll be back unless they tie me down."

"No, seriously, Mother. I think that this trip is more than just a routine matter. If Bishop Byrne wanted to talk to you about the loan, why didn't he talk to you here?"

"He was much too rushed to talk in particulars then, Sister."

"If you ask me there's something in the wind when a cardinal, a bishop, and a letter all come in the same month."

"You're getting suspicious, Sister. Watch that," Mother Praxedes teased.

As the buggy swung a full circle and started back along the road from the green frame depot, the trim gentleman in the driver's seat looked over his right shoulder and asked in a deep voice tinged with a Kentucky drawl, "Did you have a long trip, Mother?"

"Yes, I did. I've come from Denver," Mother Praxedes replied as she braced herself in the seat.

"Well, now that's quite a piece. What do you think of that, Bay Boy, all the way from Denver." This remark was evidently meant for the chestnut stallion that flicked his ears in response.

The buggy springs squeaked to the accompaniment of Bay Boy's hoofbeats on the hard-packed road. The air was warm for March.

"I 'spose those hills look kinda cut down after looking at mountains."

"Yes." Mother laughed. "But Kentucky has a beauty all its own."

"Indeed it has." He smiled, drawing a deep breath as if to savor its more volatile beauty.

"How are things at the mother house?" she asked.

"Oh, things are happening there." At this he straightened in the seat and glanced at her out of the corner of his eye. Bay Boy whinnied and went into a gallop. After a few minutes Mr. Elder slowed the horse to a trot.

"Bishop Byrne of Nashville has been here for some time. He's a very likable man," Mr. Elder said.

Mother looked across the fields. She had forgotten that earth could be so richly black and trees so lushy green. She watched for familiar rises of land and forgotten signs of curve or brook or fences. She wondered how dear old Mother Dafrosa was. Would she remember her novice after all these years? I wonder if all novices have as much trouble with obeying bells as I did? Give yourself time, Mother Dafrosa had said. Serving God was getting His point of view. Mother Praxedes wondered if she had followed Mother Dafrosa's advice. Sometimes it had been more difficult than the bells.

"If you watch the tops of the trees to your left there, you'll soon see the roof of the academy," Mr. Elder was saying.

She watched. Yes, he was right. Just for a moment she caught a glimpse of something white above the trees.

Bay Boy's hoofs made a clap, clap and then the buggy bounced across a few feet of wooden bridge. The stallion seemed to slow instinctively as he approached the gate to the road that led through pastureland to the convent and its surrounding buildings. Once past the gate Bay Boy kept a steady trot.

"Does the place look familiar?" Mr. Elder asked.

"Oh yes, quite as I remembered it."

In a few minutes they were at the top of the long hill, and then Mother could see the cluster of buildings forming three sides of a slightly irregular rectangle. The closer they drew, the more Mother Praxedes realized that the buildings, from the two-room house built by Father Badin long before the sisters had come here to the new, four-story brick academy, spoke a saga of change which spanned a near-century. For a few moments she was puzzled by the new academy. She knew that she had not seen it before, and yet, it looked familiar. Why of course! It was almost a replica of the academy at Florissant.

Before the buggy reached the walk leading from the driveway to the chapel, Mother Praxedes saw two sisters and a priest, whom she recognized as Bishop Byrne, coming to meet them.

As the buggy slowed to a stop, Bishop Byrne called, "Welcome home to Loretto, Mother."

Mr. Elder assisted Mother Praxedes as she stepped down from the buggy, and then reached for her suitcase.

Mother glanced at the two sisters. Perhaps she should know them, but neither looked familiar.

"How did you leave things at the Heights, Mother?" the Bishop asked.

"Just fine. We'll have five to graduate from twelfth grade this June."

The Bishop smiled and the sisters exchanged glances. Mother Praxedes, assured that the Bishop's interest in the Heights indicated that the loan was indeed the reason for her trip, congratulated herself for thinking to bring a copy of the mortgage.

"Do you know Sister Winifred and Sister de Sales?" the Bishop asked.

"Not personally, although I know them, of course." Oh, now she knew, two of Mother Catherine's assistants.

As the group walked toward the chapel, Mother said, "I'd like to make a visit if you don't mind."

"Go right ahead, Mother," the Bishop said. "If you'll excuse me, I'll leave you. May I see you in the academy parlor in about half an hour?" he asked.

"Of course, Your Grace. Thank you."

"I'll take your bag to your room, Mother," Sister de Sales said.

"Oh, really, Sister, I can manage it nicely."

"No, indeed. You make your visit," she insisted.

Inside all was solemn. The statues, draped in purple, came as an abrupt reminder that this was Passion Friday. The painting of the crucifixion—one of the many Father Nerinckx had brought from Belgium—looked familiar above the main altar. Mother knelt in the back pew to pray. The Church was recalling Christ's hidden life during this season. These statues draped in purple were a double reminder of the way of seclusion He had chosen for Himself. He had chosen, too, to hide Himself when they would make Him king. It was to the Hidden Christ in Loretto's chapel that she addressed her first moments of return. It was so peaceful here in the quiet hills of Kentucky. Loretto, too, was hidden from the world.

Mother Praxedes made the Sign of the Cross and left the chapel, with Sister Winifred following close behind her.

"Mother, would you like to go to your room before seeing the Bishop?" she asked when they were outside again.

"Please, Sister."

Mother Praxedes was escorted through a silent convent to a room just to the left of the stairs on the second floor. It was a fairly large room with a white iron bed, a washstand, a chest of drawers, and two stiff chairs.

"Sister, if Mother Catherine is available, I'd like to pay my respects to her first."

"Well, Mother . . ." Sister Winifred began weakly. "I think it would be just as well to wait until after you have seen the Bishop." She hestitated. "Do you have everything you need, Mother?"

"Yes, thank you."

When the door was closed, Mother Praxedes tried to collect her thoughts. Had it been her imagination or had the sister acted rather uneasy? Why had Sister Winifred been so flustered when she asked about Mother Catherine? Perhaps Mother Catherine was ill. If so, that will delay my return to Denver, she thought. Realizing, however, that there was nothing to be gained by speculation, she decided to wash her hands. Clean hands would help some.

She walked to the washstand near the window and poured some water into the china basin. After much rubbing, the soap and the hard water finally yielded a thin suds. Somehow she was having almost as much trouble ridding her hands of grit as she was quieting a rising anxiety within. There was something strange about all this.

When only a fragment of the half hour remained, she straightened her veil and took a clean handkerchief from her suitcase. She also took the long brown envelope from the pocket inside the suitcase lid. Having the mortgage with her would save time.

Going from the second floor of the convent to the side entrance of the academy, Mother Praxedes met no one. She had not realized that a place that housed so many could seem so deserted. As she turned the door knob, she found herself startled for a moment by the sound of voices coming from a room somewhere at the far end of the corridor. She closed the door softly, tempted to tiptoe so that no one would know that she was there. Annoyed by her own uneasiness, she cleared her throat and gave the door a firm push. She walked down the hall. Through a doorway to the right she could see a room that was undoubtedly the parlor. The shutters were partially closed, keeping the room in shadow.

"Someone should have opened these shutters," a crisp voice scolded. Mother Praxedes felt her heart jump as a sister swept past her. Without saying more, the sister crossed the room and adeptly folded back the upper half of the shutters on one window and then with the same quick movement went to the other. As suddenly as she had come, the sister was gone and Mother Praxedes' "thank you" was spoken to an empty room. Perhaps the sister hadn't seen her. But she must have!

Mother Praxedes sat on one of the hard leather chairs without noticing the kind eyes of the Virgin looking from the canvas on the far wall. She did not even hear the quick footsteps of the academy girls as they passed the parlor door a few minutes later. She removed the papers from the brown envelope in order to review the financial matter.

Suddenly she caught the Bishop's firm step in the hall and quickly he swept into the room.

"Well, Mother, sit down. I am so pleased to see you here. We have some big problems to solve."

"Yes, I know we do, Bishop Byrne. I have the copy of the mortgage and the loan right here. I thought you'd want to see them first."

"Yes, of course, Mother, but later." He waved aside the envelope. "That can wait." He cleared his throat. "There are more pressing matters to discuss first."

She looked at him. More pressing matters? What could be more pressing at the moment?

"I didn't ask you to come all the way to Kentucky to talk about Loretto Heights, although it is important," he said as if apologizing for the way he seemed to be minimizing her problem. "You have been summoned here because I want you to assume Mother Catherine's position as Mother Superior."

Had she heard correctly? Mother Catherine's position?

Before she could find the words for her questions, he went on. "Let me try to explain." The Bishop shifted his position. He was obviously trying to make the matter as simple as possible. "As you probably know, there has been a history of trouble between Bishop McCloskey and the superiors here."

"I was really not aware that there was anything seriously wrong," she said.

"The basic trouble, as I see it, is the wording of the Rule, which does not make it explicit whether the Mother Superior or the Ecclesiastical Superior—a priest appointed by the Bishop—possesses the final authority on certain matters. But to go back a bit; last August Mother Catherine asked Cardinal Satolli, the Apostolic Delegate, to send an impartial judge to settle matters between her and the Bishop. Actually, the Ecclesiastical Superior, in this case Father Gambon, was not well suited to be in such a delicate position. I feel that he only complicated matters." He paused. "Am I making this too complicated?"

"No, I think I follow you."

"So in October the Cardinal appointed me to conduct an inquiry, which I did. As you know from my visit to Denver, I tried to acquaint myself with the financial and disciplinary conditions of the Society. In my report to Cardinal Satolli, I said that I would need more time to appraise the problems fully. However, I told him that I felt the Rule would have to be revised before some matters could be solved."

"But why must Mother Catherine resign, Your Excellency?"

"At first I didn't think that that would be necessary, but the trouble is not quite as simple as I have made it. Two factions have grown up here at the mother house—some sisters are very loyal to Mother Catherine and others to Father Gambon and the Bishop. Then in December another complication appeared when Mother Catherine received a letter from Rome saying that the time was opportune for presenting the Loretto Rule for final confirmation—apparently there is no record of that ever being done. Then it was that I discovered that Mother Catherine had written to Rome at the same time that she had appealed to Cardinal Satolli. That was not hard to understand because she was distraught at the time over the whole situation. But Mother's failure to mention this request to either Cardinal Satolli or to me created an awkward situation for the Cardinal since he was then in the process of conducting this investigation. Then it was that Cardinal Satolli decided that the best thing to do would be to have both Mother Catherine and Father Gambon resign and get around this problem of satisfying the two opposing factions here at Loretto. Mother Catherine has many loyal followers, Mother Praxedes."

His tone was kind, but Mother Praxedes felt that she should

make her position clear, so she asked, "And you do not think that I am loyal to Mother Catherine?"

"I think that you are loyal to the Sisters of Loretto. That is the loyalty we need now—not loyalty to persons or to opinions."

Before she could ask why an election might not be held, Bishop Byrne went on.

"Mother, I will be quite frank with you. A revision of the Rule and Constitutions is needed. If such a revision is to be made satisfactorily, I need someone at the helm—at least temporarily—whom I can rely upon to win the respect of the sisters—and, let's be frank, the respect of the Bishop. An election at this time would be too risky. This whole situation could so easily be misunderstood and misinterpreted—and, through no one's fault. With the best will in the world, people can make some very serious mistakes."

After some minutes Mother Praxedes betrayed another worry. What about Mother Catherine? "Bishop Byrne, does Mother Catherine know about this? I mean has she consented to resign?"

"Yes, she has. Obviously it put her in a very peculiar position; however, I think she is genuinely interested in the good of the community and if this will solve the problems, she is willing. I certainly admire her. As I said, she has been through a great deal."

Again Mother Praxedes became silent. This was all so strange. How would the sisters who cherished their right to elect their higher superiors take this unusual situation?

"Your Grace, you must be aware that such an unprecedented step will be the cause of discontent? How are the sisters to know that all of this is with proper authority?"

"That is precisely why I only *ask* that you take the appointment. It is not a very pleasant position, Mother. I will tell you quite frankly that I would not want to be in your place."

An oppressive silence filled the room. What could she say? How could she accept? How refuse?

"Mother, you are in my opinion and in the opinion of Cardinal Satolli the only woman in the Loretto Society who is capable of weathering the difficulties ahead. I ask you in the interest of your sisters, many of whom may not understand, to accept the responsibility. It will be very much like leading the blind, Mother. Until everything is settled, some may find it hard to believe that you are not usurping authority."

"I find that hard to believe myself," she answered, with a sad, half smile. Suddenly she felt twice her forty-two years.

"You can be at ease about that, Mother. The authority is undeniably from God, straight from Pope Leo to Cardinal Satolli to you. The authority you will have"—he paused—"the cooperation may be harder to attain, but God will supply grace to your sisters through your submission to His will."

It was then that she unconsciously raised her eyes and saw the painting of the Virgin on the wall. Mary was not looking at the Child in her arms but beyond Him. She had known even in His infancy that He must leave His hidden life with her and face the passion. Mary had breathed in the suffering. Mother Praxedes turned to the Bishop.

"Your Grace," she said, "I will accept." She paused, her voice grew softer. "I say yes only because I cannot say no."

For a moment he did not speak.

"That is my answer, Mother. You will be given the cross of office this afternoon. I will get out a letter in the next day or so announcing your appointment and giving the sisters my reasons."

He stood up. Slowly she arose.

"Is there anything I can do for you, Mother?"

"If I could have your blessing, Your Lordship?" Her voice was low.

As she knelt, he raised his hand in benediction. She did not see his hand tremble or know that there were blisters of perspiration on his forehead.

Mother Praxedes did not realize then that Bishop Byrne was literally bestowing on her a lifetime of crosses. Had she been aware, her hesitation might have been prolonged to refusal. The blessing of the future was in its obscurity. She felt as if she were blind.

At the very moment, a conversation was going on in the convent across the court that would have shaken her decision.

"I think it is quite clear what is happening," a tall, slender nun said with a nod of her head.

"Well, it's plainly in opposition to Father Nerinckx's wish that we always elect our own Mother Superior."

"I can't see how Mother Praxedes would be a party to such an arrangement. I always heard what a good religious she was."

"Oh, my dear, even the best can fall when a little authority is in question. Who could resist such an offer?"

"But it isn't like her."

"From what I've heard about her," another added, "she is the kind to take over. I heard from someone in Las Cruces—and not a sister either—that she practically ran the parish there. Worried the poor pastor until he built a new church. Why she even blessed religious articles! Of course, I'm not sure that part is true. It seems unbelievable, but I do know for certain that she took up the collection right during the Mass."

"No!"

"Yes, and you know, of course, that she just took the business about Loretto Heights right out of the council's hands. She just told them she'd take care of it."

"I can't believe she's like that. Mother Cecilia always spoke so highly of her. She was related to her in some way, you know."

"You'll see, Sister. She has been a superior all her religious life. It's second nature. She loves power."

"Well, I don't envy her."

Similar conversations, some more pointedly critical, others skeptical, were to follow rapidly upon the official announcement of her appointment, but the final conclusion was always that hers was not an enviable position.

Mother Praxedes followed the Bishop to the parlor door. Her throat was tight, every swallow requiring effort. Neither of them spoke as they walked down the hall.

"I'm going over to the priest's house. I will see you after dinner." He started to open the door, then he paused. "Don't worry, Mother. God will see us through. He has already answered the big prayer."

Mother Praxedes waited in the doorway, purposely allowing him to go on. She could not be alone too soon. Somehow she could not bear to hear another word—not now. She had to think.

As soon as Bishop Byrne was out of sight, she descended the cement steps and followed the walk to the chapel door.

Inside, she genuflected; she felt her legs tremble. Kneeling in the back pew, where she had knelt just an hour before, she found her whole body trembling. Closing her eyes, she felt the beat of her heart in her temples. The nerves in her arms and hands seemed to flow with tension. Had her hands been clenched so tightly? She could not remember. She could not remember anything.

The new Mother Superior . . . Mother Catherine has suffered . . . you are the only woman . . . like leading the blind . . . after dinner . . . the cross . . . don't worry. "What have I consented to do?" she whispered.

"Mother Praxedes?" a voice beside her asked.

She turned, and there in the aisle stood a sister who was perhaps sixty, her face drawn, and deep circles shadowed her eyes.

"Yes?"

The sister closed her eyes and drew a deep breath. The sister opened her mouth but Mother Praxedes could not tell whether she had said something or whether she had only made a little sound in her throat.

As Mother Praxedes tried to stand, the sister walked away from her and down the middle aisle toward the altar. Mother Catherine! That must be Mother Catherine. Suddenly she had the desire to call out to her.

Mother Praxedes followed her out of the chapel. She must try to help her.

"Mother Catherine?" she called, her voice a strained whisper.

The older nun turned. She did not speak. Her face showed her suffering.

"I am so sorry, Mother. Could I do anything for you?" Mother Praxedes asked.

"No, dear, you are the one who needs the prayers. You will

have a hard time. They will never accept an unelected Superior General."

The next two days were a nightmare. Mother Praxedes was officially installed in office, too dazed to see or to care that many faces were hardened against her. She heard the name of Father Lassaigne mentioned, and something about blessing religious articles. On Saturday when the Bishop asked whom she would suggest to take over her office at the Heights, the only name that came to her was Mother Francisca. Then he decided that Mother Catherine should replace Mother Francisca in Santa Fe. When told, Mother Catherine asked to leave quietly before many of the sisters knew she was going. Although Mother Praxedes walked with her to the carriage, she had two other sisters accompany her to the station. Somehow she knew that Mother Catherine would be relieved to be out of her company. Mother Praxedes was too overwhelmed with the gravity of the whole situation to guess or to wonder what Mother Catherine really thought of her having accepted the Bishop's appointment to succeed her.

"Mother," Bishop Byrne said, when they met on Sunday to outline the work ahead, "I think it might be better to ask the whole council to resign."

"Oh, Your Grace, no more resignations. Please. I am sure that Mother Placide and Sisters Winifred and de Sales will do everything in their power to help us solve the difficulties."

"Well, perhaps, but you do not know them; they do not know you. I think they feel that Mother Catherine was treated unjustly. Somehow I don't think we can expect them suddenly to change their way of thinking. However, we'll see, but the vital thing right now is for you to return to wind up your business at the Heights. Mother Francisca must understand all the details about the interest on the loan. Then you can go down to Santa Fe. I am not too sure that Mother Catherine is in the right frame of mind to assume responsibility there, but you can see when you get there. When you return, I will have the first drafts of the Constitutions finished for you to consider."

Before leaving for Denver, Mother Praxedes went to the infirmary to find Mother Dafrosa.

"Sister, where will I find Mother Dafrosa?" she asked a little sister carrying a tray.

"Oh, Mother, right there. The second door. I think she's alone."

Near the window, its sill lined with geraniums, sat the still figure of an elderly nun. Her hands lay motionless in her lap; twined about her fingers were the black beads of a rosary, which caught the morning sunshine in slivers of light. Mother Praxedes stood for a moment watching the dozing figure. Time had not changed her physical appearance as much as Mother had expected; and yet, she was undoubtedly an old lady now.

Mother Dafrosa turned, blinking her eyes. "Is someone there? Come, come in, child."

Mother Praxedes crossed the room and knelt on the floor beside her.

"Pull that chair over, child, and sit down." The voice was thin but sweet.

Mother Praxedes pulled over a straight-backed chair, feeling a little tremble of emotion in her stomach.

"My memory is not so good, Sister. You'll have to pardon me if I ask your name."

Mother Praxedes wanted to say that once they had had quite a time deciding it, but instead she said, "I'm Sister Praxedes."

"Sister Praxedes," she repeated. "Oh yes, Sister Praxedes. She went to Santa Fe. Now let me see. Oh yes, she went with—now let me see—she went with a bishop."

"Bishop Salpointe," Mother Praxedes offered.

"Yes, that's right. She went with him because she was not too well. We thought the West would help her." Mother Dafrosa paused. "But you can't fool me. You aren't Sister Praxedes." She got a new glint in her eyes. "You are *Mother* Praxedes. Oh, dear child, what have they done to you?"

"I'm not too sure, Mother," she answered softly.

"Well, dear child, God will work it out. The Bishop is a good man. He means well. It is just that there are some things he does not understand."

"Do you mean Bishop Byrne, Mother?"

"Oh my no, not the young bishop, the old bishop, Bishop McCloskey. The one in Louisville. You'll meet him. Just wait."

"You had some trouble with him, didn't you?"

"Oh yes," she nodded her head. "But I was too old and too sick to do much. You know, Mother, the Irish are of only two kinds—the fighters and those who won't fight. I was never a fighter."

"Maybe a different kind of fighter, Mother."

"As I said, the Bishop is a good man. A very learned man in fact. When he would get started with his theology, I was no match for him. You younger people know more about those things. But, Mother, dear child, be careful. Be careful. It is so hard to know what is right when people in authority do not understand."

Mother Praxedes did not say anything for a few moments. Then she asked, "How are you now?"

"Oh, the dear Lord takes good care of me. Yes, indeed. I have many hours to talk to Him. At first I used to find it hard not to be busy doing many things, but then I found out that I can keep as busy as anyone by praying, praying."

"You will have to pray much for me, Mother."

"Oh yes, and especially for one thing in particular. You will have to suffer much before you see things set in order. There will be many to criticize. Our Dear Lord was criticized and if you are a friend of Jesus and Mary—how that phrase kept coming back to her—you are bound to suffer criticism too. But it isn't in adversity that you will need my prayers. You'll stay on your own knees as long as the troubles come. It is when the clouds are gone and the sun comes again that you'll need the warm rain of prayer. Many of us can suffer, but in your position you will have to live with success too. Success can be hard on sanctity, Mother Praxedes. But have faith and serve. This is, after all, His work."

ST. LOUIS, MISSOURI—1897

"What time is Mr. Wade coming, Mother?" Sister Antonella, Mother's secretary, called from the doorway.

"One o'clock, Sister. Mrs. Wade is coming too. They are taking us to see some property out by Forest Park."

"Fine! I should have time to finish another letter before they get here."

Mother Praxedes smiled to herself. It was refreshing to have such energy around. Sister Antonella reminded her of an ant, always intent on business, always heading every way at once.

Lately she had felt that she herself was headed every way at once. This was already May; for six months she had been living here in St. Louis, trying to get all the property consolidated, and where had she gotten? Mother Francisca had said it would be risky to move her headquarters here. Mother Praxedes could remember just where they had been standing and just the way Mother Francisca had said it.

Mother Praxedes had said, "What would you say if I told you that I intend asking the council to approve making St. Louis my temporary headquarters?"

"I'd say that it's practical but—"

"But what?"

"Risky."

"What do you mean?"

"Oh, I don't mean that it is risky to ask. That is no problem. It would certainly be better until all the property is evaluated. St. Louis is more centrally located, but anything that is a change just now is bound to draw criticism."

"No criticism could be worse than what I've had," she remembered saying.

That had been on September 15. Everything seemed to promise a bright future. Bishop Byrne had just distributed copies of the revised Rule. The Sisters had filed up to the altar where he sat to receive their pledge of obedience. She had felt so safe because he was to stay on as Ecclesiastical Superior and everyone seemed to have accepted the new council which he had appointed. She could thank God for that. What would she have done without Mother Francisca's loyalty. But how little I knew, she thought, about criticism!

She knew now that it would be years before some sisters would forget what they could only see as injustice to Mother Catherine. The poor tormented soul. Mother Catherine had lasted only four months in Santa Fe, five in Pueblo. Each time it had been the same. Her insistence that she was still the rightful Superior of the Society was disturbing to the sisters. Now she was at Florissant. The poor woman would probably go to her grave convinced that she had been wrong in resigning, sure that she had neglected her responsibilities. Mother Praxedes did not know what else could be done.

Mother Praxedes closed her eyes, trying to close out the worry over Mother Catherine. There were still the irritating matters connected with Loretto's financial status. After six months what had she accomplished? In January she had written to all the Loretto-owned houses in the Society asking for exact appraisals of equipment and property; but the answers were so slow—and many times so incomplete. She knew the sisters were overworked and that many of them had no idea about evaluating property; but she had to have everything under corporate ownership or they would never be able to move ahead with any new schools, to say nothing of keeping the present ones.

That was still the problem with the Heights. The two-year extension on the loan was up and she still could not show on paper that they had sufficient assets to guarantee the investment. There was always the possibility that the company would call for payment before she could actually meet it. In time, the Heights would pay for itself; but until it could, she would have to keep borrowing.

Here she was over a year Mother General and still taken up with the problem of financing Loretto Heights, the same problem which got her into this job in the first place.

She had spoken to dozens of investment brokers here in St. Louis. Mr. Papin had tried to negotiate a loan from England—the interest was too high. Mr. Kingsley at Penn Mutual in Denver had almost settled a deal—the board of directors vetoed the loan. She had tried Mexico again—the rate of exchange was still too low. She had spent two days in Milwaukee—the answer: no extension. Always she ran into the same old difficulty: not enough security.

Maybe this jaunt out into the country would do her good. She was losing her perspective. After all, she reminded herself, the work of the sisters was education, not finance. She picked up the copy of the course of studies which Mother Francisca had prepared for the young sisters studying at the mother house. She knew Bishop Byrne would be pleased. It was splendid, she thought. He had suggested not too long ago that she go to Philadelphia to see one of the normal schools there. Maybe she would. "I can't forget everything else while I look for money," she told herself. "After all, these are Your buildings," she said to God. "You have to open doors or I am locked out, totally helpless."

She thought she had heard the doorbell. She got up from her place behind the desk and walked to the front window. She couldn't see anyone. Maybe it had been her imagination. Looking at Pine Street she could not help but notice how the neighborhood had run down since her childhood. She glanced at the old house. It seemed impossible that no Cartys lived there any more. When David died suddenly only a year ago, Kitty and Delia had moved to Carondolet. Standing at the window now, she realized that that house and this house where she stood—this small compass of Pine Street—had been the scene of exodus for all the people who had constituted her world: Maria, Papa, Mama, John, and David had all died in that house; Sister Cecilia had died in this house.

"Mother, Mr. Wade is here," Sister Antonella said from the doorway.

"I don't see his carriage. Don't tell me we're going to walk!" she laughed.

"He's at the side entrance. Are you wearing gloves?"

"Naturally," Mother's voice rose with pretended surprise. "We must look stylish when we ride through Forest Park."

Festus Wade stood almost statuelike with his tall gray hat resting against the wide lapel of his gray suit coat. "He's my idea of dapper," Sister Antonella had said after the first time she saw him. "He's my idea of ingenious," Mother thought now. Mother Praxedes had learned enough about this young business genius to know she was right. One day he had been in a talkative mood and she had found out why he was so involved in so many business ventures at thirty-eight. "I was wrapping bundles at Crawford's before I could reach the counter," he had said.

"Good afternoon, Mother Praxedes. I think we're early. Don't hurry."

"I'm not hurrying. I am just anxious to see what a good buy you have for me."

"You'll like this location, I think," he said as he opened the door and waited for the two sisters to step outside. "It is out of the business district, not too far from transportation, with a good view of Forest Park. By the way, Mother, I brought Kate along today."

"Oh, I'm so glad. How are the children?"

The carriage driver helped Mother in, then gave Sister Antonella his hand. Festus Wade climbed in and seated himself across from Mother and next to Mrs. Wade.

"Mother Praxedes, it is good to see you again. I hope you don't mind my barging in on a business affair." Mrs. Wade smiled, and Mother noticed how pretty her eyes were.

"I'm delighted that you wanted to come. How are the girls? Did Marie get over that cold?"

"Oh yes. She's fine. Mother, you can settle an argument. Festus says that someday Forest Park will be in the heart of the city. Do you believe that?"

"Oh, I'm sure he would be the one to say about that, but if the prediction is for the next ten to twenty years, I wouldn't want to build there."

As the carriage moved west on Pine Street, Festus Wade listened to Mother's description of what she wanted. "I'd like a place that will still be residential thirty or forty years from now. Our academy in Florissant is ideally located as a boarding school. What I would like is a place out from the city in order to attract boarding students; yet sufficiently close to make commuting possible for those who wish to live at home."

"That's a big order, Mother, too big for the particular location I had in mind. What you need is a place in Webster Groves," he said, laughing. "That's a good fifteen miles from town."

"Fifteen miles," she repeated. "Would it be too much trouble to ride out there now?"

"Why, Mother, I was only joking. Webster Groves is a country town! Not even two hundred families live out there."

"Is there any transportation?"

"Well, the Missouri Pacific Railroad goes through there, but I—"

"Mr. Wade, could we ride out to Webster Groves this afternoon?"

"Certainly, but I don't have any property out there. A few weeks ago Ben Webster, a lawyer friend of mine, was saying something about thinking he might sell his farm out there; but I don't know how serious he was."

"I'd like to see it. We can look over the Forest Park district on our way back, or is it even in that direction?"

"It wouldn't be out of our way." Mr. Wade picked up the tube and told the driver to go straight through the park and out to Big Bend Road. "Ben Webster's farm," he said.

"I doubt that anyone but the caretaker will be around, but you can get an idea of it."

As they got out into open country, Mother said, "I'm still interested in city property, Mr. Wade. Just before you came, I was looking at the neighborhood there on Pine Street. It's rapidly becoming a commercial area."

"You're right. Many of the homes are already boarding and rooming houses. That's the first step. Everyone seems to be moving to the west end."

Mother looked out at the rolling fields. St. Louis always seemed so flat to her, but the countryside around it really wasn't. She wondered if the house on the Webster farm would be large enough to start a school. Maybe they wouldn't even need to build right away. She smiled inside; she was getting a little ahead of herself.

"By the way, Mother, how are you coming along on your Denver property?"

"Not too well. Mr. Papin is still trying, but so far we've had nothing but refusals. However, I still have hopes."

The carriage continued out Big Bend Road for well over an hour. Finally they came to a stop and the driver called down to Mr. Wade that he wasn't sure which way to go.

"It's just up a bit to the right. That's Big Bend Road," he said, pointing to the left. "It runs along the back of Ben's place. Let's go in the front way."

The carriage started again and as they ascended the hill, Mr. Wade explained that if they all watched to the left they would see the house through the trees. "It's a nice-looking place."

Mother Praxedes watched closely and finally she could discern a whiteness beyond the trees. She watched, and as they turned into the drive she got a full view of the three-story, white frame house. This is just the place, she thought to herself.

The carriage stopped at the front door. From the general appearance of the house, the closed shutters and the dust on the porch, it was evident that no one was there.

"Looks like no one's here, Festus," Mrs. Wade said.

"I'm not surprised. I guess Ben doesn't even keep a caretaker here any more. Let's get out. I know Ben won't mind if we look around."

This is just the place, Mother Praxedes was thinking again. A large house, pretty good acreage, magnificent old trees. "Are there any other buildings on the property?" she asked.

"As I remember, there is a barn and a greenhouse in the back."

The party of four walked around the house. Although the grounds were generally well kept, the flower beds had not been weeded.

"This just might make a good place for a school," Mr. Wade said, looking up at the side of the house.

"There's the greenhouse," Sister Antonella said.

"And that must be a coach house," Mrs. Wade added.

"Well, what do you think of a place we may not even be able to buy, Mother?"

"I think it just might be what we want, Mr. Wade; however, I would want to see the inside and the other smaller buildings. How much land does Mr. Webster have here?"

"I really don't know, but I can find out."

"Do you think, provided, of course, that he wants to sell, that we could get it for a reasonable price?"

"Well, I don't know that either. Ben is a shrewd businessman. If he knew you intended making it into a school, he might ask a pretty penny for it."

"It's up to you to drive the bargain, Mr. Wade. You know what I can pay. I'm sure that if Mr. Webster is thinking about selling, he would be willing to let you have it."

"Could we walk down to the barn?" Sister Antonella asked.

"Yes, let's do," Mother agreed. "We would have to use some of these outbuildings. Perhaps the coach house could be turned into a music conservatory."

"When do classes begin?" Mr. Wade teased.

Mother Praxedes just smiled.

In late December of the same year, Mother Praxedes sat alone in her Pine Street office watching the snow fall. Inadvertently she sighed. The plans for the new school, to be called the Loretto Seminary, in Webster Groves were coming along fine, but she still had nothing but failure to show on the Loretto Heights property. Lately she had begun to think that this was the cross that jeweler had once predicted she'd carry through the streets of St. Louis. It was not just the present failure to get money to pay off the mortgage that disturbed her, but rather it was that such a failure meant for the future. With the approach of the twentieth century, educators were predicting undreamed-of expansion in education. And from the way things looked, Catholic education was going to be right in the midst of it. New academies and perhaps even colleges would be in the offing. How could the Sisters of Loretto meet this challenge if they had no way of financing new buildings? They had started the normal school to prepare the sisters to be better teachers, but teachers needed schools.

Two words kept going through her mind: *double security*. That was what every company that had refused asked: double security. And we have it, she thought. We have triple security, but it just isn't available yet.

The evaluation of the Society's property was a slow, slow process. Some houses had replied with all holdings well itemized, but in other cases there were difficulties in clearing titles and locating deeds. The maze was unraveling but it seemed so slow.

"I'm too impatient," she said audibly. "Give me more faith."

Just then there was a knock on the door.

"Yes, come in," she said.

"Mother," Sister Antonella began, "I have the tickets for Loretto!"

"That's fine, Sister."

Sister Antonella smiled. "Won't it be good to be home for Christmas?"

"It will. I wonder if they'll recognize us, we've been gone so long."

On Christmas Eve snow began to fall just as the sisters were going to night prayers. By the time prayers were over, the ground was white and Christmas was in the air. Mother Praxedes shivered slightly as she ascended the stairs to her room. This was the kind of night to form ice on the water pitcher. It hadn't been her imagination; Kentucky cold did have long penetrating fingers that reached into the bone.

She opened the door. The lamp on her desk was already lighted and a small fire was burning in the fireplace. Weary, she decided to sit by the fire for a while before going to bed. On the mantel over the fireplace were branches of evergreen with three red candles at the center; a wide green bow decked the base of the tallest candle. Mother looked at them and smiled. Then she closed her eyes for a moment. In a matter of a few days, 1897 would be gone, she was thinking. She opened her eyes, watching the flames lick at the crumbling logs. Time crumbled that way too. A year and a half had crumbled that way and still the financial problems were not solved.

Strange isn't it, she thought, that we who vow poverty should be so concerned about money; and I guess people looking at schools like the Heights think we are well-off. They don't realize that what they see exists for others; no one sees the simplicity of the sisters' quarters. Which is all right, except that when we ask for loans, they somehow think that it is for ourselves. But she knew she must not show resentment; she must not allow herself to feel resentment. It was only relative. Eventually it would work out if He wanted it to.

As Mother Praxedes sat there, she was keenly aware that saving buildings went with saving souls. It isn't buildings for buildings' sake; it is a matter of a place to impart truth. Not only truth about God, but God's truth. How the world needs to know, to know everything to be known. Christ, who called Himself Truth, meant, she was sure He meant, that the more of truth, all truth, that man knows, the more of God he knows.

She glanced again at the candles and the evergreen on the mantel. Christmas, she thought. A time of rebirth. "Oh, how I need a rebirth. A rebirth in You. I feel that I've been away, away from more than the physical Loretto. I've been wandering around like a blind woman. How long has it been since I just sat down and looked at You? If I weren't so convinced that serving others is serving You, I could not go on because I seem to have so little time to pray, so little time to collect my thoughts, to sort motives, to weigh values. Let this Christmas be a revival, a new beginning. Don't let the work You have given me shut You out." She glanced down at the bright red of the two embroidered hearts on the cape-like front of her black veil. The firelight made them almost brilliant. "They mean a great deal. They mean I am Your friend. Don't ever let me forget."

She smiled to herself. Sometimes she found herself growing so eloquent within that the words spilled out. Had she been talking aloud? Walking across the room to turn down the lamp on her desk, she knew that all was not dark. They had thirty-five young sisters preparing to teach. Mother Francisca was expecting to have the oral exams soon after Christmas so Mother Praxedes could be there. No doubt the poor young things would prefer that Mother Francisca not try to arrange the exams that way, but Mother Praxedes felt sure that they would do well in spite of her presence.

The days of Christmas week bounded by. It was good to see the novices come into the chapel, to hear them singing Christmas hymns. Mother had many letters to answer and many sisters to see. The normal school exams took hours, but still she found time to walk down to the cemetery each morning before going to work. She had to keep reminding Father Nerinckx that he had lots to do for them in heaven.

One morning as she walked briskly down the path, snow piled on both sides, she looked up suddenly to see Old Tim, the man who cared for the grounds, throwing bread crumbs on the snow for the birds.

"Mornin', Mother," he called, doffing his brown work cap.

"Good morning, Tim. St. Francis would be proud of you."

"Yessum, Mother. This snow is a fright to little birdeens."

"Why, Tim. Sure and I haven't been hearing anyone say birdeen since St. Patrick left Ireland."

"Ah, Mother, that's the pity of things. Not enough good Irish blood around to keep up our thoughts of the Emerald Isle."

Mother smiled. "Well, Tim, when you want to be talking about Ireland, come up to me office," she said.

Tim laughed and rubbed his mittened hands together. "That I'll do, Mother. And may the blessing of Himself be on you."

"Thank you, Tim, and God go with you on this holy day," she answered; and turning, she continued down the path to the cemetery. "May the blessing of Himself be on you," she said as she walked.

ST. LOUIS, MISSOURI—1898

Thin rivulets of heat rose visibly from the sidewalk as Mother Praxedes and Sister Flaget approached the office of the Anderson-Wade Realty Company at Eighth and Locust. It was a hot day, a hot June day in St. Louis.

Glad for the less oppressive heat of the office building, Mother Praxedes smiled at the young woman behind the reception desk.

"Go right in, Mother," she said. "Mr. Wade is expecting you."

Mother knocked lightly on the door, then opened it.

"Come in, come in." His voice had a genuine quality of good humor. Rising to his full stature behind the paper-littered desk, he indicated two chairs to the left of the desk, which had evidently been placed there in anticipation of their arrival.

"Mr. Wade, this is Sister Flaget, who will be in charge of the school in Webster Groves."

"I am happy to know you, Sister. Won't you both be seated?" Then, turning to Mother Praxedes, he asked, "How are things coming in Webster?"

"Fine. School will begin in September."

"I think I have a little news for you, Mother. It is rumored that your sisters are going to be asked to staff the parish school out there too."

Mother glanced at Sister Flaget. "It's no longer rumor but fact, Mr. Wade. We've been asked and we have accepted."

"Grand. I'm glad to hear that. By the way, Mother, have you reached the end of your rope in the Loretto Heights affair?"

"Yes! And I'm about to tie the knot on it."

"What do you mean?"

"I mean we finally have a loan."

"May I ask who has had the foresight to set you up?"

"A bank in Amsterdam."

"You don't mean it!"

"In a few words, when I was at the mother house for Christmas, Bishop Byrne mentioned that he had heard about a bank in Amsterdam which could possibly help us. Since a priest friend of his was then planning a trip to Europe, we asked him to make an investigation for us. In March I received a wire from the Bishop's friend saying that he could get the money if I cared to delegate him to act in the matter. Yesterday I received the bonds. My principal reason for coming to see you today was to have your notary to witness my signature on them."

"Mother Praxedes," he was unusually serious, "couldn't you wait a few days before signing the bonds?"

"Wait? Why should I wait? I've been almost two years trying to get this money."

"I know. I realize what this means to you." He hesitated.

"I'm very anxious to be finished with this matter, Mr. Wade."

"Oh, I realize that. Of course, you would be. Naturally." Again he hesitated.

Obviously, something was on Festus Wade's mind. She could not figure out why he should be bothered by this. He above all people knew how many fruitless attempts she had made to get a loan.

"What seems to be troubling you? I thought you would be relieved too."

"No. On the contrary, I am disturbed. I think that we should never let an American woman be forced to go from our country to get a loan."

" 'Forced' is indeed the word, Mr. Wade. I've tried every American source possible. But as long as we get the money, it doesn't much matter to me which country it comes from."

"It matters to me, Mother Praxedes." He actually sounded indignant.

He stood up. "Will you excuse me? I'll try not to be gone too long. Please wait here." At that, Festus Wade grabbed his straw hat from the rack in the corner, plunged it on his head, and stalked out of the room.

"Where do you think he's going?" Sister Flaget asked.

"I have no idea, but you can be sure that it has something to do with those bonds. I've never seen him so determined. As long as he wants us to wait, we might as well finish deciding on the rooms. Where were we?"

"On the library." Sister Flaget took a rough sketch of the floor plan of the Webster house from her pocket. "Where do you think the library should be?"

Both sisters grew silent as they looked at the pencil markings which indicated the location of classrooms and living quarters for the sisters.

"If we use this large room on the second floor for the chapel, the only other place for the library is here on the first floor," Sister Flaget said, pointing to a rectangular marking on the first-floor plan.

"That's right, Sister. Write library in that space then. The arrangement that thrills me is the music conservatory in the coach house. It couldn't be better if it had been built for that purpose. Sister Mary Albert is pleased too."

By the time Festus Wade returned, mopping his perspiring brow, Mother Praxedes and Sister Flaget had already planned their Loretto Seminary in the air.

"I see you have been busy while I was gone. I'm sorry to have kept you waiting, but I think you'll be glad to hear what I've been doing. Do you have those bonds with you?"

"Yes. Here they are," and she handed him a large brown envelope.

"Mother Praxedes, if you don't mind, I'll put these in my safe for a few days. I just spoke to Judge Madill over at the St. Louis Union Trust Company. I think he is willing to meet the terms made by the firm in Amsterdam."

"Why, he doesn't even know what the terms are! Mr. Wade, I appreciate your interest, but this loan is final as far as I am concerned. All that is needed is my signature on the bonds."

"I know, but Judge Madill agrees with me that we would be guilty of a grave injustice to allow you to get help from abroad."

"I don't feel that way about it. I'm so relieved to be getting this matter settled. I haven't the slightest ill feeling toward the many people I have contacted. The reasons for refusing us were sound. I couldn't have offered sufficient security; however, our property has been put under the name of the Loretto Literary and Benevolent Institution—doesn't that sound elegant?—so I feel sure that some of those same banks would reconsider now."

"Mother Praxedes, won't you do me the personal favor of not signing these bonds today?"

"Mr. Wade, if you put it that way, why of course I'll wait for a few days."

"Let me put the bonds in my safe." He took the folder, and, going to the door at the far end of the room, asked his secretary to place them in the safe. "You won't ever sign those bonds, Mother Praxedes."

Mother Praxedes was more adamant in her decision than Festus Wade knew. Even after an interview with Judge Madill the following day, at which he offered to meet the terms from abroad, she was not inclined to turn down the other offer. She returned to Loretto and called a meeting of the council. The final decision would be theirs.

"Only one thing makes me think that perhaps we should accept this new offer," she said finally, after voicing her opinion against accepting. "The day is coming when we will want to build in Webster Groves. If we have the backing of the Union Trust Company, we will have local investment behind us. Judge Madill and Festus Wade are being generous and both consider this a personal favor. Perhaps, under these conditions, we should accept."

Bishop Byrne was inclined to think that, under these conditions, they should accept the Union Trust's loan; consequently, the council decided to cancel the loan in Amsterdam and to accept the other. As a result, the bonds were issued to be effective July 1, 1898.

"This bond issue is a feather in your cap," Bishop Byrne remarked to Mother Praxedes as he looked over the papers. "I'm afraid that you have endeared yourself to the hearts of your sisters. You will hardly be able to escape election on the sixteenth."

The Bishop's words caught her unaware. Oh, he couldn't mean that! She was counting on being relieved of this office, on having some of those responsibilities lifted, on returning to a more peaceful way of life.

The Bishop did not look up, but continued to scrutinize the sheet of paper before him. After several moments, he realized that she had not answered.

"You don't look pleased about it."

"Should I be?"

"After all you've gone through!"

"Oh." She smiled. "Of course I'm pleased about the loan. I thought—"

"I see, we were thinking about two different things. You mean the election. Frankly, I think you might as well face the fact."

There was no response again. What was to be said?

"As I see it, Mother Praxedes, the election won't even go to a second ballot. Two years ago you were the only one to hold this office, and right now, even though things have been set in working order, anyone else would have a frightful time carrying on. The chapter is bound to recognize that."

Mother Praxedes made no reply. Bishop Byrne was voicing what she would not allow herself to consider.

"One thing worries me more than the possibility of my being elected, Your Excellency."

"And that?"

"Who will take your place as Ecclesiastical Superior?"

Now it was his turn to be silent. After a moment, he said, "That is impossible to predict, Mother; but if you are re-elected, I have no fears for Loretto. I feel sure that Bishop McCloskey respects your ability."

By the end of the first week of July, the first of the twenty-one sisters chosen by their communities as electors began to arrive at

Loretto for the General Chapter. When the date for this election, July 16, 1898, had been set by Cardinal Satolli two years before, it had seemed a ridiculously long time to wait; now in retrospect it was a short time to everyone except to those who had carried the burden of office.

The evening before the retreat, preparatory to the election, Mother Praxedes stood on the walk beside the chapel talking to Mother Francisca and to Mother Rosine. Mother Rosine had just arrived as a delegate from the convent in Colorado Springs.

"Did you know that Mother Francisca was my mistress of novices too?" Mother Rosine asked Mother Praxedes.

"Really?"

"The youngest and the most determined novice I ever had." Mother Francisca smiled.

"I'm afraid to ask how you would have described me." Mother Praxedes raised her eyebrows and sniffed.

"That would be too hard," Mother Francisca came back at her.

Sister Ita interrupted the conversation to ask if she might see Mother Praxedes privately for a moment.

"Of course, dear. Will you excuse me?" She glanced at Mother Francisca and Mother Rosine.

"I feel that the Holy Ghost will be with us during the election," Mother Rosine said to Mother Francisca now that they were alone.

"Oh, Mother, pray that He is!"

"These two years have been hard for Mother Praxedes, haven't they?"

"No one knows. I marvel at her ability to seem so free and relaxed when I know she can't be. She certainly has deep faith. That is the only way I can account for it. The obstacles that Mother Praxedes has surmounted in these two years took nothing less than the kind of faith that Our Lord said would move mountains."

"Mother Francisca, you amaze me!"

"I do?" she asked.

"I've never heard you wax eloquent over anyone else."

"Ah, but there is only one Mother Praxedes!"

On the last evening of the retreat, the night before the election was to begin, Mother Praxedes walked toward the cemetery. "God doesn't expect us to cast away plain sense and live on the moon," the retreat master had said several times during the retreat. And for some reason the words kept gnawing at her consciousness.

Looking through the silent guard of trees that lined the path to the cemetery, she could see the sky, a glow of red far beyond the fields. The whole earth seemed to be hushed as if stunned to find day over. She sighed. "God doesn't expect us to cast away plain sense and live on the moon."

As she walked, another thought came to her. A thought she had had to chase away repeatedly this past week; and yet, it kept coming back. Sometimes when she knelt in chapel early in the morning, other times when she was just dropping off to sleep. At unexpected moments, she would remember New Mexico—the rolling desert, the towering mountains, the lilt of Spanish voices, the feel of a grimy little hand in hers. If she failed to catch the thought, it formed a question, a question always unanswered. Tonight she did not stop it. Tonight as she walked, she let the question take words. When? When could she go back to New Mexico? When could she return to the children? Were they never to be hers again? Was she never again to share the light of wonder in eyes that mirrored discovery? There are hundreds in my family, Mother Bridget had said many years ago when Susan had asked a question. And there are hundreds in mine, too—she knew—but couldn't some of them be children?

"God doesn't expect us to cast off plain sense and live on the moon," the priest had said. She looked away from the sky to find herself already at the cemetery gate. One hand reached out automatically and the gate creaked on its hinges. She stopped and looked across the rows of white crosses. Is the Southwest my moon, she wondered. Tomorrow I could be the person I was. Teaching, cooking, planting—that was the real Susan Carty. Tomorrow I could be going west to live again, free of buildings and loans, free of making decisions and deciding for others, of sometimes feeling forced to take care of God's worries.

Once more she had started to walk, a bit more quickly now as if trying to chase away something she did not want to feel. Standing at the foot of Father Nerinckx's grave, she looked down at the date, 1824. He had been dead seventy-four years. The Society had multiplied and spread since then. So many sisters! Then she thought of the election. Three more years if she were elected tomorrow. Three more years of interpreting the Rule, three more years of travel from house to house, of money, of begging. She looked at the sky again. The glow was almost gone now. It is still light in New Mexico, she thought. Looking away from the western sky and back at the sanctuary of Loretto's dead, she thought of Father Nerinckx again. Once he had been asked to take a bishopric, but he had begged to remain a common missionary. He wished no position of honor. His request had been respected. But to whom could she appeal? God knew, but would He save her from this? "Plain sense," yes, plain sense told her that she could not escape this. But again she wondered, who would take Bishop Byrne's position as Ecclesiastical Superior? Plain sense also told her that his revision of the Rule had not taken care of all the possibilities for disagreement if Loretto got a difficult Ecclesiastical Superior.

Walking with the dignity that was natural to her, in some ways she seemed older than just forty-four. Her countenance, her whole bearing showed a maturity that was responsibility-formed, a maturity that recognized that the future of Loretto was, by far, more important than where she lived or what she did.

The next day she had forgotten the feelings which had done battle in her heart. There was reality to face here on this planet, and she faced it. The only change in the members of the council was Mother Rosine's election as treasurer. Mother herself, Mother Francisca, and Mother Laurentia were all elected to the offices they had held for two years by appointment. Now at least they had the assurance that they had been chosen by their own sisters.

"It looks as if the Southwest has come east to stay," Mother

Francisca said to Mother Rosine, who still seemed stunned by what had happened to her.

"Well, if we live long enough, Mother, perhaps we'll all get back there before we die." Then she added wistfully, "I always told myself not to get attached."

"Did you take your own advice?"

"No, I just let myself fall in love with everything about it."

"Well, to tell the truth, I think God wants it that way. As long as we are willing to give it up when the time comes," she added.

"I've heard Mother Praxedes say that she belongs to the adobes of the Southwest. I wonder if she, too, ever longs to return."

With this election Bishop Byrne's term as Ecclesiastical Superior ended. Now again, according to the Rule, the right to appoint his successor reverted back to the Bishop of the diocese in which the Society had its mother house. Anxiously, then, Mother Praxedes and her three assistants waited to see who would be appointed for this delicate office, an office which, judiciously handled, would be advisory rather than administrative. On August 12, the answer came.

Mother Praxedes sat at her desk staring at a letter from Bishop McCloskey. Mother Francisca, standing next to her, looked pale, her lips pinched with concern.

"This will put the Society right back where it was two years ago," Mother Praxedes was saying.

"I'm afraid I do not understand why you are so opposed to this Father Gambon as Ecclesiastical Superior."

"Mother Francisca, reinstating him in the position which Bishop Byrne asked him to resign two years ago puts us where Mother Catherine and her council were: we must do business with Bishop McCloskey through a man whom past experience has proven incapable. If we are to have any conflicts of opinion with the Bishop, I would by far prefer to deal with him directly. From everything Bishop Byrne could find out, Father Gambon had no concept of the obligations of an ecclesiastical superior to further the well-being of the sisters. Bishop Byrne saw him as totally incapable and I trust the Bishop's judgment."

"What can you do?"

"I shall have to see Bishop McCloskey personally and tell him that we will not accept this man." Mother Praxedes let the letter slip from her fingers. "How would you like to join me in a trip to Louisville?"

Miles are measured in myriad ways, but on that warm August day of 1898, Mother Praxedes measured them in half-sentences of prayer. She had thought over her objections so well that to rehearse them was unnecessary. However, to object to any act of authority, no matter how trivial, could never be an easy or a pleasant task; but to object to the act of a bishop previously antagonistic to her sisters, and about a serious matter, was a bitter business which even she found hard to take calmly. Too soon she found herself in the Bishop's residence. Then like a confused and disconnected dream, she found herself going through the motions of an ordeal that could not be true except that the cold sweat on her hands was so real.

When she entered the Bishop's study, a priest was there. Although she did not think she had ever seen him, she knew instinctively—maybe it was by a gesture of the Bishop, that this was Father Gambon. She asked that she might see the Bishop alone, but he said—yes, she was sure he had said—that whatever she had to say could be said in the presence of the priest. So, fully conscious that the man she had come to denounce was listening, she voiced her objections to his appointment.

"I regret that I must speak in this way, Your Excellency; but in conscience I cannot stand by and see a situation arise which cannot but take us back to the troubled times from which we are just now emerging. I am sure that Father Gambon himself realizes that it just would not work. I am sorry, Father."

When she found herself void of words, the Bishop continued to stare at her. Without a question or a comment, without an indication of compliance or disapproval, he dismissed her as he might dismiss a chronic complainer, and turned to the priest.

Relieved to have the ordeal over—yet stunned by the Bishop's attitude, she left the room. Arriving at Cedar Grove Academy, she asked if she might lie down.

"Never have I had to do anything like that. When I saw that Father Gambon was there, I asked the Bishop if we might speak privately, hoping to save the priest the embarrassment; hoping, too, that I might get a chance to really talk to His Excellency; but I think he knew what I wanted and perhaps thought that I would not speak about it in Father's presence."

"But he gave you no satisfaction. Will he do anything?" Mother Francisca was worried too.

"I don't know, but I think I should write immediately to the Apostolic Delegate and send Bishop McCloskey a copy. One of the last things Bishop Byrne told me was to keep the delegate informed about any difficulties that might arise."

"But Cardinal Satolli has been replaced."

"Yes, but I am sure the records are there. Surely all of Bishop Byrne's letters and recommendations are filed there in Washington."

Within six days Father Gambon resigned. With no time to feel the relief of this, another appointment followed which was almost as impossible. A young priest who could have no knowledge of the administration of a religious community of women was named to the office. Again Mother Praxedes objected to the Bishop and to Cardinal Martinelli in Washington. Finally, on August 26, a third appointment came from the Bishop's office: Reverend Henry Westermann, an experienced priest, well respected in the diocese, a man who Mother Praxedes felt confident would work well with them. For the first time in two weeks, Mother Praxedes could relax and turn her mind to other matters.

Within a few days Loretto had settled back to its quiet way of life, with the chapel bell marking the hours. Day followed day with the steadiness that only God-ordained regularity can have. September brought earlier sunsets and less-warm evenings; September carried letters concerning the opening of another school year; with September came the arrival of new aspirants to the religious life, postulants in search of a life with God. Some seemed to be mere children; others were more mature. Some had never known any sisters other than Lorettines; some had never met a Sister of Loretto until they arrived. But all were important to Mother Praxedes. And now, at last, she felt that she could take time to welcome them to Loretto herself.

The lawn was flooded with sunshine the September morning that Mother Praxedes walked from the chapel out onto the lawn to meet Dorothea Norton, a young lady from Chicago, a young lady who had only heard of the Lorettines.

"Miss Norton," Mother said, taking her hands, "welcome to Loretto."

"Thank you, Mother." The young lady looked even more petite than she was standing next to Mother Praxedes.

Sensing that Dorothea was a bit excited, Mother suggested that they sit for a little while on one of the green benches near the sidewalk that ran from the drive to the chapel. "It's lovely out of doors this time of the year."

As they walked to the bench, Mother recalled the Jesuit's letter of recommendation. "An able secretary," he had called her.

"How was your trip from Chicago?"

"A very warm one, Mother." Glancing around, Dorothea smiled and said, "This is a beautiful place. I've always wanted to live in the country."

As they sat chatting about the Jesuits they both knew in Chicago, especially Father J. R. Rosswinkel, through whom Dorothea had first heard about the Sisters of Loretto, the young lady remarked, "Father Rosswinkel paid many compliments to your sisterhood, Mother Praxedes. Among other things, he said that it is a product of our own American soil, and it had no old-world ideas to outgrow. He said that he felt it has preserved its original spirit better than any community he knows."

"That was very kind of Father," Mother answered, wishing that Bishop McCloskey thought the same thing.

"I have a letter for you from Father. It happens to be in my baggage; but when my things are brought from the station, I will give it to you, Mother."

After the young lady had been whisked away to the postulants' quarters, Mother Praxedes turned toward the convent. Perhaps there was time for a visit with Mother Dafrosa. Two items in the morning mail would interest her. She really ought to tell Mother Dafrosa about Father Rosswinkel's compliment, no old-world ideas to outgrow. Mother Praxedes smiled.

Mother Praxedes passed the chapel, turned right, and walked to the convent door. The infirmary rooms were to the right of the entrance, close enough to the chapel for those who could make some of the spiritual exercises.

The door to Mother Dafrosa's room stood open. Mother Praxedes could see her seated near the window. Mother knocked.

"Come in! Oh, Mother Praxedes, dear child, come in." Mother Dafrosa attempted to stand, but Mother Praxedes restrained her. Without a word Mother Praxedes pulled over a chair and sat in front of the elderly sister.

"How are you, Mother Dafrosa? Did you get my message last week?"

"Yes," and she shook her finger at Mother Praxedes. "But don't send any more like it. I'm quite aware that you haven't a minute to yourself. I don't expect you to be coming over all the time, so don't you think about it." She patted Mother's hand. "You look tired. Are you well? You know you have to be careful."

Mother Praxedes laughed. "Oh, I'm fine. I have several bits of good news to share with you. First of all, Sister Flaget wrote that they have sixty pupils at Webster Groves." Mother Praxedes reached into her pocket, drawing out several letters with a rubber band around them. "Here's her letter. She says, 'The enrollment has—' I told you that. Oh yes, 'Only God knows what good this school may do.'"

"That's fine. I like to hear that our sisters are spreading their talents to new places."

"And then I received this yesterday. It's a copy of a report from the United States Indian Service." Mother Praxedes unfolded the single-page report. "Would you like to read it?"

"Oh, dear child, you read it to me. With my old eyes, I'll miss half of it."

"It is a copy of a report by a Mr. Charles Burton made to the United States Indian Service in regard to the Indian girls boarding at our school in Bernalillo. He says, 'I noted with pleasure the peculiar excellence of that school. The teachers are careful and painstaking, and the children are remarkably bright, clean, and attractive. The intellectual advancement of the children is beyond that of any of the schools under my care. The buildings are ample, clean, and well cared for; the grounds are very attractive. The superintendent, Sister Margaret Mary, is a woman of fine attainments and excellent character and possesses great executive ability. I, therefore, take great pleasure that the contract be increased from thirty-four to seventy-five children.' And then he signs his name."

"How fine! God knows it is time the government did something for the poor dispossessed Indians."

"Mother Dafrosa, there is so much to be done in New Mexico; and yet, I think our sisters are doing more than they realize. The exams to renew state certificates for those teaching in the public schools are coming up again. I'm hoping that every sister gets a first-class certificate this year. Teaching in the public schools in New Mexico is really the only way to help educate the very poor."

"Did the sisters take them when you were out there?"

"Oh yes, even those of us who didn't teach in the public schools took them to give the people the assurance that we were qualified teachers. I can't remember if I first took them in '80 or '81."

"But how do the sisters live on the meager salary the state pays?"

"They manage, Mother. There are always generous people who give us things."

"Mother Praxedes, dear child, you miss the Southwest, don't you?" Mother Dafrosa patted her hand again.

"Yes, but I think it is a selfish missing. I cannot tell you what it is to work with people who so warmly respond to love. Mother

Dafrosa, when a little Spanish American loves you, you can feel it all the way into your own heart. I'm afraid I like that kind of love." She smiled.

"You shall go back." Mother Dafrosa nodded her head. "You shall go back a hundred times in the sisters you will send there. True, someone else will feel the love that is returned; but the love will be yours all the same."

ROME, ITALY—1903

"I always suspected that there must be some place colder than Kentucky in the wintertime," Mother Praxedes said as she put another bundle of fagots into the squatty, black stove in the middle of the stone floor.

"Sunny Italy?" asked the sister rooting through the trunk at the foot of one of the room's two iron bedsteads.

"Next time we come to Rome, we will make sure it is sunny," Mother said, laughing. "And I hope we won't have to try four convents before we find one that will take us in." Turning around, she watched Sister for a moment. "Sister Wilfrid, what *are* you doing?"

"You'll see." When Sister seemed on the point of toppling head first into the trunk, she stood up again. "Here it is! My new watch pocket! After bringing it five thousand miles, I'd never be able to explain to the poor novice who made it that I didn't wear it the day I saw the Pope." Sister Wilfrid seemed to glide from one end of the room to the other as she finished dressing.

Mother Praxedes smiled. No wonder the novices enjoyed this waspish little woman, part poet, part wit. Walking over to the awkward table at the far end of the gloomy eighteenth-century room, Mother Praxedes placed her new, black silk gloves on it. She glanced again at the last paragraph of the letter she had been reading.

> It may have escaped you that the report to be made in view of a final approbation of your Rule must be signed by the Bishop of the diocese in which the Motherhouse is located, as a certificate of its correctness and exactness. As I have not seen one single item of the report, especially that regarding its financial condition, I cannot lend my name

to any recommendation that might be interpreted by Rome as an approval of all you say in the report. You will pardon me, then, if Rome expects from me more than a mere perfunctory letter of recommendation.

Mother Praxedes did not doubt Bishop McCloskey's words at all. She knew that his years as rector of the North American College in Rome had made him keenly aware of Rome's way. She also realized that his statement sounded highly reasonable. Of course, he could not be expected to endorse recommendations he had not seen. But surely Bishop McCloskey knew as well as she why her letter to him had been only a gesture. Cardinal Martinelli, whose advice she had taken in coming, knew too. If Bishop McCloskey had formerly forced both Mother Dafrosa and Mother Catherine to withdraw appeals to Rome, obviously he would never have sanctioned her request.

"How do I look?" Sister Wilfrid asked as she swung around. She was as small of stature as Mother Praxedes was tall.

"Simply elegant." Mother laughed.

Sister Wilfrid frowned. "I have a suspicion that I look no more handsome than I did yesterday when it took me only fifteen minutes to dress."

"Well, Sister, the Holy Father will never know. Do you have the admission card?"

"Right here. I was just thinking that it's a month today that we sailed from New York."

"So it is. But somehow Christmas doesn't seem four days away." She had lost all sense of time during the last six months. So much had happened. "If you are ready, we'll start. Father Lanciotti expects us to meet him by two-thirty."

Although the ride to the Vatican was short, it took half an hour because every pedestrian along the way decided to cross the street in front of their carriage.

"It was good of Father Lanciotti to make the arrangements for us," Mother Praxedes said.

"We will have to write to Sister Josepha and tell her that her kindness to a sick seminarian years ago has returned a hundred-fold."

Stepping from the cab, Mother Praxedes greeted Father Lanciotti. "Will we have to wait long, Father?"

"Oh no, His Holiness keeps strictly to schedule. There is no diplomatic margin of fifteen minutes at the Vatican. Our audience is for three-fifteen and it will be three-fifteen."

Having been admitted to Vatican City by the Swiss guard at the outside gate, the party of three found themselves mounting many marble stairways, meeting at each landing another Swiss guard in yellow and black who raised his white-gloved hand at sight of the card. On the upper floor of the Vatican palace they began walking from one suite of rooms to another, where an usher in livery conducted them silently from one door to the next, where they were in turn met by another usher.

Finally they entered a large room more richly decorated than any of the others through which they had passed. Four guards wearing rose-colored damask and quilted satin, looking like figures from a storybook kingdom, eyed them and bowed courteously. A stately gentleman in black evening suit with a white cravat came forward to greet them. He spoke softly to Father Lanciotti, who whispered in turn to Mother Praxedes that they might take off their shawls and leave them there.

When they were ready, the gentleman, who they learned was Pio Centro, a favorite domestic of the late Pope Leo XIII, and now in the service of Pius X, showed them to the next room. He indicated three brilliant red velvet chairs which faced a rose-colored plush throne, trimmed in gold, above which hung a canopy of the same color.

As they seated themselves on the red velvet chairs, Sister Wilfrid looked at Mother Praxedes and wondered if she had noticed the pendant chandelier which hung like a cluster of jewels from the frescoed ceiling. Mother Praxedes was too busy sorting through the events which had brought her here—events which made a personal appeal to Rome imperative. How much could she tell the Holy Father? Should she mention that not since that day almost five years ago when she had to reject Father Gambon's appointment in Father's presence had Bishop McCloskey accepted her appeals for an audience? No, that was petty in itself. That did not constitute any major problem although it had made understanding considerably more difficult. She would say only as much as the Pontiff asked. Oh, but she hoped he would ask many, many questions.

They had just caught their breath when a door opened. Was the Holy Father coming? They turned as a short man robed in purple entered. It was Monsignor Bisleti, Maestro di Cámera, who, as he smiled, beckoned for them to follow him. Opening a door that led into a still more private room, he told them that His Holiness would see them in just a moment.

Instinctively, Mother Praxedes' eyes looked toward a door on the far side of the room. As she looked, a figure clothed in white entered. She knelt. This was indeed the Vicar of Christ. Her heart hammered in her ears. She was thankful to be on her knees for she found herself trembling.

His Holiness came forward and extended his hand, which bore the green emerald of the Fisherman. Mother Praxedes caught her breath. Bowing her head, she kissed the ring. Then the Holy Father raised his hands and blessed her. While he blessed Sister Wilfrid, Mother Praxedes found herself thinking over and over, "Thank you . . . Thank You!"

When they had greeted His Holiness, he invited them to be seated. Monsignor Bisleti put everyone at ease by reminding His Holiness that Mother Praxedes had come to Rome to receive papal approbation for the Rule of her society. Although the founder, Father Charles Nerinckx, had had the Rule temporarily approved in Rome by Pius VII in 1816, no final papal approbation had ever been received for the original Rule or for any of the many revisions made through the years. Monsignor explained to His Holiness: repeatedly in the past four and one half years conflicts have arisen between Mother Praxedes and the Bishop as to who holds the final authority over internal matters in the Society. Is it the elected

Council of Sisters headed by Mother Praxedes or the Bishop? Although Monsignor spoke in Italian, Mother Praxedes, with her knowledge of Spanish, was able to follow. She watched the Holy Father closely as the Monsignor spoke.

Pius X listened attentively. When he paused, His Holiness turned to Mother Praxedes. "And you have letters of recommendation from the bishops in whose dioceses your sisters work," he said solemnly. "I have looked them over; I note that one from the Bishop of Louisville does not sound so good for you."

As Father Lanciotti translated these words to Mother, the Pontiff looked at her with a hint of a smile. Then he told the monsignor to ask Mother to tell him something about her community.

The Holy Father listened as she told him that there were almost six hundred Sisters of Loretto teaching in the central and southern parts of the United States as well as others in the Southwest, where their work was with the Spanish-speaking people. Ours is an educational apostolate Mother said. She paused and Monsignor Bisleti translated for His Holiness, who nodded his head, signifying that he understood.

"So many schools; so much good to be done," the Pontiff murmured.

Mother Praxedes prayed that he would ask more about their trouble with the Bishop. She could not very well return to the matter unless he asked. There was more he should know.

The Holy Father began paging through the papers which Monsignor Bisleti had handed to him. Perhaps something there would bring more questions. At last he said, "That is fine. Father Lanciotti will see that these are referred to the Propaganda as soon as possible."

Mother Praxedes took the papers again. She and Sister Wilfrid knelt to receive Pius X's blessing, which he extended to the members of their families and all of Loretto's sisters and novices in America.

His Holiness then left the room to greet other visitors and the little company of three retraced their steps through the many galleries and down the countless flights of stairs. There were no words to speak.

Standing outside the gate to Vatican City, Father Lanciotti asked if they would care to visit Saint Peter's.

"Yes, Father, we would. We must thank Our Dear Lord for the graces we have just received."

"They must surely be praying for us in America," Sister Wilfrid added.

"Have they no idea when Father Lanciotti expects to return?" Mother Praxedes asked Sister Wilfrid as Sister entered the room which had been both office and bedroom for them for almost a month.

"No, Mother, apparently he thought he would be gone only a week. Each time I inquire they say 'maybe tomorrow.'"

"They have been saying 'maybe tomorrow' for two weeks, and it had been three since we saw the Holy Father. It's the tenth of January and we've done nothing."

Mother Praxedes crossed the room for the third time. Sister Wilfrid looked at her helplessly. She had never seen her distraught before.

"I have to do something, Sister. If Father Lanciotti isn't here by Monday, I'm going to see Cardinal Satolli. We are wasting precious days."

"Mother, please don't worry so. Everything will be all right."

"I must talk to someone who can advise me. The Superior here thinks it would be improper to go to Cardinal Satolli directly; you think we will hurt Father Lanciotti's feelings if we don't wait. In the meantime, we have no idea what kind of communication may have been sent from Louisville about us."

"Mother, everything will be all right."

"Sister Wilfrid, if you say 'everything will be all right' once more I think—well, please don't."

Mother Praxedes crossed the room again. "Sister, why don't you go with Mother Fidelis to visit St. Maria Maggiore? There is no reason for two of us to wait for Father. I must write to Mother Francisca anyway."

When Sister Wilfrid was gone, Mother felt ashamed that she had jumped at her. This delay wasn't Sister's fault any more than it was Father Lanciotti's fault that he had been called back to his mission in Mentorello before he had time to deliver their papers to the Propaganda. But waiting might be serious if Bishop McCloskey were to protest to the Propaganda before her appeal was in. What would prevent the Cardinals from viewing her as a rebellious religious who wanted personal power, and, therefore, felt it necessary to shake off the jurisdiction of her Bishop?

A letter from Mother Francisca had added to her fears. Mother said that Father Riley, the chaplain at the mother house, was telling the young sisters that Mother Praxedes was in Rome without proper permission, and that she would never be successful. Of course, she thought, how is he to know that I came on Cardinal Martinelli's advice? "But maybe he is right. Maybe I won't be successful."

Well, she would wait until Monday. If Father Lanciotti did not return then, she would go directly to Cardinal Satolli, risking a breach in diplomacy. But would Cardinal Satolli recall their previous difficulties? It had been almost eight years since, as Apostolic Delegate, he had appointed Bishop Byrne to revise Loretto's Rule.

Father Lanciotti did not return on Sunday; so early Monday morning Mother Praxedes sent a message to Cardinal Satolli. His answer came immediately. He would see her that afternoon.

"Sister Wilfrid, you stay here in case Father Lanciotti comes. If he does, explain to him that I have been terribly upset about the delay. Ask him to wait until I return. Cardinal Satolli said that he would see me at two. I'm sure that it won't take more than an hour. And pray. Go to the chapel and beg Our Lord to help me. Pray that I'm not making a mistake. Ask Him to help the Cardinal remember us and our previous troubles."

"Will Mother Fideles go with you?"

"Yes. Fortunately she knows the Cardinal; so, at least, he will know that I come in good company," she said as she put several more papers into the portfolio.

As the two sisters rode to the appointment with the Cardinal, Mother Praxedes turned to the English nun who somehow seemed like an old friend already. "I was just thinking that I don't know where I would be if you hadn't taken us in that rainy night."

"You were drenched, weren't you? Rome does nothing by halves. Even a rain is a deluge."

"And no room for us. You cannot imagine how depressing it was to go from convent to convent and find no room."

"I am sure God wanted you to find the Little Helpers of Mary, Mother Praxedes. I am glad that no one would take you in."

They rode along in silence for a few minutes. Neither could bring herself to speculate on what might happen when they reached the Cardinal's residence.

"Have you gotten any reaction from your sisters at home about the change in the style of your veil?"

"No, that will come when they receive the letter I am sending this week; but if I know women, there will be more talk about putting a few inches of stiff lining in the veil than over getting the decree."

When they reached Cardinal Satolli's residence there was no delay. He was expecting them.

"Your Eminence, this is Mother Praxedes from the United States of America," Mother Fideles said in her well-chiseled English accent.

"Yes, we are old friends; but I did not expect to find you halfway around the world, Mother. Don't tell me that you are in Rome trying to borrow money for your Colorado property. We are very poor here, you know," he said, as he motioned for them to be seated.

After eight years he had remembered! He remembered even that! "No, Your Eminence, but I must admit that I have made other debts since then."

"Ah! That's the sign of a good religious administrator! Won't you both be seated. What can I do for you, Mother? You did not leave America just to spend a miserable winter in Rome."

"Your Eminence, I am in Rome to present our Rule to the Propaganda."

"Oh, you have come to Rome to get the final approbation!"

"Not exactly, Your Eminence, I have come to Rome to have it revised and then, I hope, approved."

"Oh?" His voice rose.

"Your Eminence, our Rule is not clear on the matter of administrative authority. We have had more difficulty with the Ordinary of Louisville."

"You do not agree with Bishop McCloskey on some matters?"

The mention of the Bishop's name surprised Mother Praxedes. How much did Cardinal Satolli know about this? Had he perhaps heard from Bishop McCloskey?

"No, I don't, Your Eminence; but that is not my reason for wanting the Constitutions changed. Our work is being hindered by the Rule and a religious Rule is intended to further God's work. Our present Rule states very explicitly that every house, no matter where it is located, is under jurisdiction of the central council; but in another place all purchases and real estate transactions come under the board of trustees, which is presided over by the Bishop of Louisville or a priest appointed by him. You can see the problems which could arise when we need permission to expand our work in other dioceses."

"But, Mother Praxedes, isn't your community a diocesan community subject to the Bishop?"

"No, Your Eminence. We were founded in Kentucky when Bardstown was the episcopal residence, but within ten years we had gone to places in Missouri which were in the diocese of St. Louis."

"Do you have a copy of your present Rule?" he asked.

She opened the portfolio, which contained all the papers that Father Lanciotti had intended presenting. She handed a small book to the Cardinal. As he read the first page, Mother Praxedes glanced at Mother Fideles. Cardinal Satolli looked away and then back at the book.

"Mother, you are certainly correct about this matter of administration; but it only makes it clearer that your community comes under the jurisdiction of the bishop of Louisville."

"Well, then it mustn't, Cardinal Satolli!" Suddenly she realized that this was the man she had to win or her cause was lost. "Unless we can get Rome's protection for our work, our community is going to be stifled. Our whole pioneer spirit will be lost. Our Society is going to be forced to split into little autonomous communities. We can't refuse sisters and houses in other dioceses in favor of Louisville without incurring the displeasure of other prelates and without severely limiting our work. I know Father Nerinckx intended our work to be missionary, to go any place we were needed. This way the whole idea of our foundation will be lost."

"But, Mother, Father Nerinckx is dead and things have changed."

"Then are you suggesting that I am wrong in trying to get Rome to give us approval as an exempt community?"

"No." He smiled; after a pause he went on. "I think you are right and a very brave woman. I will do whatever I can to help you."

Riding back to the convent, Mother Praxedes seemed reluctant to talk. Finally she said to Mother Fideles, "Do you think Cardinal Satolli had heard from Bishop McCloskey?"

"Oh, I doubt it, Mother. If he had, I believe he would have mentioned it. Don't worry, Mother. Cardinal Satolli could not doubt that your interest is any but serving your community."

"I should have softened my words, I suppose; and yet, after debating my position for so long, I feel sure that I must fight for this. A hundred times I have asked myself: should I accept disagreement with the Bishop as God's will? Should I be resigned to things as they are? Am I wrong in fighting God's authority in this man? But always I have concluded that to curl up and refuse to defend our position would be unfair to the sisters I represent and to the people we serve." She looked out the carriage window. "Sometimes it is harder to fight, Mother."

Mother Praxedes turned toward Mother Fideles again. "That has been part of my problem, too," she said. "You see, Mother, I know that I am strong willed. I know that I am, after all, a stubborn Irishwoman. There has always been the personal battle within myself, the battle not to let this become a conflict of personalities."

"That could hardly be possible since the Bishop has not, as you say, even consented to meet you face to face for years."

"Oh, I am not sure that that alone would prevent the personal from entering in."

Mother Fideles could not restrain her curiosity about one thing, so she asked, "I suppose you have been criticized by the very blind you have tried to lead?"

Mother Praxedes did not answer directly. Instead she said, "Eight years ago a very dear sister, who has since gone home to God, told me that criticism goes with being a friend of Jesus and Mary. That is why these hearts must mean a great deal or they mean nothing." She ran the slender forefinger of her right hand over the red embroidery on her veil.

Sister Wilfrid's heels made a quick, definite click on the stone floor. Reaching the door, she turned. "It is a relief to know that you are on the mend, Mother." She opened the heavily carved wooden door. "I'll be back at six," she said.

Mother Praxedes shifted in the high bed on the far side of the room. Even my attack of appendicitis has not hampered her gadding about, Mother thought. And right on top of the thought she laughed at her nice bit of Irish self-pity. "Thank the Lord," she finally said aloud, "that one of us can forget these agonizing days of delay."

She closed her eyes. What was the date anyway? Thinking back across the haze of weeks, she tried to separate the days since January, when she had seen Cardinal Satolli. Perhaps her worries now were as groundless as those concerning the Cardinal had been. Even Father Lanciotti had said on his return that they couldn't have contacted a better person than the Cardinal. But why all these weeks of continued delay? The canonists were being so careful, but so slow. Was it possible that, after all this, Bishop McCloskey would succeed in stopping them?

She thought back to Mother Francisca's last letter. Each day now seemed to bring word of another place where Father Riley had stopped in his tour of the Loretto convents. From the questions he was asking, in the interest of Bishop McCloskey, it was evident that he was trying to sow dissatisfaction. He was obviously not simply a mother-house chaplain on a spring vacation. Everything concerned finances. In Kansas City he questioned the workmen about the cost of the new academy. In Colorado Springs he told the young sisters that Mother Praxedes had mortgaged the mother house. "Who does she think she is? Rothchild's daughter?" he had exclaimed. If he kept up these tactics, her authority to be an effective leader would surely be frittered away, no matter what the Roman decree said, before she could even return to America.

What *was* the date anyway? She had had the attack on April 15. On the seventeenth Sister Wilfrid had checked the translation with Father Esser, one of the canonists; the next day Sister had visited Cardinal Satolli and Cardinal Martinelli. Yesterday Father Lanciotti had stopped on his way to Mentorello. Then this was the twenty-first, April 21. She took a deep breath. Even thinking tired her. How many more days would they have to wait? No matter what else happened, she was going to make the trip to the Holy House of Loreto near Ancona. Even if the legend that the small house there was Our Lady's home which had been carried by angels were only a pious tradition, the simple faith of the thousands of pilgrims who had sought consolation there for over six hundred years made the place holy. Yes, she would go to Loreto, Italy, to pray for her Loretto, Kentucky.

As Mother Praxedes planned her pilgrimage high into the mountains above the Adriatic, Bishop McCloskey arrived at the Loretto mother house in the hills of Kentucky.

"This makes the third visitation he has conducted since we came into office," Mother Francisca was saying to Mother Rosine as they met to decide what they should do.

"And not even one when Reverend Mother was here," Mother Rosine added.

"Sometimes I think he must be afraid to face her."

"Well," Mother Rosine said, wrinkling her nose, "I'll tell you *I* don't relish meeting *him*."

"I'll welcome it." Mother Francisca underlined her words with a lift of her head. "I intend to tell him exactly how difficult he has made Mother Praxedes' job."

Without delay Bishop McCloskey began sending for the sisters, from the eldest to the youngest novice; but he did not send for Mother Francisca. Some sisters were asked if they knew what Mother Praxedes was doing in Rome. Others were asked if they knew when Mother Praxedes would return from Rome. Several were told that she would never succeed. Mother Rosine was asked the nature of the telegrams she had sent to Mother Praxedes. But still Mother Francisca was not called. Three weeks passed. Tension grew. One by one the sisters came to Mother Francisca to report what they had been asked, but still Mother Francisca was not called. Abruptly Bishop McCloskey returned to Louisville. On May 24, Mother Francisca received an overwhelming list of recommendations from him. They ranged all the way from instructions to send out the announcement for the coming election for the positions of Mother General and her council, to a request that a younger sister replace the acting mistress of novices, to such details as removing the overseer, Mr. Elder, from residence in the priest's house.

"What did you answer?" Mother Rosine sounded almost frantic.

"I took each item, one after another, and said that I would do exactly as he requested; but I told His Excellency that I did *not* think it necessary at this late date to countermand Mother Praxedes' appointment of Sister Joanna as acting mistress of novices. I reminded him that Sister Joanna is some years younger than himself. I also asked his pardon if I seemed to express myself rather freely since I had not been granted the privilege of speaking while he was here."

"Oh, Mother Francisca, everything seems to be falling apart," Mother Rosine lamented. "Father Riley has been asking again at the telegraph office to see messages from here. Oh, I wish Mother Praxedes were here."

"Did you hear someone knock, Mother Rosine? Come in," Mother Francisca called.

Sister Antonella glided into the room, waving a piece of paper. "Mothers, look what I have. Mr. Riggs just called it over from the station. It's a cablegram!"

LORETTO CONFIRMED FOREVER. SAIL FOR HOME PRINCESS IRENE MAY 27. MOTHER PRAXEDES.

LORETTO, KENTUCKY—1904

Stunned, still trying to fathom the cause, trying to determine an answer, Mother Praxedes sank to her knees. Her head throbbed, she had not slept all night. Some place in the haze of the chapel, she heard a sob. What had she done to her sisters? She who thought she saw so clearly, she had been the blind one. Why had she not fought her way in to him when he refused to see her and to receive the decree? Perhaps with God's help she could have made him see that she was simply trying to save Loretto. The feeling of failure made a knot of her heart. She could not restrain her tears. At last she wept. She wept all the unshed tears of the last eight years. The decree—the work of so many months of anxiety—had made no difference. If anything, she thought, it has made things worse.

When the moment for the priest's communion came, the great silence of the chapel grew thunderous. Each sound as the Host broke in the priest's hands lashed across her heart. Strange that now as Christ's body was being consumed, taken from them—strange that now, almost for the first time, she realized what His presence really meant.

Kneeling there through the agonizing minutes as Father Werner devoured Host after Host, eating Life itself, she could hear the words spoken just before he had commenced the Holy Sacrifice. "Because the council has disobeyed the Bishop's orders, Loretto is being placed under interdict. I have been instructed by the Bishop to say Mass and to consume the Sacred Species."

As Christ's life ebbed away, leaving them helpless, desolate, and alone, she weighed again the question of disobedience. What could he mean? True, she had reinstated Mr. Elder in the priest's house because he was the only one she could rely upon to answer important phone calls at night; but that certainly was not cause for an interdict. Then why, she pleaded to her God, whom she felt was departing.

In the haste of these days since her return, had they failed somehow to inform her of something the Bishop wanted done? She was sure Mother Francisca had looked after everything. No, it was her own fault; her own courage had failed. She should have demanded to see him when he would not receive her. She should have put an end to this game of blindman's buff which they had played so long.

When the Mass was over, the Eucharistic Christ was gone. Gone, too, was her feeling of confusion. She knew now that she must take some final and decisive action.

Mother Praxedes left the chapel. Mother Francisca followed her. In a few seconds, the four council members were a black cluster of concern.

"What is the disobedience?" Mother Rosine asked.

"I don't know."

"Why not ask Father Werner, Mother. He is still here."

"He doesn't know. Last night when he told me that he had received these instructions from the Bishop, he said that no explanation had been offered."

Mother Francisca looked worried. Finally she said, "Perhaps this is my fault. Perhaps my refusal to appoint a substitute for Sister Joanna is the disobedience he means."

They all looked at Mother Praxedes. Could that be it perhaps?

Mother Praxedes grasped Mother Francisca's arm, almost as if she were trying to support herself. "Mother Francisca, it could be that. It could be Mr. Elder's return. The particular reason doesn't matter. I cannot help but think that all this could have been avoided had I insisted that he see me when I returned from Rome."

"But what could you do? You went twice. You asked for an appointment. If he didn't want to see you, you couldn't force yourself in."

"Yes, I could have, but I was afraid. But the only thing to do now is to act."

"Couldn't you telegraph Cardinal Satolli in St. Louis? Maybe it is providential that he is in the United States now when we need help," Mother Francisca suggested.

"Yes, or I could go to the delegate in Washington." She hesitated. "We seem to be starting all over again, don't we?"

They stood almost transfixed. Mother Rosine and Mother Laurentia were too dazed to offer any suggestion. They had all been so jubilant, so confident only two weeks before when Mother had returned with the decree; now all joy seemed so far away.

"What do you think about asking Dom Obrecht, the Abbot at Gethsemani, what we should do? He is close by and he would be able to advise us without fear of incurring the Bishop's displeasure."

"Oh, that sounds fine!" Mother Francisca's voice was still strained.

Later that same morning Mother Praxedes sat before Dom Obrecht, head of the Trappist monastery of Our Lady of Gethsemani, hearing herself rehearse the events of the past six months. Even as she spoke it seemed incredible. Had all of this actually happened? Was this she speaking? Occasionally the Abbot would ask a question. When she had finished, he did not speak. He was silent for some moments; then he said simply, "I could go to Washington for you. This has to be presented to Monsignor Marchetti, but it would be bad for you to leave your sisters. You have already been away too long."

"But, Dom Obrecht, I cannot expect you—"

"I know, but God sent you here for help and since we are dealing with a man who is, I'm afraid, too old to be really responsible for his actions, this is a very delicate situation. An interdict is a serious punishment, used only for the gravest wrongs."

The Abbot was silent for a few minutes again. Then he added, "Monsignor Marchetti will need to understand everything that preceded this interdict so I want you to go back to Loretto and gather together everything you can. Get a statement from the man at the station about Father Riley's requests to see telegrams. Also a transcript of the talk the Bishop gave before he concluded the visitation. Have Father Werner write out what he was instructed to say. Then write to Bishop McCloskey requesting a specific statement of the reason for the interdict. We will need that, too."

Mother Praxedes returned to Loretto. First she wrote to the Bishop requesting the reason for depriving one hundred eight persons of the Blessed Sacrament. "Even if the council were guilty, the penalty seems to be quite disproportionate to the offense and includes the innocent as well as the guilty. If it can be proven that the council has done anything contrary to ecclesiastical rights, we desire to know it. If it cannot be proven, we protest against this injustice and therefore hold you responsible for all the lost graces, Holy Mass and the Sacraments."

When the letter had been posted, she began collecting the data which Abbot Obrecht had requested. This took several days; but, in the meantime, Mother Rosine came over from the post office with a letter from Louisville. Mother Praxedes recognized the wild flurry of the Bishop's handwriting, the handwriting which was more familiar than the man himself.

Mother opened the envelope carefully, unfolded the letter, and read aloud the one long sentence. "You having disobeyed our decree regarding the removal of Mr. John Elder from the priest's house by reinstating him and that after Mother Assistant had obeyed our decree, we have withdrawn Very Rev. Father Riley and we hereby forbid any ecclesiastic whatsoever to offer up the Holy Sacrifice at Loretto without our permission in writing. With respect—"

"That is all?" Mother Rosine asked.

"Yes, that's our answer." Mother put the letter down. She turned toward the window, but without looking out she turned around again. "I think we had better have a short meeting right now. Mother Rosine, would you ask Mother Francisca and Mother Laurentia to join us as soon as possible?"

While Mother Praxedes waited for them to come, she realized that she would have to ask Mr. Elder to vacate his quarters again.

She could have another telephone put in this building; but so often the chaplain was away and when they had laymen as guests, who would act as host? She shook her head. That wasn't the real problem. Such petty vexations and all for no reason!

When Mother Praxedes had read the Bishop's letter to the whole group, she said, "I see nothing to do just now but to ask Mr. Elder to move again, but I feel that we should definitely protest Father Riley's return."

"I certainly agree!" Mother Francisca said. "His requests at the telegraph office alone require it."

"And all the things he said when he went around to our houses all over the country!" Mother Laurentia, usually so quiet and peaceable, sounded almost angry.

"I think we can all understand that, since the Bishop had appointed him Ecclesiastical Superior, he felt such actions were within his province, but now with our new Constitutions no such office exists. But even to have Father return as chaplain would be impossible for him and for us."

The decision was to protest Father's return. Mother Praxedes wrote:

> In reply to your favor of the 24th instant just received, I beg to state that Mr. John Elder will be removed this afternoon from the priest's house, as you decree; but the council emphatically protests against the return of the Reverend J. H. Riley as either chaplain or confessor to our community, for he has both publicly and privately been undermining authority and has sown discord and dissensions among the sisters."

With no word about removal of the interdict, Mother Praxedes wrote to Monsignor Marchetti, informing him that Dom Edmond Obrecht would soon leave for Washington in Loretto's behalf. In closing her letter to him, she mentioned another decision which the council had reached concerning the forthcoming general election. "As our general election will take place next month and our Constitutions give us the privilege of holding it elsewhere than in the diocese of Louisville, we find it expedient to do so."

On the morning of June 29, Mother Francisca brought the mail to Mother Praxedes' office. She hesitated in the doorway and glanced again at the letters she was carrying.

"Oh, Mother Francisca, come in. I didn't see you there."

"I think you are getting more copies of that same letter," Mother Francisca said, as she placed the stack of envelopes on the desk in front of Mother.

"Evidently the Bishop did send a copy to every Loretto convent." She opened one. Yes, a duplicate of Bishop McCloskey's announcement of the reason for the interdict.

"Mother Praxedes, this interdict must be ended!"

Mother Praxedes looked at Mother Francisca. She sounded almost panicky.

"Sit down, Mother Francisca. You look tired." Mother Praxedes shuffled through the rest of the letters but she did not open any others. "Mother Francisca, do you sense a spirit of dissatisfaction in all these letters being sent to me?"

"Well, Mother, I am afraid I do. I've been hesitant to add to your concern, but I think that this interdict is seriously undermining your authority. I suppose you've heard the rumor that, while you were in Rome, a group of our own sisters—probably those who never forgave you for 'what you did to Mother Catherine'—sent a petition to someone in Rome condemning you personally. I'm afraid this interdict, publicized by the Bishop's letter, has revived that same spirit of—of revolt. Oh, Mother, if we don't get rid of this interdict soon, I'm afraid some of the sisters might turn against you to your face."

"What more can I do? Dom Obrecht leaves this afternoon for Washington. It may be days before we see any results."

"I know; but—oh, Mother, here's what I mean. One sister came to me this morning. She said that she honestly felt that by your going over the Bishop's head (that's the way she put it) you have put the community into an impossible position in the Louisville diocese which could only lead to our being forced to leave Kentucky. She says that some of the sisters think you are actually planning to move the mother house to St. Louis since you want to have the election at Florissant. In a few words I showed what I thought of her disloyalty to you; but, Mother, that doesn't solve the problem. My greatest fear is that we will have some defections from the community unless this trouble with Bishop McCloskey stops."

"I know you are right. And I can understand why some sisters feel this way. What else could be expected? But I am absolutely helpless at this point. I have done all I can. I even wrote to Cardinal Satolli yesterday. We must pray that Dom Obrecht is successful in getting the interdict lifted. God can't abandon us now, not after all we've been through."

Mother Francisca looked at her. How could they not trust her? How could anyone speak against her after all she had suffered for them?

When Mother Francisca was gone, Mother Praxedes decided to walk down to the cemetery to visit her friends there. As she started down the stairs, the chapel bell tolled the hour. She said the aspiration Father Nerinckx had given them. "O Suffering Jesus! O Sorrowful Mary!" Then like an echo out of the past, she remembered the words, her own words, "Bells a bother or bells a blessing." It was all in having God's point of view. She realized now, walking along protected by the canopy of Loretto's elms, that at fifty the lessons of twenty are at least half learned. Perhaps that was what old Moira had tried to explain when she had said that it was not everything that God kept from her eyes. How differently most things looked from the side of age.

Mother Praxedes knelt by Father Nerinckx's grave. She prayed for his soul. Then she thought how differently he had handled opposition. He had chosen not to fight. He had let them take the sisters from him. He had willingly gone into exile. And she? Mother walked to Mother Dafrosa's grave. She, too, had chosen not to fight. But Mother Praxedes knew that the lesson of seeing things from God's point of view, which Mother Dafrosa had taught, was not a one-answer lesson. It did not make for the same answer for everyone. One fights; another submits. Both can do His will.

Standing there in the cemetery, she knew that the dead were not as far away as she had once thought. Once long ago, that day when she had held her father's limp hand, she had thought that he was gone. That she was alone. But she had never been alone. Gradually she knew, too, that Christ, the One she had chosen to serve by serving others, had not really gone from Loretto either. He was here and they were here. And the kind Archbishop, too. He who had held the poppy, the flaming poppy of full-blown love. They were all a part of the community of love. Love had kept them together.

A peace came over her. Mother Francisca *was* right. The interdict must be lifted, but the lifting was His. If her efforts now were to end in failure, she could not prevent it. The fighting was over.

She looked around the cemetery. She seemed to be discovering herself standing there. She did not know why, but for the first time in years, she found herself wondering just who she really was. Was she in any way her father's Susan with gold in her heart? Was she the Sister Praxedes who had found a new life in a bishop's garden? Was she a friend of Jesus and Mary? Truly she was at the foot of the cross. Only one thing she had never wanted to be. She had never wanted to be a bishop's adversary. But that is what they think I am, she thought. That is all I seem to be.

After three more days of waiting, Dom Obrecht returned from Washington with the Apostolic Delegate's promise that he would write to Bishop McCloskey. But June turned into July. The first passed and the second, and then late on July 5 Father Werner came to the convent.

"Dom Obrecht has been successful, Mother. Tomorrow Christ returns to Loretto."

"And look what has come," Mother Praxedes said as she held up a small black book.

"The Rule books, Mother? You mean our new Rule books are here, too?" Mother Francisca's voice squeaked with excitement.

"Yes, and listen to these words." She opened the small book. "'The supreme authority over the whole Society shall be exercised in the ordinary way by the Mother General and her council; in an extraordinary way by the General Chapter.' And the General Chapter means the sister-delegates chosen by the *sisters* who represent the *community*."

Mother closed the book. She must remember that one did not grasp the poppy too tightly. Success could be hard on sanctity. But now the words of Father Werner drowned out all other thoughts:

"Tomorrow Christ returns to Loretto."

LORETTO, KENTUCKY—1916

The July heat had already been heavy on the air when the delegates entered the auditorium; the room was stifling now. But Mother Praxedes shivered, as severed from the heat as she was from the movement about her. Since early morning she had not been able to concentrate on the present. Because she could find no structure for tomorrow, because she could not foresee what the election would bring, she kept returning to what had been. The years shifted, making disconnected designs with the present.

Just a while before, so it seemed, she had sat in this same place on another election day, a day in 1904. Then she had wondered who would bind up the wounds of the interdict? Who would see the new Rule through the days of trial? Who would guide the return to routine? Surprised, she had heard her own name repeated and repeated. She had been elected to serve a first term under the new Rule. When she had wept that day, who had known why? Had it been exhaustion from those months in Rome and the bitter time of the interdict? Had it been relief that her sisters somehow, in spite of criticisms, in spite of anxieties still believed in her? Had it been the dread of going on after so many valleys of discouragement?

And then the routine did come. And the days became days marked by the planned and the expected. Years telescoped into yesterday and she could not recall exactly when all returned to normal. One day she realized that the new academy in Kansas City was beginning its fifth year, a second group of sisters was attending the Catholic University, the new veil was no longer a subject for comment, and she had been doing certain things in a certain way for months without grave decisions or grave reverses. Even the second trip to Rome after the three-year probation of the Rule had had a routineness—a settled security. But today was to be the end of her years as Mother General, today was to be the end of elections for her and the beginning of . . . she did not know. Only one thing seemed sure. She had served six years and then another six under the new Rule and Constitutions. According to Canon Law—Rome's law—twelve years were enough. And she, having served twenty through the strange workings of a troubled time, now could rejoice at Rome's wisdom.

The promise of an end had somehow been a spur during this last year. Enlivened by the prospect of soon being able to serve in a more simple way, she had launched energetically into her last big project—the long-desired Loretto College, the ultimate reason why she had pioneered in sending sisters to Vanderbilt University before any Catholic university would accept women. Already the building was going up on the old Webster farm near St. Louis. Already the college had started temporarily in Kansas City. But now seated here, waiting for ballots to be cast, that was farther away than the past. Suddenly she seemed to be standing in the gray light of a cemetery. People were weaving in and out between the graves. It struck her how much they looked like children playing some weird game. Why were they in the cemetery? Someone put out a hand to her. Now the battle is really over, a voice said. What battle? What had they known of a battle? The man, Bishop McCloskey, was dead. He was dead and they were all walking away in tight clusters, mumbling. That had been a strange day in 1909. A day which had been over years before it happened. She had stood there wanting to feel the way one should, not knowing, feeling nothing; for long before his death, long before the pain of conflict had dulled, his place in the pattern of Loretto was clear to her. He had played a part. That day in the cemetery, fleetingly, for a moment, before the clusters of people edged away forever, she had wondered whose part had mattered more—his or hers.

As the sisters were filing by in two's to the scrutineers' table to deposit their votes, Mother Praxedes found herself thinking about Mother Francisca, who also was gone now. Perhaps the cemetery had reminded her. They had stood one sunny afternoon in Loretto's own little green cemetery just outside there on the quiet hill.

"Father Nerinckx must have a monument," Mother Francisca had said. And they had planned a monument of the Crucifixion to mark his grave and to mark one hundred years of Loretto's being. She remembered the day, while the monument was being placed, when Father Nerinckx's body was brought into the chapel. She had knelt watching her spiritual daughters walk in solemn procession to venerate the body of their holy founder. When she was told that his body would be taken to the chapel, she had planned what she would whisper to the saintly priest. She would enumerate her hopes for Loretto's second century, tell him of her dreams for a college, for some foreign mission. Yet when the time came, she had forgotten her plan. Instead she heard Mother Dafrosa's voice traveling across the years, reminding her, "You will have as much opportunity for sanctity as Father Nerinckx." Father Nerinckx had breathed in suffering; he had not resisted. And she? "Success can be hard on sanctity," Mother Dafrosa had said. Was it as easy to breathe in success as it was to breathe in suffering? She wondered. Success was not her problem now, nor was suffering. She would be free at last when the ballots were in and counted and tabulated, then she would have only peace, obscurity, seclusion to master. And this she would like to try. Perhaps in some quiet convent in New Mexico she could cook again, renew her Spanish. She could teach the little dark round faces about the "Good God." Yes, that would be old Moira's blessing come true—some quiet place in New Mexico.

When Mother Praxedes looked up again, the last of the sister-delegates were returning after depositing their ballots. The muted sounds of feet passing ceased. The room was quiet. Mother whispered a prayer for the woman who would leave this hall burdened with responsibility. That woman would have a college to complete; she would have almost twice the number of convents and schools to visit as Mother had had these twenty years before. More, she would take office against the background of a world already at war.

Mother Praxedes watched Bishop O'Donaghue's face as the two sister-scrutineers counted the votes. She smiled; at least her successor would find no crusty traditions to sustain. These had been years of change.

Finally a high voice called the first name for the office of Mother General. Mother Praxedes had not caught what was said.

"Mother Praxedes," she heard the voice call.

My name? Why my name?

"Mother Praxedes," the voice seemed to repeat.

Why hadn't the vicaress reminded the Bishop to announce that according to Canon Law . . .

"Mother Praxedes," the sister called again.

Didn't they know that she could not be re-elected?

"Mother Praxedes."

This needless delay annoyed her. An election was a serious matter—no time for making gestures. If this was meant as some sort of pledge or honor to her, it was certainly ill-placed! Had they no thought of the sister who would be elected?

Over and over she heard her name. Evidently this had been planned. No doubt they meant well.

When all the votes had been tabulated, Bishop O'Donaghue rose. He drew an envelope from inside his scarlet-piped cassock. He read.

No, she shouted within herself. Rome would not do this. She had been there. She had been to Rome twice, Rome would not approve this. God would not approve! Not six more years! The Bishop was reading a paper from Rome. She must see that paper. Don't you know I am tired, she wanted to shout. I must be allowed—

"The Bishop asks if you accept, Mother?" she heard Mother Olivette whisper.

Accept? Twenty years ago she had been asked. She had answered then. She had not refused; she must refuse now. She walked forward. She must see the paper. Must she accept? Must she say yes again?

The bishop offered his hand to her as she ascended the steps to the stage. He held out the paper. He was smiling. She looked at the paper. She could not see the words. What good would it do? They were asking her for six more years. What right had she to say no? What reason? What excuse? I am tired? I've had enough of decisions? I want to go back to New Mexico?

"Mother Praxedes, do you accept the office?" the Bishop asked.

She looked at him. She looked at the paper, the paper that gave Rome's permission to waive Rome's law.

"Yes, Your Excellency."

"We felt that the new college at Webster Groves and the instability of world conditions were sufficient reason to petition Rome," Mother Olivette said.

But there were always new buildings; there was always instability!

"The council made the request, Rome consented, and you have been elected."

Mother Praxedes crumbled within herself. "I can't," she thought. Almost audibly the words were squeezed out, "I can't."

The cold October rain hammered against the window. For three days it had pounded down. Would it never stop, Mother wondered as she turned again to read over to herself the final draft of the letter she had just completed. "October 26, 1918 . . . under conditions unique in the history of our country, I desire to call your attention again to the obligation we are under of eliminating everything not in accord with the spirit of the time . . . I wish to urge the greatest economy . . . President Wilson exhorts the people to curtail unnecessary traveling . . ." Her voice trailed off. She stared vacantly at the little black letters in front of her. Almost imperceptibly, the little black letters became big black letters which seemed to scream from newspapers: SPANISH INFLUENZA HITS ARMY CAMPS . . . SCHOOLS CLOSE . . . WAR TOLL RISES . . . NURSES NEEDED AT CAMP TAYLOR. The headlines in their own turn became snatches of conversations. They beat into Mother Praxedes' ears as she grasped her head to stop its spinning. "Mother, they need nurses . . . 9000 cases at the camp, 90 deaths in the last forty-eight hours . . . the Sisters of Loretto are teachers, not nurses! . . . Mother, I'll go . . . I'll go, Mother . . . we are teachers! . . . Sister Mary Jean can't go. She's too young . . . too young? Sister Mary Jean has . . . Mother, is Sister Mary Jean dying? . . . the mining camp needs nurses, too . . . please, Mother, more sisters . . . the war can't last forever . . . yes, go ahead. Yes, plan the college at the Heights . . . yes, go ahead . . . Father, I can't even pray . . . I can't . . . no, everything is beating down on me . . . I can't . . ."

"Mother Praxedes, Mother—"

"Oh, Sister Antonella!" She ran one hand across her forehead. "I didn't hear you."

"A headache, Mother?"

"Oh no. It's nothing. Did you want something, Sister?"

"Yes, Mother. I said they called again from Louisville. Sister Mary Jean is worse."

"Worse?"

"Sister said they don't think she'll live through the night."

"And now I'm letting another group go to the mining camp. Oh, Sister Antonella, I should not have let them go."

"But they volunteered, Mother. Everyone wanted to go."

"I know." She put her hand to her head again. "I must see Sister Mary Jean. She's worse you say?"

As Mother Praxedes entered the hospital room, the still figure on the bed stirred. Sister Mary Jean opened her eyes, blinking like a sleepy child. Mother put one hand gently on Sister's feverish forehead. In her mind Mother could still see those coffins—coffins stacked four deep at the depot. My God, I had no idea!

"Oh, Reverend Mother, how good of you," the young sister whispered. Her smile was radiant. "Are you all right, Mother?"

"Why, of course. You are the one who is sick, you know."

Sister closed her eyes. "But you had chills, Mother."

What did the child mean? She must be—oh, I know. She means the day before the group left Loretto. Strange that she should remember that I was sick that day.

Mother Praxedes glanced around the room. Sister Mary Jean opened her eyes again.

"Sister, has Father been here today?"

"I think it was today. He gave me the Last Sacraments." She sighed. Her eyes closed for a moment. "I'm not afraid, Mother." She took a deep breath. "God answered my prayers."

Mother stroked Sister's forehead. "Oh?"

"I told Him to take me and to spare you many years for the sisters." She closed her eyes again.

She told him? Her life for mine? For mine? She told Him to take her life? She must not do that! She must tell God she had no right to do that.

"But, child, your life is not yours to give away." Mother Praxedes was not sure what she was saying as tears came to her eyes.

Sister Mary Jean just smiled at her and closed her eyes.

Mother watched, but Sister did not open her eyes. Her breathing seemed steady. This was all like a dream. Mother caught the edge of the sheet in her left hand. Was this all real? She could see herself sitting at the table with the council just three weeks ago. The list of volunteers to nurse the sick soldiers at Camp Zachary Taylor was in front of her.

"*Now* how many do we have?" she was asking.

"Seven, Reverend Mother. You said we would send eight."

"Read the list again, please."

"Sister Assumpta, Sister Bonaventure, Sister Mary Carmel, Sister Mary Leo, Sister Marcellas, Sister Liberata, Sister Patricia."

"What about Sister Mary Jean, Reverend Mother?"

"Oh, I don't know. She's only just made her first vows."

"But she's twenty-eight, Reverend Mother, and she's a good practical nurse."

She had thought for a moment. Twenty-eight was not so very young. Had she herself been twenty-eight, she would have thought it quite old enough to serve the soldiers.

Coming back to the reality of the hospital room, Mother Praxedes looked at Sister Mary Jean again. Sister had not even made her final profession. If she was really going to die—

"Sister," Mother patted her hand. "Sister Mary Jean, my dear."

Sister opened her eyes again.

"Sister, would you like to become completely His now?" Mother's voice was strained. "Would you like to pronounce your final vows?"

Sister nodded. Mother took her own crucifix and held it for Sister to see. "Repeat the words after me," Mother said.

"Prostrate before my God." Prostrate—Mother was jarred by the word. "And actuated by the desire of wholly consecrating myself"—wholly, entirely—"to His Divine Majesty and to the honor of His Sorrowful Mother Mary, I, Sister Mary Jean, into your hands, Reverend Mother General, do vow perpetual poverty, chastity, and obedience."

Sister closed her eyes. Mother Praxedes sank to her knees, still holding the young nun's hand.

My God, Mother Praxedes cried out in her heart, this was the greatest service. This was the kind of service I once desired, the kind of service I withheld that morning in the chapter hall; the "I can't" that has made these two years, outwardly so successful, so filled with building and growth, but inwardly so barren. I was too tired and too old, I thought, to take on six more years. I have failed to give myself.

"Sister Mary Jean, help me to serve as long as He wants," she said aloud. She straightened up. Standing, she looked down at the still figure. "Because I must, I can."

EL PASO, TEXAS—1933

Two workmen in paint-spattered overalls climbed down from their ladders. It was time to stop for the day. Large beads of perspiration stood out on their foreheads. Although it was past mid-December, the day had been warm even for El Paso.

Silently they covered their paint cans and together they rolled back the paint-flecked tarpaulin.

"How would you say that?" the taller man asked as he peered down at the words in blue tile on the floor they had just uncovered.

"Praxedes Hall," the other replied. "Say, Fred, you mean to tell me you never heard of Mother Praxedes?"

"Oh, sure, she's the kinda old sister who goes around here in the wheel chair. She's sick now, isn't she? But why's the place got her name?"

"Good Lord, Fred, everybody in El Paso knows that. This place was her idea. Back in the spring of '22, when I was working for Morgan, we got the contract for this place. We were all set up over by Mt. Franklin when this Mother Praxedes—man, was she a hustler—comes out from back East. She was the big wheel—the Mother General or whatever they call it. And just like that she decides to build here instead. This was way out in the desert even more than it is now and people started calling it 'Praxedes Folly' instead of Praxedes Hall."

"Yah, I can see how it must have shocked 'em. All this fancy stuff out in the middle of the desert. Buff brick, red tile roof and all."

"And more marble in that chapel than in all the churches in El Paso put together!"

"You know, I think the old girl really knew what she was doing after all."

The crimson trail of a vanished day faded into darkness as the lights of El Paso flickered on. Faraway from sky and city, another small light burned. Its pale yellow rays reached through the shadows of the room where Mother Praxedes waited on the brink of another world. Her tired head propped against the pillows, she opened her eyes for a moment. "Have they come?" she asked.

A prim little woman in her late sixties walked over to the bed. Gently she took her sister's hand and patted it. As the light caught her face, she looked more like Ellen Carty than like Ellen's daughter.

"No, Susie, they have not come; but I'll tell you when they do."

Mother Praxedes smiled wearily as she closed her eyes again. Delia continued holding her hand, stroking it. After several minutes, she carefully placed it on the covers and returned to her place of watching near the window. Delia remembered Susie gazing up at her from the bed after she had broken her hip. "Don't cry, dear, I'm getting all kinds of attention."

That had been in St. Louis in February 1931. They had not known then that the fractured hip would never heal. Delia turned to look at her sister again. Mother had been so happy when the doctors said they could take her back to El Paso. "How good God is to let me come back to the place I so love," she had said as she saw the roofs of El Paso. "Oh, I am God's spoiled child. Is He not good to me?"

No one thought then that she would ever be about again, but she had. "I'll use a wheel chair. Wheels are faster than feet anyway," she had said.

Delia noticed that Mother stirred slightly. She walked over to the bed again. "Yes, Susie, what is it, dear?"

"Have they come, Delia?"

"No, not yet."

There was a hesitation, then Mother said softly, as if to herself, "She's never taken so long before. I hope nothing has happened to her." Then she looked up at Delia. "We must pray."

Delia hoped, too, that nothing had happened. Mother had worried from the time the sisters set sail for China. She had somehow retained a feeling of responsibility for the Chinese mission. "It was the last house I requested to open," Delia had once heard her say. And then she had gotten that little look of mischief in her eyes. "We couldn't have gone any farther west, Delia."

Delia stroked her sister's slender hand. "Strange that her hands have stayed young," she was thinking. "Always graceful, these hands are beautiful even now."

"I remember," Delia thought to herself, "I remember you saying that it wasn't your fault you had nice hands since you had done practically everything including mixing adobe. The only thing they never did was milk a cow."

Realizing that tears were gathering in her eyes and that her throat felt tight, Delia made an effort to swallow back her sorrow. "How will I ever get along without you?"

A whisper came from the doorway. "Has Mother gone to sleep?"

Delia turned and nodded that she had. Then, smoothing a wrinkle in the covers, she tiptoed toward the door and stepped out into the hallway to speak to someone.

Mother Praxedes opened her eyes again. Noticing that Delia was not near the window now, she listened for sound of her. Yes, Delia was there near the door. Satisfied, Mother closed her eyes again.

"Maybe tomorrow I will be able to go outside," she was thinking. "I must show Mother Olivette the shrubbery in front of the chapel. Maybe tomorrow . . ."

That smells good, Mother. What is it? a voice was asking.

I thought it was apple butter in Cruces, but it's soup in El Paso, she heard herself say. . . . Who was that kneeling on the ground? Soil, too, must feel love before it becomes fruitful, she was saying as her fingers kneaded the black earth. What are you doing, Sister, a little boy asked. I hope I'm helping the Good God to grow things. Does He need help? The child's eyes had grown wide. No, He really doesn't. Sometimes He lets me think He does.

"Yes, Mother?" Had she said something? Delia wondered.

"You must have the sisters pray that Reverend Mother arrives safely. Perhaps there has been a storm at sea."

"The sisters have just had word from San Francisco that the ship docked this evening. Mother Olivette will be here tomorrow. They will come tomorrow to tell you all about China."

"Oh, isn't God good! He is so good. Thank you. Now I will sleep." Smiling, she closed her eyes.

They were coming. They were coming from China. All of them were coming. Papa was coming. Papa was coming with gold in his heart. . . . Yes, and the friends of Jesus and Mary. They would be coming too. . . . And would the kind Archbishop? What did he have in his hand? "Angelica, you must not pick the Archbishop's flowers." You must not hold the poppy too tight. It will rob the gold in your heart. . . . Six more years? Oh no! Not that! Why were they so blind? . . . Mr. Shawn, I will show you how to make the mill disappear. One step, two steps. Mr. Shawn, take my hand!

What did they say? Was someone calling her? She opened her eyes. The voice was more distinct, and familiar, too.

"Well, really have you come?" she said, reaching up both hands.

"Mother, dear."

Mother Praxedes closed her eyes once more, saying over and over again, "Mother! Mother!"

That was who she was. She was not Susie. No, she was Mother.

Lying there, her heart beating out the last hours of life, she did not see them come in two's and three's to kneel beside her. She did not see her children, her family, hundreds of them.

It happened then, that in the space of time which linked consciousness to the threshold of eternity that, little girl-like, she was sure she found a bit of winding road, clover-hugged and rocky. The road stretched out between cool patches of green which touched the distant purple hills. She felt her feet upon the road, a road familiar because it led across the hill to home. Then she reached out and took Moira's hand and they led each other, and she heard a voice saying to her, "Look, alannah. Look to the end of the road. I *can* see, and I see Him coming." And she turned, and with a lift of her heart she saw Him where the road reached up to the beginning of the sky.

"Weigh Well What I Say"

The first time I spoke to Mother Olivette, then a slightly bent old lady with a kind face and the elegance of another era, she said to me, "You will have to weigh well what I say for there have been those who called me a hero worshiper and I suppose as far as she was concerned I was; but they did not know her the way I knew her."

Time and time again I returned to her room in the infirmary at the Loretto mother house to ask about this woman she so loved. As the years progressed, I came to know from letters and documents that hers was a true picture. I ceased to question what had become, to me, the real woman who lived so vividly in the heart of her friend.

Today they lie close together on that same windswept hillock in Kentucky, where Mother Praxedes alone pondered the problems of several generations. The last time I visited them there, I was still perplexed by the problems a long life gives a biographer. But since then I have come to know that had they not both lived beyond the height of middle age into the days of less activity, there could have been no book, for both left for us a legacy in writing that only the old have time to make.

This book is the real story of a real woman. The heavy use of conversation creates questions for those who want only dry facts. In some few instances I did create conversations entirely from imagination and in others I reconstructed them from letters and narratives left by Mother Praxedes. In all cases these conversations were made in support of factual information. In a few places where details were lacking I took the liberty of supplying them. That young Susan led blind beggars I know because her memoirs have told me so. Moira's name and personality I created, but Moira was real. Hilliker's Dry-Goods Store and Burgess Hilliker existed, but I do not know their real names or the minute details as they were. On the other hand, the portraits of Archbishop Lamy and Bishop McCloskey came to me in detail from letters and documents in the Loretto Archives so they, as the many other persons in the book, are in no way my creation.

For those who find the El Paso years paced too swiftly, may I say, turn to the living who were there and ask those who now know the story of the years before to tell you about the woman, the Mother Praxedes who lived beyond the scope that this book could reach. With Mother Olivette weigh carefully what they say, for greatness is illusive to those who have not known the suffering of the great. To be old and passive after one has been young and active is the crowning cross to life. She had all the other crosses and at the end she had that one too. The very length of her life was a mark of God's enduring care of her. To the end, she had only one heart and that was His.

Sister Patricia Jean
Loretto Heights College
Feast of St. Praxedes, July 21, 1962

BIBLIOGRAPHY

BOOKS

BARBOUR, SISTER RICHARD MARIE. *Light in Yucca Land*. Santa Fe: Schifani Brothers, 1952.

BENEDICT, BROTHER ALPHONSUS, F.S.C. *One Hundred Years of Service*. Privately printed, 1959.

CASEY, SISTER CELESTINE, AND FERN, SISTER EDMOND. *Loretto in the Rockies*. Denver: privately printed, 1943.

CLEMENT, BROTHER ANTHONY, F.S.C. *Seventy-five Years of Service*. Privately printed, 1934.

COMPTON, RICHARD J., ED. *Pictorial St. Louis, the Great Metropolis of the Mississippi Valley*. Chicago: Compton & Company, 1896.

DACUS, J. A., PH.D., AND BUEL, JAMES W. *A Tour of St. Louis*. St. Louis: Western Publishing Co., 1878.

DAVIS, WILLIAM WATT HART. *El Gringo or New Mexico and Her People*. Santa Fe: Rydall Press, 1938.

FINN, BRENDAN A. *Twenty-four American Cardinals*. Boston: B. Humphries, 1948.

FLANIGAN, REV. GEORGE J., ED. *Catholicity in Tennessee*. Nashville: Ambrose Print Co., 1937.

HORGAN, PAUL. *The Centuries of Santa Fe*. New York: Dutton, 1956.

HOWLETT, REV. W. J. *Life of Bishop Macheboeuf*. Pueblo: Franklin Press, 1908.

MAES, RT. REV. CAMILLUS, D.D. *Life of Father Charles Nerinckx*. Cincinnati: Robert Clark & Co., 1880.

MINOGUE, ANNA C. *Loretto Annals of the Century*. New York: American Press, 1912.

SALPOINTE, RT. REV. J. B. *Soldiers of the Cross*. Banning, Calif.: St. Boniface Press, 1898.

WARNER, LOUIS A. *Archbishop Lamy, An Epoch Maker*. Santa Fe: New Mexican Publishing Corp., 1936.

Centennial Discourses. Kentucky: privately printed, 1912.

Prospectus, Loretto Academy. Florissant, Mo.: privately printed, 1895–96.

St. Louis City Directories from 1865 to 1875.

ARTICLES

CLUM, JOHN P. "Santa Fe in the Seventies," *New Mexico Hostorical Review*, Vol. II.

CROCCHIOLA, REV. STANLEY. "Death Comes for the Archbishop," Santa Fe *Register* (Aug. 25, 1950).

HOWLETT, REV. W. J. Sermon, Louisville *Record* (Dec. 28, 1933).

MCKINNON, BESS. "The Toll Road over Raton Pass," *New Mexico Historical Review*, Vol. II.

O'HAGAN, DR. THOMAS. "Loretto Heights," *Rosary Magazine* (May 1901).

POMEROY, C. A. "This Out Loud," El Paso *Times* (Dec. 21, 1933).

ROUAULT, T. LETTER, Mesilla *News* (Aug. 24, 1880).

TERRY, ROBERT JAMES, M.D. "Memories of a Long Life," *Missouri Historical Society Bulletin*, Vol. XI, p. 124.

"Centennial Celebration," *Loretto Magazine* (April 1912).

"Here We Are All Aboard," Mesilla *News* (April 30, 1881).

"Sisters of Loretto in the Mining Regions." *Queens Work* (June 1919).

UNPUBLISHED MANUSCRIPTS

ANSON, SISTER GENOVEVA, AND DRISCOLL. *Mother Praxedes*, Loretto Motherhouse Archives.

CARTY, MOTHER PRAXEDES. "Second Loan," LMA.

DOYLE, SISTER MARY BERNARD. "Memoirs," LMA.

EVERIN, SISTER MARY BARBARA. "Memories of the Long Ago," LMA.

GREEN, MOTHER ROSINE. Diary, LMA.

LAMOTTE, MOTHER WILFRID. European Diary, 1903–04, LMA.

LAMOTTE, MOTHER WILFRID, AND NORTON, MOTHER OLIVETTE. "A Sketch," LMA.

LAMY, MOTHER FRANCISCA. Santa Fe Annals, 1887–88, LMA.

LASSAIGNE, REV. PEDRO. Journal, 1886–90, St. Gertrude's Rectory, Las Cruces, New Mexico.

LYONS, PEGGY. "Mother Herself," LMA.

NORTON, MOTHER OLIVETTE. "Memories of Kansas City," LMA.

———. "Random Memories Concerning Mother M. Praxedes Carty," LMA.

SCHNEIDER, SISTER MARY JANICE. "The Hayden Sisters as Educators," Master Thesis, LMA.

House Annals from Bernalillo, Cedar Grove Academy, El Paso,

Kansas City, Las Cruces, Loretto Heights, Florissant, Loretto Normal School, Loretto Motherhouse, Santa Fe, Webster, LMA.
Las Cruces Cash Book, 1880–81, LMA.
Sketches from Biography Book, LMA.

UNPUBLISHED LETTERS IN LORETTO MOTHERHOUSE ARCHIVES. QUOTED IN BOOK.

ASCARATE, GERTRUDE A. Las Cruces: Feb. 20, 1952.
BONFILS, MOTHER PANCRATIA. Colorado Springs: April 10, 1904.
BOURGADE, RT. REV. PETER. Santa Fe: March 4, 1899; April 15, 1899.
BYRNE, RT. REV. THOMAS S. Loretto: June 26, 1896; Aug. 1, 1896; Sept. 12, 20, 1896.
CARTY, MOTHER PRAXEDES. Taos: Oct. 10, 1900; Conejos: Dec. 24, 1900; Aug. 28, 1903; Rome: Dec. 4, 22, 1903; Jan. 12, 13, 15, 23, 27; Feb. 18, 20, 1904; Loretto: June 11, 13, 23, 25, 26; July 1, 2, 16; Rome: Nov. 4, 12, 17; Loretto: Jan. 19, 1912; May 16, 1916; April 15, 1918. And several hundred others not quoted but used for background information.
CHAPELLE, RT. REV. PLACID, D.D. Santa Fe: July 28, 1896.
CONNOR, MOTHER CATHERINE. Santa Fe: Aug. 13, 1896.
FERN, SISTER MARY EDMOND. March 2, 1950.
FIDELES, MOTHER. Rome: 1907.
KIRGAN, REV. DAVID J. Las Cruces: June 30, Nov. 28, 1951.
LAMOTTE, MOTHER WILFRID. Rome: Dec. 16, 22, 1903; Feb. 2, 9; April 2, 1904.
LAMY, MOTHER FRANCISCA. Loretto: May 24, 1904.
LANCIOTTI, REV. V. T., C.R. Rome: Dec. 20, 1903; Mentorella: May 20, 1904; March 29, 1905; Feb. 24, 1908.
MCCLOSKEY, RT. REV. WILLIAM. Louisville: Nov. 18, 1903; May 17, 23; June 24, 1904.
MATZ, RT. REV. NICHOLAS. Denver: Aug. 24, 1897.
OBRECHT, DOM EDMOND M., O.S.O. Gethsemani: June 29, 1904; Washington, D.C.: June 30, 1904.
O'CONNELL, REV. C. J. Bardstown: Sept. 14, 1893.
RODEN, MOTHER CECILIA. St. Louis: 1886; Loretto: 1892; Louisville. Dec. 20, 1893.
SATOLLI, FRANCIS CARDINAL. Washington, D.C.: Sept. 8, 14, 1896.
STEPHENSON, MRS. HORACE F. Las Cruces: Aug. 1893.
VALENA, SISTER. El Paso: March 29, April 11, 1948, interviews with Miss Delia Carty.
WISE, SISTER LOUISE. Kansas City: April 4, 1904.

ACKNOWLEDGMENTS

In addition to the persons listed in the bibliography, may I say a special thank you to Sister Dafrosa, whose idea the book was, to Mother Edwarda, who first approved it, and to Mother Mary Luke, who provided the impetus for its completion.

The book could not have been without them or the following persons whose contributions are too varied to describe here: Mrs. W. M. Adair, Las Cruces, N.M.; Rev. John Brady, PPVF, Templeporte, County Cavan, Ireland; Mrs. Larry Dillenbeck, Sterling, Ill.; Preston F. Grandon, Sterling, Ill; my brother J. Thomas Manion, St. Louis, Mo.; Sister Mary Cecily, Milwaukee, Wisc.; Sister Matilda, archivist, Loretto, Ky.; Rt. Rev. F. N. Pitt, Louisville, Ky.; Mrs. Sewell Thomas, Denver, Colo.; Elizabeth Tindall, Missouri Historical Society; Rt. Rev. Charles M. Williams, Nashville, Tenn.

Lastly, special mention must be made of the book's first critics, Dr. Donald P. Costello, Notre Dame University, and Sister Mary Louise, Loretto Heights College. To them I say Amen.